Stanley Gibb
Commonwealth Stam

St. Helena, Ascension & Tristan da Cunha

5th edition 2014

STANLEY GIBBONS LTD
London and Ringwood

By Appointment to
Her Majesty The Queen
Stanley Gibbons Ltd
London
Philatelists

Published by Stanley Gibbons Ltd
Editorial, Publications Sales Offices
and Distribution Centre:
7 Parkside, Christchurch Road, Ringwood,
Hants BH24 3SH

British Library Cataloguing in
Publication Data.
A catalogue record for this book is available
from the British Library.

Errors and omissions excepted
the colour reproduction of stamps is only as
accurate as the printing process will allow.

ISBN-10: 0-85259-916-1
ISBN-13: 978-0-85259-916-7

Item No. R2875-14

Printed by
Latimer Trend

Contents

Stanley Gibbons Holdings Plc

Stanley Gibbons Limited, Stanley Gibbons Auctions
399 Strand, London WC2R 0LX
Tel: +44 (0)207 836 8444
Fax: +44 (0)207 836 7342
E-mail: help@stanleygibbons.com
Website: www.stanleygibbons.com
for all departments, Auction and Specialist Stamp Departments.

Open Monday–Friday 9.30 a.m. to 5 p.m. Shop. Open Monday–Friday 9 a.m. to 5.30 p.m. and Saturday 9.30 a.m. to 5.30 p.m.

Stanley Gibbons Publications Gibbons Stamp Monthly and Philatelic Exporter
7 Parkside, Christchurch Road, Ringwood, Hampshire BH24 3SH.
Tel: +44 (0)1425 472363
Fax: +44 (0)1425 470247
E-mail: help@stanleygibbons.com
Publications Mail Order.
FREEPHONE 0800 611622

Monday–Friday 8.30 a.m. to 5 p.m.

Stanley Gibbons (Guernsey) Limited
18–20 Le Bordage, St Peter Port, Guernsey GY1 1DE.
Tel: +44 (0)1481 708270
Fax: +44 (0)1481 708279
E-mail: investment@stanleygibbons.com

Stanley Gibbons (Jersey) Limited
18 Hill Street, St Helier, Jersey, Channel Islands JE2 4UA.
Tel: +44 (0)1534 766711
Fax: +44 (0)1534 766177
E-mail: investment@stanleygibbons.com

Stanley Gibbons (Asia) Limited
Level 10
Central Building
1-3 Pedder Street
Hong Kong
Tel: +852 3975 2988
E-mail: ganandappa@stanleygibbons.com

Benham Collectibles Limited
Unit K, Concept Court,
Shearway Business Park
Folkestone Kent CT19 4RG
E-mail: benham@benham.com

Fraser's
(a division of Stanley Gibbons Ltd)
399 Strand, London WC2R 0LX
Autographs, photographs, letters and documents
Tel: +44 (0)207 836 8444
Fax: +44 (0)207 836 7342
E-mail: sales@frasersautographs.com
Website: www.frasersautographs.com

Monday–Friday 9 a.m. to 5.30 p.m. and Saturday 10 a.m. to 4 p.m.

Stanley Gibbons Publications Overseas Representation
Stanley Gibbons Publications are represented overseas by the following

Australia ***Renniks Publications PTY LTD***
Unit 3 37-39 Green Street, Banksmeadow, NSW 2019, Australia
Tel: +612 9695 7055
Website: www.renniks.com

Canada ***Unitrade Associates***
99 Floral Parkway, Toronto, Ontario M6L 2C4, Canada
Tel: +1 416 242 5900
Website: www.unitradeassoc.com

Germany ***Schaubek Verlag Leipzig***
Am Glaeschen 23, D-04420 Markranstaedt, Germany
Tel: +49 34 205 67823
Website: www.schaubek.de

Italy ***Ernesto Marini S.R.L.***
V. Struppa, 300, Genova, 16165, Italy
Tel: +3901 0247-3530
Website: www.ernestomarini.it

Japan ***Japan Philatelic***
PO Box 2, Suginami-Minami, Tokyo 168-8081, Japan
Tel: +81 3330 41641
Website: www.yushu.co.jp

Netherlands also covers Belgium Denmark, Finland & France
Uitgeverij Davo BV
PO Box 411, Ak Deventer, 7400 Netherlands
Tel: +315 7050 2700
Website: www.davo.nl

New Zealand ***House of Stamps***
PO Box 12, Paraparaumu, New Zealand
Tel: +61 6364 8270
Website: www.houseofstamps.co.nz

New Zealand ***Philatelic Distributors***
PO Box 863
15 Mount Edgecumbe Street
New Plymouth 4615, New Zealand
Tel: +6 46 758 65 68
Website: www.stampcollecta.com

Norway ***SKANFIL A/S***
SPANAV. 52 / BOKS 2030
N-5504 HAUGESUND, Norway
Tel: +47-52703940
E-mail: magne@skanfil.no

Singapore ***C S Philatelic Agency***
Peninsula Shopping Centre #04-29
3 Coleman Street, 179804, Singapore
Tel: +65 6337-1859
Website: www.cs.com.sg

South Africa ***Peter Bale Philatelics***
P O Box 3719, Honeydew, 2040, South Africa
Tel: +27 11 462 2463
Tel: +27 82 330 3925
E-mail: balep@iafrica.com

Sweden ***Chr Winther Sorensen AB***
Box 43, S-310 20 Knaered, Sweden
Tel: +46 43050743
Website: www.collectia.se

USA ***Regency Superior Ltd***
229 North Euclid Avenue
Saint Louis, Missouri 63108, USA

PO Box 8277, St Louis, MO 63156-8277, USA
Toll Free Tel: (800) 782-0066
Tel: (314) 361-5699
Website: www.RegencySuperior.com
Email: info@regencysuperior.com

General Philatelic Information and Guidelines to the Scope of Stanley Gibbons Commonwealth Catalogues

These notes reflect current practice in compiling the Stanley Gibbons Commonwealth Catalogues.

The Stanley Gibbons Stamp Catalogue has a very long history and the vast quantity of information it contains has been carefully built up by successive generations through the work of countless individuals. Philately is never static and the Catalogue has evolved and developed over the years. These notes relate to the current criteria upon which a stamp may be listed or priced. These criteria have developed over time and may have differed somewhat in the early years of this catalogue. These notes are not intended to suggest that we plan to make wholesale changes to the listing of classic issues in order to bring them into line with today's listing policy, they are designed to inform catalogue users as to the policies currently in operation.

PRICES

The prices quoted in this Catalogue are the estimated selling prices of Stanley Gibbons Ltd at the time of publication. They are, unless it is specifically stated otherwise, for examples in fine condition for the issue concerned. Superb examples are worth more; those of a lower quality considerably less.

All prices are subject to change without prior notice and Stanley Gibbons Ltd may from time to time offer stamps below catalogue price. Individual low value stamps sold at 399 Strand are liable to an additional handling charge. Purchasers of new issues should note the prices charged for them contain an element for the service rendered and so may exceed the prices shown when the stamps are subsequently catalogued. Postage and handling charges are extra.

No guarantee is given to supply all stamps priced, since it is not possible to keep every catalogued item in stock. Commemorative issues may, at times, only be available in complete sets and not as individual values.

Quotation of prices. The prices in the left-hand column are for unused stamps and those in the right-hand column are for used.

A dagger (†) denotes that the item listed does not exist in that condition and a blank, or dash, that it exists, or may exist, but we are unable to quote a price.

Prices are expressed in pounds and pence sterling. One pound comprises 100 pence (£1 = 100p).

The method of notation is as follows: pence in numerals (e.g. 10 denotes ten pence); pounds and pence, up to £100, in numerals (e.g. 4.25 denotes four pounds and twenty-five pence); prices above £100 are expressed in whole pounds with the '£' sign shown.

Unused stamps. Great Britain and Commonwealth: the prices for unused stamps of Queen Victoria to King George V are for lightly hinged examples. Unused prices for King Edward VIII, King George VI and Queen Elizabeth issues are for unmounted mint.

Some stamps from the King George VI period are often difficult to find in unmounted mint condition. In such instances we would expect that collectors would need to pay a high proportion of the price quoted to obtain mounted mint examples. Generally speaking lightly mounted mint stamps from this reign, issued before 1945, are in considerable demand.

Used stamps. The used prices are normally for fine postally used stamps, but may be for stamps cancelled-to-order where this practice exists.

A pen-cancellation on early issues can sometimes correctly denote postal use. Instances are individually noted in the Catalogue in explanation of the used price given.

Prices quoted for bisects on cover or large piece are for those dated during the period officially authorised.

Stamps not sold unused to the public (e.g. some official stamps) are priced used only.

The use of 'unified' designs, that is stamps inscribed for both postal and fiscal purposes, results in a number of stamps of very high face value. In some instances these may not have been primarily intended for postal purposes, but if they are so inscribed we include them. We only price such items used, however, where there is evidence of normal postal usage.

Cover prices. To assist collectors, cover prices are quoted for issues up to 1945 at the beginning of each country.

The system gives a general guide in the form of a factor by which the corresponding used price of the basic loose stamp should be multiplied when found in fine average condition on cover.

Care is needed in applying the factors and they relate to a cover which bears a single of the denomination listed; if more than one denomination is present the most highly priced attracts the multiplier and the remainder are priced at the simple figure for used singles in arriving at a total.

The cover should be of non-philatelic origin; bearing the correct postal rate for the period and distance involved and cancelled with the markings normal to the offices concerned. Purely philatelic items have a cover value only slightly greater than the catalogue value for the corresponding used stamps. This applies generally to those high-value stamps used philatelically rather than in the normal course of commerce. Low-value stamps, e.g. ¼d. and ½d., are desirable when used as a single rate on cover and merit an increase in 'multiplier' value.

First day covers in the period up to 1945 are not within the scope of the system and the multiplier should not be used. As a special category of philatelic usage, with wide variations in valuation according to scarcity, they require separate treatment.

Oversized covers, difficult to accommodate on an album page, should be reckoned as worth little more than the corresponding value of the used stamps. The condition of a cover also affects its value. Except for 'wreck covers', serious damage or soiling reduce the value where the postal markings and stamps are ordinary ones. Conversely, visual appeal adds to the value and this can include freshness of appearance, important addresses, old-fashioned but legible handwriting, historic town-names, etc.

The multipliers are a base on which further value would be added to take account of the cover's postal historical importance in demonstrating such things as unusual, scarce or emergency cancels, interesting routes, significant postal markings, combination usage, the development of postal rates, and so on.

Minimum price. The minimum catalogue price quoted is 10p. For individual stamps prices between 10p. and 95p. are provided as a guide for catalogue users. The lowest price charged for individual stamps or sets purchased from Stanley Gibbons Ltd is £1

Set prices. Set prices are generally for one of each value, excluding shades and varieties, but including major colour changes. Where there are alternative shades, etc., the cheapest is usually included. The number of stamps in the set is always stated for clarity. The prices for sets containing *se-tenant* pieces are based on the prices quoted for such combinations, and not on those for the individual stamps.

Varieties. Where plate or cylinder varieties are priced in used condition the price quoted is for a fine used example with the cancellation well clear of the listed flaw.

Specimen stamps. The pricing of these items is explained under that heading.

Stamp booklets. Prices are for complete assembled booklets in fine condition with those issued before 1945 showing normal wear and tear. Incomplete booklets and those which have been 'exploded' will, in general, be worth less than the figure quoted.

Repricing. Collectors will be aware that the market factors of supply and demand directly influence the prices quoted in this Catalogue. Whatever the scarcity of a particular stamp, if there is no one in the market who wishes to buy it cannot be expected to achieve a high price. Conversely, the same item actively sought by numerous potential buyers may cause the price to rise.

All the prices in this Catalogue are examined during the preparation of each new edition by the expert staff of Stanley Gibbons and repriced as necessary. They take many factors into account, including supply and demand, and are in close touch with the international stamp market and the auction world.

Commonwealth cover prices and advice on postal history material originally provided by Edward B Proud.

GUARANTEE

All stamps are guaranteed originals in the following terms:

If not as described, and returned by the purchaser, we undertake to refund the price paid to us in the original transaction. If any stamp is certified as genuine by the Expert Committee of the Royal Philatelic Society, London, or by BPA Expertising Ltd, the purchaser shall not be entitled to make any claim against us for any error, omission or mistake in such certificate.

Consumers' statutory rights are not affected by the above guarantee.

The recognised Expert Committees in this country are those of the Royal Philatelic Society, 41 Devonshire Place, London W1G, 6JY, and BPA Expertising Ltd, PO Box 1141, Guildford, Surrey GU5 0WR. They do not undertake valuations under any circumstances and fees are payable for their services.

MARGINS ON IMPERFORATE STAMPS

Superb | Very fine | Fine | Average | Poor

GUM

Unmounted | Very lightly mounted | Lightly mounted | Mounted/ large part original gum (o.g.). | Heavily mounted small part o.g.

CENTRING

Superb | Very fine | Fine | Average | Poor

CANCELLATIONS

Superb | Very fine | Fine | Average | Poor

Superb | Very fine

Fine | Average | Poor

CONDITION GUIDE

To assist collectors in assessing the true value of items they are considering buying or in reviewing stamps already in their collections, we now offer a more detailed guide to the condition of stamps on which this catalogue's prices are based.

For a stamp to be described as 'Fine', it should be sound in all respects, without creases, bends, wrinkles, pin holes, thins or tears. If perforated, all perforation 'teeth' should be intact, it should not suffer from fading, rubbing or toning and it should be of clean, fresh appearance.

Margins on imperforate stamps: These should be even on all sides and should be at least as wide as half the distance between that stamp and the next. To have one or more margins of less than this width, would normally preclude a stamp from being described as 'Fine'. Some early stamps were positioned very close together on the printing plate and in such cases 'Fine' margins would necessarily be narrow. On the other hand, some plates were laid down to give a substantial gap between individual stamps and in such cases margins would be expected to be much wider.

An 'average' four-margin example would have a narrower margin on one or more sides and should be priced accordingly, while a stamp with wider, yet even, margins than 'Fine' would merit the description 'Very Fine' or 'Superb' and, if available, would command a price in excess of that quoted in the catalogue.

Gum: Since the prices for stamps of King Edward VIII, King George VI and Queen Elizabeth are for 'unmounted' or 'never hinged' mint, even stamps from these reigns which have been very lightly mounted should be available at a discount from catalogue price, the more obvious the hinge marks, the greater the discount.

Catalogue prices for stamps issued prior to King Edward VIII's reign are for mounted mint, so unmounted examples would be worth a premium. Hinge marks on 20th century stamps should not be too obtrusive, and should be at least in the lightly mounted category. For 19th century stamps more obvious hinging would be acceptable, but stamps should still carry a large part of their original gum—'Large part o.g.'—in order to be described as 'Fine'.

Centring: Ideally, the stamp's image should appear in the exact centre of the perforated area, giving equal margins on all sides. 'Fine' centring would be close to this ideal with any deviation having an effect on the value of the stamp. As in the case of the margins on imperforate stamps, it should be borne in mind that the space between some early stamps was very narrow, so it was very difficult to achieve accurate perforation, especially when the technology was in its infancy. Thus, poor centring would have a less damaging effect on the value of a 19th century stamp than on a 20th century example, but the premium put on a perfectly centred specimen would be greater.

Cancellations: Early cancellation devices were designed to 'obliterate' the stamp in order to prevent it being reused and this is still an important objective for today's postal administrations. Stamp collectors, on the other hand, prefer postmarks to be lightly applied, clear, and to leave as much as possible of the design visible. Dated, circular cancellations have long been 'the postmark of choice', but the definition of a 'Fine' cancellation will depend upon the types of cancellation in use at the time a stamp was current—it is clearly illogical to seek a circular datestamp on a Penny Black.

'Fine', by definition, will be superior to 'Average', so, in terms of cancellation quality, if one begins by identifying what 'Average' looks like, then one will be half way to identifying 'Fine'. The illustrations will give some guidance on mid-19th century and mid-20th century cancellations of Great Britain, but types of cancellation in general use in each country and in each period will determine the appearance of 'Fine'.

As for the factors discussed above, anything less than 'Fine' will result in a downgrading of the stamp concerned, while a very fine or superb cancellation will be worth a premium.

Combining the factors: To merit the description 'Fine', a stamp should be fine in every respect, but a small deficiency in one area might be made up for in another by a factor meriting an 'Extremely Fine' description.

Some early issues are so seldom found in what would normally be considered to be 'Fine' condition, the catalogue prices are for a slightly lower grade, with 'Fine' examples being worth a premium. In such cases a note to this effect is given in the catalogue, while elsewhere premiums are given for well-centred, lightly cancelled examples.

Stamps graded at less than fine remain collectable and, in the case of more highly priced stamps, will continue to hold a value. Nevertheless, buyers should always bear condition in mind.

The Catalogue in General

Contents. The Catalogue is confined to adhesive postage stamps, including miniature sheets. For particular categories the rules are:

(a) Revenue (fiscal) stamps are listed only where they have been expressly authorised for postal duty.
(b) Stamps issued only precancelled are included, but normally issued stamps available additionally with precancel have no separate precancel listing unless the face value is changed.
(c) Stamps prepared for use but not issued, hitherto accorded full listing, are nowadays foot-noted with a price (where possible).
(d) Bisects (trisects, etc.) are only listed where such usage was officially authorised.
(e) Stamps issued only on first day covers or in presentation packs and not available separately are not listed but may be priced in a footnote.
(f) New printings are only included in this Catalogue where they show a major philatelic variety, such as a change in shade, watermark or paper. Stamps which exist with or without imprint dates are listed separately; changes in imprint dates are mentioned in footnotes.
(g) Official and unofficial reprints are dealt with by footnote.
(h) Stamps from imperforate printings of modern issues which occur perforated are covered by footnotes, but are listed where widely available for postal use.

Exclusions. The following are excluded:

(a) non-postal revenue or fiscal stamps;
(b) postage stamps used fiscally (although prices are now given for some fiscally used high values);
(c) local carriage labels and private local issues;
(d) bogus or phantom stamps;
(e) railway or airline letter fee stamps, bus or road transport company labels or the stamps of private postal companies operating under licence from the national authority;
(f) cut-outs;
(g) all types of non-postal labels and souvenirs;
(h) documentary labels for the postal service, e.g. registration, recorded delivery, air-mail etiquettes, etc.;
(i) privately applied embellishments to official issues and privately commissioned items generally;
(j) stamps for training postal officers.

Full listing. 'Full listing' confers our recognition and implies allotting a catalogue number and (wherever possible) a price quotation.

In judging status for inclusion in the catalogue broad considerations are applied to stamps. They must be issued by a legitimate postal authority, recognised by the government concerned, and must be adhesives valid for proper postal use in the class of service for which they are inscribed. Stamps, with the exception of such categories as postage dues and officials, must be available to the general public, at face value, in reasonable quantities without any artificial restrictions being imposed on their distribution.

For errors and varieties the criterion is legitimate (albeit inadvertent) sale through a postal administration in the normal course of business. Details of provenance are always important; printers' waste and deliberately manufactured material are excluded.

Certificates. In assessing unlisted items due weight is given to Certificates from recognised Expert Committees and, where appropriate, we will usually ask to see them.

Date of issue. Where local issue dates differ from dates of release by agencies, 'date of issue' is the local date. Fortuitous stray usage before the officially intended date is disregarded in listing.

Catalogue numbers. Stamps of each country are catalogued chronologically by date of issue. Subsidiary classes are placed at the end of the country, as separate lists, with a distinguishing letter prefix to the catalogue number, e.g. D for postage due, O for official and E for express delivery stamps.

The catalogue number appears in the extreme left-column. The boldface Type numbers in the next column are merely cross-references to illustrations.

Once published in the Catalogue, numbers are changed as little as possible; really serious renumbering is reserved for the occasions when a complete country or an entire issue is being rewritten. The edition first affected includes cross-reference tables of old and new numbers.

Our catalogue numbers are universally recognised in specifying stamps and as a hallmark of status.

Illustrations. Stamps are illustrated at three-quarters linear size. Stamps not illustrated are the same size and format as the value shown, unless otherwise indicated. Stamps issued only as miniature sheets have the stamp alone illustrated but sheet size is also quoted. Overprints, surcharges, watermarks and postmarks are normally actual size. Illustrations of varieties are often enlarged to show the detail. Stamp booklet covers are illustrated half-size, unless otherwise indicated.

Designers. Designers' names are quoted where known, though space precludes naming every individual concerned in the production of a set. In particular, photographers supplying material are usually named only where they also make an active contribution in the design stage; posed photographs of reigning monarchs are, however, an exception to this rule.

CONTACTING THE CATALOGUE EDITOR

The editor is always interested in hearing from people who have new information which will improve or correct the Catalogue. As a general rule he must see and examine the actual stamps before they can be considered for listing; photographs or photocopies are insufficient evidence.

Submissions should be made in writing to the Catalogue Editor, Stanley Gibbons Publications at the Ringwood office. The cost of return postage for items submitted is appreciated, and this should include the registration fee if required.

Where information is solicited purely for the benefit of the enquirer, the editor cannot undertake to reply if the answer is already contained in these published notes or if return postage is omitted. Written communications are greatly preferred to enquiries by telephone or e-mail and the editor regrets that he or his staff cannot see personal callers without a prior appointment being made. Correspondence may be subject to delay during the production period of each new edition.

The editor welcomes close contact with study circles and is interested, too, in finding reliable local correspondents who will verify and supplement official information in countries where this is deficient.

We regret we do not give opinions as to the genuineness of stamps, nor do we identify stamps or number them by our Catalogue.

TECHNICAL MATTERS

The meanings of the technical terms used in the catalogue will be found in our *Philatelic Terms Illustrated.*

References below to (more specialised) listings are to be taken to indicate, as appropriate, the Stanley Gibbons *Great Britain Specialised Catalogue* in five volumes or the *Great Britain Concise Catalogue.*

1. Printing

Printing errors. Errors in printing are of major interest to the Catalogue. Authenticated items meriting consideration would include: background, centre or frame inverted or omitted; centre or subject transposed; error of colour; error or omission of value; double prints and impressions; printed both sides; and so on. Designs *tête-bêche*, whether intentionally or by accident, are listable. *Se-tenant* arrangements of stamps are recognised in the listings or footnotes. Gutter pairs (a pair of stamps separated by blank margin) are not included in this volume. Colours only partially omitted are not listed. Stamps with embossing omitted are reserved for our more specialised listings.

Printing varieties. Listing is accorded to major changes in the printing base which lead to completely new types. In recess-printing this could be a design re-engraved; in photogravure or photolithography a screen altered in whole or in part. It can also encompass flat-bed and rotary printing if the results are readily distinguishable.

To be considered at all, varieties must be constant.

Early stamps, produced by primitive methods, were prone to numerous imperfections; the lists reflect this, recognising re-entries, retouches, broken frames, misshapen letters, and so on. Printing technology has, however, radically improved over the years, during which time photogravure and lithography have become predominant. Varieties nowadays are more in the nature of flaws and these, being too specialised for this general catalogue, are almost always outside the scope.

In no catalogue, however, do we list such items as: dry prints, kiss prints, doctor-blade flaws, colour shifts or registration flaws (unless they lead to the complete omission of a colour from an individual stamp), lithographic ring flaws, and so on. Neither do we recognise fortuitous happenings like paper creases or confetti flaws.

Overprints (and surcharges). Overprints of different types qualify for separate listing. These include overprints in different colours; overprints from different printing processes such as litho and typo; overprints in totally different typefaces, etc. Major errors in machine-printed overprints are important and listable. They include: overprint inverted or omitted; overprint double (treble, etc.); overprint diagonal; overprint double, one inverted; pairs with one overprint omitted, e.g. from a radical shift to an adjoining stamp; error of colour; error of type fount; letters inverted or omitted, etc. If the overprint is handstamped, few of these would qualify and a distinction is drawn. We continue, however, to list pairs of stamps where one has a handstamped overprint and the other has not.

Albino prints or double prints, one of them being albino (i.e. showing an uninked impression of the printing plate) are listable unless they are particularly common in this form (see the note below Travancore No. 32fa, for example). We do not, however, normally list reversed albino overprints, caused by the accidental or deliberate folding of sheets prior to overprinting (British Levant Nos. 51/8).

Varieties occurring in overprints will often take the form of broken letters, slight differences in spacing, rising spaces, etc. Only the most important would be considered for listing or footnote mention.

Sheet positions. If space permits we quote sheet positions of listed varieties and authenticated data is solicited for this purpose.

De La Rue plates. The Catalogue classifies the general plates used by De La Rue for printing British Colonial stamps as follows:

VICTORIAN KEY TYPE

Die I

1. The ball of decoration on the second point of the crown appears as a dark mass of lines.
2. Dark vertical shading separates the front hair from the bun.
3. The vertical line of colour outlining the front of the throat stops at the sixth line of shading on the neck.
4. The white space in the coil of the hair above the curl is roughly the shape of a pin's head.

Die II

1. There are very few lines of colour in the ball and it appears almost white.

2. A white vertical strand of hair appears in place of the dark shading.
3. The line stops at the eighth line of shading.
4. The white space is oblong, with a line of colour partially dividing it at the left end.

Plates numbered 1 and 2 are both Die I. Plates 3 and 4 are Die II.

GEORGIAN KEY TYPE

Die I

A. The second (thick) line below the name of the country is cut slanting, conforming roughly to the shape of the crown on each side.
B. The labels of solid colour bearing the words "POSTAGE" and "& REVENUE" are square at the inner top corners.
C. There is a projecting "bud" on the outer spiral of the ornament in each of the lower corners.

Die II

A. The second line is cut vertically on each side of the crown.
B. The labels curve inwards at the top.
C. There is no "bud" in this position.

Unless otherwise stated in the lists, all stamps with watermark Multiple Crown CA (w **8**) are Die I while those with watermark Multiple Crown Script CA (w **9**) are Die II. The Georgian Die II was introduced in April 1921 and was used for Plates 10 to 22 and 26 to 28. Plates 23 to 25 were made from Die I by mistake.

2. Paper

All stamps listed are deemed to be on (ordinary) paper of the wove type and white in colour; only departures from this are normally mentioned.

Types. Where classification so requires we distinguish such other types of paper as, for example, vertically and horizontally laid; wove and laid bâtonné; card(board); carton; cartridge; glazed; granite; native; pelure; porous; quadrillé; ribbed; rice; and silk thread.

Wove paper Laid paper

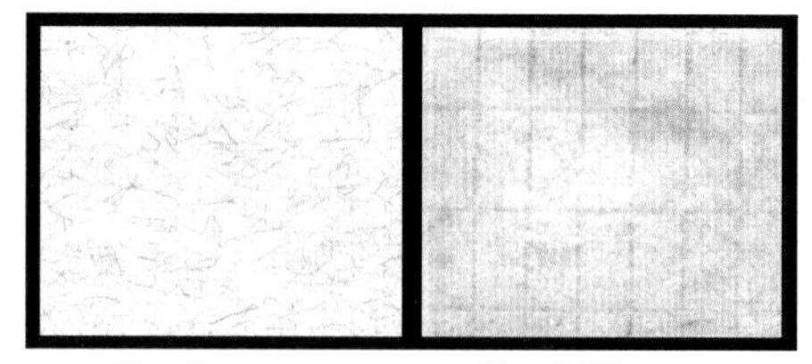

Granite paper Quadrillé paper

Burelé band

The various makeshifts for normal paper are listed as appropriate. The varieties of double paper and joined paper are recognised. The security device of a printed burelé band on the back of a stamp, as in early Queensland, qualifies for listing.

Descriptive terms. The fact that a paper is handmade (and thus probably of uneven thickness) is mentioned where necessary. Such descriptive terms as "hard" and "soft"; "smooth" and "rough"; "thick", "medium" and "thin" are applied where there is philatelic merit in classifying papers.

Coloured, very white and toned papers. A coloured paper is one that is coloured right through (front and back of the stamp). In the Catalogue the colour of the paper is given in italics, thus:

black/*rose* = black design on rose paper.

Papers have been made specially white in recent years by, for example, a very heavy coating of chalk. We do not classify shades of whiteness of paper as distinct varieties. There does exist, however, a type of paper from early days called toned. This is off-white, often brownish or buffish, but it cannot be assigned any definite colour. A toning effect brought on by climate, incorrect storage or gum staining is disregarded here, as this was not the state of the paper when issued.

"Ordinary" and "Chalk-surfaced" papers. The availability of many postage stamps for revenue purposes made necessary some safeguard against the illegitimate re-use of stamps with removable cancellations. This was at first secured by using fugitive inks and later by printing on paper surfaced by coatings containing either chalk or china clay, both of which made it difficult to remove any form of obliteration without damaging the stamp design.

This catalogue lists these chalk-surfaced paper varieties from their introduction in 1905. Where no indication is given, the paper is "ordinary".

The "traditional" method of indentifying chalk-surfaced papers has been that, when touched with a silver wire, a black mark is left on the paper, and the listings in this catalogue are based on that test. However, the test itself is now largely discredited, for, although the mark can be removed by a soft rubber, some damage to the stamp will result from its use.

The difference between chalk-surfaced and pre-war ordinary papers is fairly clear: chalk-surfaced papers being smoother to the touch and showing a characteristic sheen when light is reflected off their surface. Under good magnification tiny bubbles or pock marks can be seen on the surface of the stamp and at the tips of the perforations the surfacing appears "broken". Traces of paper fibres are evident on the surface of ordinary paper and the ink shows a degree of absorption into it.

Initial chalk-surfaced paper printings by De La Rue had a thinner coating than subsequently became the norm. The characteristics described above are less pronounced in these printings.

During and after the Second World War, substitute papers replaced the chalk-surfaced papers, these do not react to the silver test and are therefore classed as "ordinary", although differentiating them without recourse to it is more difficult, for, although the characteristics of the chalk-surfaced paper remained the same, some of the ordinary papers appear much smoother than earlier papers and many do not show the watermark clearly. Experience is the only solution to identifying these, and comparison with stamps whose paper type is without question will be of great help.

Another type of paper, known as "thin striated" was used only for the Bahamas 1s. and 5s. (Nos. 155a, 156a, 171 and 174) and for several stamps of the Malayan states. Hitherto these have been described as "chalk-surfaced" since they gave some reaction to the silver test, but they are much thinner than usual chalk-surfaced papers, with the watermark showing clearly. Stamps on this paper show a slightly 'ribbed' effect when the stamp is held up to the light. Again, comparison with a known striated paper stamp, such as the 1941 Straits Settlements Die II 2c. orange (No. 294) will prove invaluable in separating these papers.

Glazed paper. In 1969 the Crown Agents introduced a new general-purpose paper for use in conjunction with all current printing processes. It generally has a marked glossy surface but the degree varies according to the process used, being more marked in recess-printing stamps. As it does not respond to the silver test this presents a further test where previous printings were on chalky paper. A change of paper to the glazed variety merits separate listing.

Green and yellow papers. Issues of the First World War and immediate postwar period occur on green and yellow papers and these are given separate Catalogue listing. The original coloured papers (coloured throughout) gave way to surface-coloured papers, the stamps having "white backs"; other stamps show one colour on the front and a different one at the back. Because of the numerous variations a grouping of colours is adopted as follows:

Yellow papers

(1) The original *yellow* paper (throughout), usually bright in colour. The gum is often sparse, of harsh consistency and dull-looking. Used 1912–1920.

(2) The *white-backs*. Used 1913–1914.

(3) A bright lemon paper. The colour must have a pronounced greenish tinge, different from the "yellow" in (1). As a rule, the gum on stamps using this lemon paper is plentiful, smooth and shiny, and the watermark shows distinctly. Care is needed with stamps printed in green on yellow paper (1) as it may appear that the paper is this lemon. Used 1914–1916.

(4) An experimental *orange-buff* paper. The colour must have a distinct brownish tinge. It is not to be confused with a muddy yellow (1) nor the misleading appearance (on the surface) of stamps printed in red on yellow paper where an engraved plate has been insufficiently wiped. Used 1918–1921.

(5) An experimental *buff* paper. This lacks the brownish tinge of (4) and the brightness of the yellow shades. The gum is shiny when compared with the matt type used on (4). Used 1919–1920.

(6) A *pale yellow* paper that has a creamy tone to the yellow. Used from 1920 onwards.

Green papers

(7) The original "green" paper, varying considerably through shades of blue-green and yellow-green, the front and back sometimes differing. Used 1912–1916.

(8) The *white backs*. Used 1913–1914.

(9) A paper blue-green on the surface with *pale olive* back. The back must be markedly paler than the front and this and the pronounced olive tinge to the back distinguish it from (7). Used 1916–1920.

(10) Paper with a vivid green surface, commonly called *emerald-green*; it has the olive back of (9). Used 1920.

(11) Paper with *emerald-green* both back and front. Used from 1920 onwards.

3. Perforation and Rouletting

Perforation gauge. The gauge of a perforation is the number of holes in a length of 2 cm. For correct classification the size of the holes (large or small) may need to be distinguished; in a few cases the actual number of holes on each edge of the stamp needs to be quoted.

Measurement. The Gibbons *Instanta* gauge is the standard for measuring perforations. The stamp is viewed against a dark background with the transparent gauge put on top of it. Though the gauge measures to decimal accuracy, perforations read from it are generally quoted in the Catalogue to the nearest half. For example:

Just over perf 12¾ to just under 13¼ = perf 13
Perf 13¼ exactly, rounded up = perf 13½
Just over perf 13¼ to just under 13¾ = perf 13½
Perf 13¾ exactly, rounded up = perf 14

However, where classification depends on it, actual quarter-perforations are quoted.

Notation. Where no perforation is quoted for an issue it is imperforate. Perforations are usually abbreviated (and spoken) as follows, though sometimes they may be spelled out for clarity. This notation for rectangular stamps (the majority) applies to diamond shapes if "top" is read as the edge to the top right.

P 14: perforated alike on all sides (read: "perf 14").

P 14×15: the first figure refers to top and bottom, the second to left and right sides (read: "perf 14 by 15"). This is a compound perforation. For an upright triangular stamp the first figure refers to the two sloping sides and second to the base. In inverted triangulars the base is first and the second figure to the sloping sides.

P 14–15: perforation measuring anything between 14 and 15: the holes are irregularly spaced, thus the gauge may vary along a single line or even along a single edge of the stamp (read: "perf 14 to 15").

P 14 *irregular*: perforated 14 from a worn perforator, giving badly aligned holes irregularly spaced (read: "irregular perf 14").

P *comp(ound)* 14×15: two gauges in use but not necessarily on opposite sides of the stamp. It could be one side in one gauge and three in the other; or two adjacent sides with the same gauge. (Read: "perf compound of 14 and 15".) For three gauges or more, abbreviated as "P 12, 14½, 15 *or compound*" for example.

P 14, 14½: perforated approximately 14¼ (read: "perf 14 or 14½"). It does *not* mean two stamps, one perf 14 and the other perf 14½. This obsolescent notation is gradually being replaced in the Catalogue.

Imperf: imperforate (not perforated)

Imperf×P 14: imperforate at top ad bottom and perf 14 at sides.

P 14×*imperf*: perf 14 at top and bottom and imperforate at sides.

Such headings as "P 13×14 (*vert*) and P 14×13 (*horiz*)" indicate which perforations apply to which stamp format—vertical or horizontal.

Some stamps are additionally perforated so that a label or tab is detachable; others have been perforated for use as two halves. Listings are normally for whole stamps, unless stated otherwise.

Imperf×perf

Other terms. Perforation almost always gives circular holes; where other shapes have been used they are specified, e.g. square holes; lozenge perf. Interrupted perfs are brought about by the omission of pins at regular intervals. Perforations merely simulated by being printed as part of the design are of course ignored. With few exceptions, privately applied perforations are not listed.

In the 19th century perforations are often described as clean cut (clean, sharply incised holes), intermediate or rough (rough holes, imperfectly cut, often the result of blunt pins).

Perforation errors and varieties. Authenticated errors, where a stamp normally perforated is accidentally issued imperforate, are listed provided no traces of perforation (blind holes or indentations) remain. They must be provided as pairs, both stamps wholly imperforate, and are only priced in that form.

Stamps imperforate between stamp and sheet margin are not listed in this catalogue, but such errors on Great Britain stamps will be found in the *Great Britain Specialised Catalogue*.

Pairs described as "imperforate between" have the line of perforations between the two stamps omitted.

Imperf between (horiz pair): a horizontal pair of stamps with perfs all around the edges but none between the stamps.

Imperf between (vert pair): a vertical pair of stamps with perfs all around the edges but none between the stamps.

Imperf between (vertical pair) — Imperf horizontally (vertical pair)

Where several of the rows have escaped perforation the resulting varieties are listable. Thus:

Imperf vert (horiz pair): a horizontal pair of stamps perforated top and bottom; all three vertical directions are imperf—the two outer edges and between the stamps.

Imperf horiz (vert pair): a vertical pair perforated at left and right edges; all three horizontal directions are imperf—the top, bottom and between the stamps.

Straight edges. Large sheets cut up before issue to post offices can cause stamps with straight edges, i.e. imperf on one side or on two sides at right angles. They are not usually listable in this condition and are worth less than corresponding stamps properly perforated all round. This does not, however, apply to certain stamps, mainly from coils and booklets, where straight edges on various sides are the manufacturing norm affecting every stamp. The listings and notes make clear which sides are correctly imperf.

Malfunction. Varieties of double, misplaced or partial perforation caused by error or machine malfunction are not listable, neither are freaks, such as perforations placed diagonally from paper folds, nor missing holes caused by broken pins.

Types of perforating. Where necessary for classification, perforation types are distinguished.

These include:

Line perforation from one line of pins punching single rows of holes at a time.

Comb perforation from pins disposed across the sheet in comb formation, punching out holes at three sides of the stamp a row at a time.

Harrow perforation applied to a whole pane or sheet at one stroke.

Rotary perforation from toothed wheels operating across a sheet, then crosswise.

Sewing machine perforation. The resultant condition, clean-cut or rough, is distinguished where required.

Pin-perforation is the commonly applied term for pin-roulette in which, instead of being punched out, round holes are pricked by sharp-pointed pins and no paper is removed.

Mixed perforation occurs when stamps with defective perforations are re-perforated in a different gauge.

Punctured stamps. Perforation holes can be punched into the face of the stamp. Patterns of small holes, often in the shape of initial letters, are privately applied devices against pilferage. These (perfins) are outside the scope except for Australia, Canada, Cape of Good Hope, Papua and Sudan where they were used as official stamps by the national administration. Identification devices, when officially inspired, are listed or noted; they can be shapes, or letters or words formed from holes, sometimes converting one class of stamp into another.

Rouletting. In rouletting the paper is cut, for ease of separation, but none is removed. The gauge is measured, when needed, as for perforations. Traditional French terms descriptive of the type of cut are often used and types include:

Arc roulette (percé en arc). Cuts are minute, spaced arcs, each roughly a semicircle.

Cross roulette (percé en croix). Cuts are tiny diagonal crosses.

Line roulette (percé en ligne or *en ligne droite)*. Short straight cuts parallel to the frame of the stamp. The commonest basic roulette. Where not further described, "roulette" means this type.

Rouletted in colour or coloured roulette (percé en lignes colorées or *en lignes de coleur)*. Cuts with coloured edges, arising from notched rule inked simultaneously with the printing plate.

Saw-tooth roulette (percé en scie). Cuts applied zigzag fashion to resemble the teeth of a saw.

Serpentine roulette (percé en serpentin). Cuts as sharply wavy lines.

Zigzag roulette (percé en zigzags). Short straight cuts at angles in alternate directions, producing sharp points on separation. US usage favours "serrate(d) roulette" for this type.

Pin-roulette (originally *percé en points* and now *perforés trous d'epingle*) is commonly called pin-perforation in English.

4. Gum

All stamps listed are assumed to have gum of some kind; if they were issued without gum this is stated. Original gum (o.g.) means that which was present on the stamp as issued to the public. Deleterious climates and the presence of certain chemicals can cause gum to crack and, with early stamps, even make the paper deteriorate. Unscrupulous fakers are adept in removing it and regumming the stamp to meet the unreasoning demand often made for "full o.g." in cases where such a thing is virtually impossible.

The gum normally used on stamps has been gum arabic until the late 1960s when synthetic adhesives were introduced. Harrison and Sons Ltd for instance use *polyvinyl alcohol,* known to philatelists as PVA. This is almost invisible except for a slight yellowish tinge which was incorporated to make it possible to see that the stamps have been gummed. It has advantages in hot countries, as stamps do not curl and sheets are less likely to stick together. Gum arabic and PVA are not distinguished in the lists except that where a stamp exists with both forms this is indicated in footnotes. Our more specialised catalogues provide separate listing of gums for Great Britain.

Self-adhesive stamps are issued on backing paper, from which they are peeled before affixing to mail. Unused examples are priced as for backing paper intact, in which condition they are recommended to be kept. Used examples are best collected on cover or on piece.

5. Watermarks

Stamps are on unwatermarked paper except where the heading to the set says otherwise.

Detection. Watermarks are detected for Catalogue description by one of four methods: (1) holding stamps to the light; (2) laying stamps face down on a dark background; (3) adding a few drops of petroleum ether 40/60 to the stamp laid face down in a watermark tray; (4) by use of the Stanley Gibbons Detectamark, or other equipment, which work by revealing the thinning of the paper at the watermark. (Note that petroleum ether is highly inflammable in use and can damage photogravure stamps.)

Listable types. Stamps occurring on both watermarked and unwatermarked papers are different types and both receive full listing.

Single watermarks (devices occurring once on every stamp) can be modified in size and shape as between different issues; the types are noted but not usually separately listed. Fortuitous absence of watermark from a single stamp or its gross displacement would not be listable.

To overcome registration difficulties the device may be repeated at close intervals *(a multiple watermark)*, single stamps thus showing parts of several devices. Similarly, a *large sheet watermark* (or *all-over watermark*) covering numerous stamps can be used. We give informative notes and illustrations for them. The designs may be such that numbers of stamps in the sheet automatically lack watermark: this is not a listable variety. Multiple and all-over watermarks sometimes undergo modifications, but if the various types are difficult to distinguish from single stamps notes are given but not separate listings.

Papermakers' watermarks are noted where known but not listed separately, since most stamps in the sheet will lack them. Sheet watermarks which are nothing more than officially adopted papermakers' watermarks are, however, given normal listing.

Marginal watermarks, falling outside the pane of stamps, are ignored except where misplacement caused the adjoining row to be affected, in which case they may be footnoted.

Watermark errors and varieties. Watermark errors are recognised as of major importance. They comprise stamps intended to be on unwatermarked paper but issued watermarked by mistake, or stamps printed on paper with the wrong watermark. Varieties showing letters omitted from the watermark are also included, but broken or deformed bits on the dandy roll are not listed unless they represent repairs.

Watermark positions. The diagram shows how watermark position is described in the Catalogue. Paper has a side intended for printing and watermarks are usually impressed so that they read normally when looked through from that printed side. However, since philatelists customarily detect watermarks by looking at the back of the stamp the watermark diagram also makes clear what is actually seen.

Illustrations in the Catalogue are of watermarks in normal positions (from the front of the stamps) and are actual size where possible.

Differences in watermark position are collectable varieties. This Catalogue now lists inverted, sideways inverted and reversed watermark varieties on Commonwealth stamps from the 1860s onwards except where the watermark position is completely haphazard.

Great Britain inverted and sideways inverted watermarks can be found in the *Great Britain Specialised Catalogue* and the *Great Britain Concise Catalogue*.

Where a watermark comes indiscriminately in various positions our policy is to cover this by a general note: we do not give separate listings because the watermark position in these circumstances has no particular philatelic importance.

AS DESCRIBED (Read through front of stamp)		AS SEEN DURING WATERMARK DETECTION (Stamp face down and back examined)
GvR	Normal	
	Inverted	
	Reversed	GvR
	Reversed and Inverted	
	Sideways	
	Sideways Inverted	

Standard types of watermark. Some watermarks have been used generally for various British possessions rather than exclusively for a single colony. To avoid repetition the Catalogue classifies 11 general types, as under, with references in the headings throughout the listings being given either in words or in the form ("W w **9**") (meaning "watermark type w **9**"). In those cases where watermark illustrations appear in the listings themselves, the respective reference reads, for example, W **153**, thus indicating that the watermark will be found in the normal sequence of illustrations as (type) **153**.

The general types are as follows, with an example of each quoted.

W	*Description*	*Example*
w **1**	Large Star	St. Helena No. 1
w **2**	Small Star	Turks Is. No. 4
w **3**	Broad (pointed) Star	Grenada No. 24
w **4**	Crown (over) CC, small stamp	Antigua No. 13
w **5**	Crown (over) CC, large stamp	Antigua No. 31
w **6**	Crown (over) CA, small stamp	Antigua No. 21
w **7**	Crown CA (CA over Crown), large stamp	Sierra Leone No. 54
w **8**	Multiple Crown CA	Antigua No. 41
w **9**	Multiple Script CA	Seychelles No. 158
w **9***a*	do. Error	Seychelles No. 158a
w **9***b*	do. Error	Seychelles No. 158b
w **10**	V over Crown	N.S.W. No. 327
w **11**	Crown over A	N.S.W. No. 347

CC in these watermarks is an abbreviation for "Crown Colonies" and CA for "Crown Agents". Watermarks w **1**, w **2** and w **3** are on stamps printed by Perkins, Bacon; w **4** onwards on stamps from De La Rue and other printers.

w **1**
Large Star

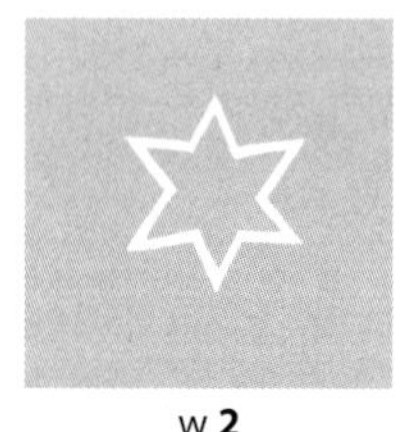
w **2**
Small Star

w **3**
Broad-pointed Star

Watermark w **1**, *Large Star*, measures 15 to 16 mm across the star from point to point and about 27 mm from centre to centre vertically between stars in the sheet. It was made for long stamps like Ceylon 1857 and St. Helena 1856.

Watermark w **2**, *Small Star* is of similar design but measures 12 to 13½mm from point to point and 24 mm from centre to centre vertically. It was for use with ordinary-size stamps such as Grenada 1863–71.

When the Large Star watermark was used with the smaller stamps it only occasionally comes in the centre of the paper. It is frequently so misplaced as to show portions of two stars above and below and this eccentricity will very often help in determining the watermark.

Watermark w **3**, *Broad-pointed Star*, resembles w **1** but the points are broader.

w **4**
Crown (over) CC

w **5**
Crown (over) CC

Two *Crown (over) CC* watermarks were used:
w **4** was for stamps of ordinary size and w **5** for those of larger size.

w **6**
Crown (over) CA

w **7**
CA over Crown

Two watermarks of *Crown CA* type were used, w **6** being for stamps of ordinary size. The other, w **7**, is properly described as *CA over Crown*. It was specially made for paper on which it was intended to print long fiscal stamps: that some were used postally accounts for the appearance of w **7** in the Catalogue. The watermark occupies twice the space of the ordinary Crown CA watermark, w **6**. Stamps of normal size printed on paper with w **7** watermark show it *sideways*; it takes a horizontal pair of stamps to show the entire watermark.

w **8**
Multiple Crown CA

w **9**
Multiple Script CA

Multiple watermarks began in 1904 with w **8**, *Multiple Crown CA,* changed from 1921 to w **9**, *Multiple Script CA*. On stamps of ordinary size portions of two or three watermarks appear and on the large-sized stamps a greater number can be observed. The change to letters in script character with w **9** was accompanied by a Crown of distinctly different shape.

It seems likely that there were at least two dandy rolls for each Crown Agents watermark in use at any one time with a reserve roll being employed when the normal one was withdrawn for maintenance or repair.

Both the Mult Crown CA and the Mult Script CA types exist with one or other of the letters omitted from individual impressions. It is possible that most of these occur from the reserve rolls as they have only been found on certain issues. The MCA watermark experienced such problems during the early 1920s and the Script over a longer period from the early 1940s until 1951.

During the 1920s damage must also have occurred on one of the Crowns as a substituted Crown has been found on certain issues. This is smaller than the normal and consists of an oval base joined to two upright ovals with a circle positioned between their upper ends. The upper line of the Crown's base is omitted, as are the left and right-hand circles at the top and also the cross over the centre circle.

Substituted Crown

The *Multiple Script CA* watermark, w **9**, is known with two errors, recurring among the 1950–52 printings of several territories. In the first a crown has fallen away from the dandy-roll that impresses the watermark into the paper pulp. It gives w **9a**, *Crown missing*, but this omission has been found in both "Crown only" (*illustrated*) and "Crown CA" rows. The resulting faulty paper was used for Bahamas, Johore, Seychelles and the postage due stamps of nine colonies

w **9a**: Error, Crown missing

w **9b**: Error, St. Edward's Crown

When the omission was noticed a second mishap occurred, which was to insert a wrong crown in the space, giving w **9b**, St. Edward's Crown. This produced varieties in Bahamas, Perlis, St. Kitts-Nevis and Singapore and the incorrect crown likewise occurs in (Crown only) and (Crown CA) rows.

w **10**
V over Crown

w **11**
Crown over A

Resuming the general types, two watermarks found in issues of several Australian States are: w **10**, *V over Crown*, and w **11**, *Crown over A*.

w **12**
Multiple St. Edward's Crown Block CA

w **13**
Multiple PTM

The *Multiple St. Edward's Crown Block CA* watermark, w **12**, was introduced in 1957 and besides the change in the Crown (from that used in Multiple Crown Script CA, w **9**) the letters reverted to block capitals. The new watermark began to appear sideways in 1966 and these stamps are generally listed as separate sets.

The watermark w **13**, *Multiple PTM*, was introduced for new Malaysian issues in November 1961.

w **14**
Multiple Crown CA Diagonal

By 1974 the two dandy-rolls the "upright" and the "sideways" for w **12** were wearing out; the Crown Agents therefore discontinued using the sideways watermark one and retained the other only as a stand-by. A new dandy-roll with the pattern of w **14**, *Multiple Crown CA Diagonal,* was introduced and first saw use with some Churchill Centenary issues.

The new watermark had the design arranged in gradually spiralling rows. It is improved in design to allow smooth passage over the paper (the gaps between letters and rows had caused jolts in previous dandy-rolls) and the sharp corners and angles, where fibres used to accumulate, have been eliminated by rounding.

This watermark had no "normal" sideways position amongst the different printers using it. To avoid confusion our more specialised listings do not rely on such terms as "sideways inverted" but describe the direction in which the watermark points.

w **15**
Multiple POST OFFICE

During 1981 w **15**, *Multiple POST OFFICE* was introduced for certain issues prepared by Philatelists Ltd, acting for various countries in the Indian Ocean, Pacific and West Indies.

w **16**
Multiple Crown Script CA Diagonal

A new Crown Agents watermark was introduced during 1985, w **16**, *Multiple Crown Script CA Diagonal.* This was very similar to the previous w **14**, but showed "CA" in script rather than block letters. It was first used on the omnibus series of stamps commemorating the Life and Times of Queen Elizabeth the Queen Mother.

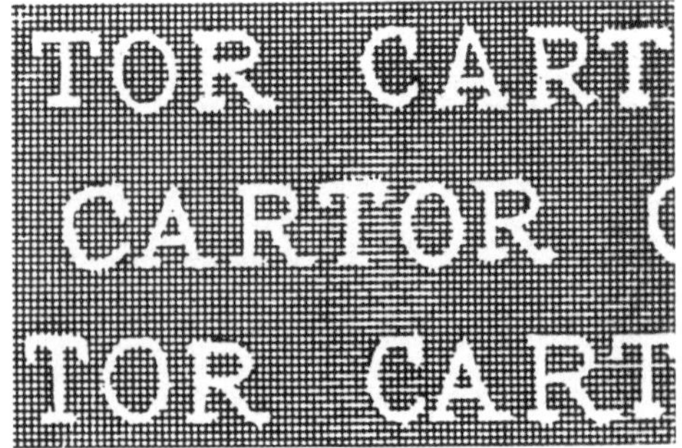

w **17**
Multiple CARTOR

Watermark w **17**, *Multiple CARTOR*, was used from 1985 for issues printed by this French firm for countries which did not normally use the Crown Agents watermark.

w **18**

In 2008, following the closure of the Crown Agents Stamp Bureau, a new Multiple Crowns watermark, w **18** was introduced

In recent years the use of watermarks has, to a small extent, been superseded by fluorescent security markings. These are often more visible from the reverse of the stamp (Cook Islands from 1970 onwards), but have occurred printed over the design (Hong Kong Nos. 415/30). In 1982 the Crown Agents introduced a new stock paper, without watermark, known as "C-Kurity" on which a fluorescent pattern of blue rosettes is visible on the reverse, beneath the gum. This paper was used for issues from Gambia and Norfolk Island.

6. Colours

Stamps in two or three colours have these named in order of appearance, from the centre moving outwards. Four colours or more are usually listed as multicoloured.

In compound colour names the second is the predominant one, thus:

orange-red = a red tending towards orange;
red-orange = an orange containing more red than usual.

Standard colours used. The 200 colours most used for stamp identification are given in the Stanley Gibbons Stamp Colour Key. The Catalogue has used the Stamp Colour Key as standard for describing new issues for some years. The names are also introduced as lists are rewritten, though exceptions are made for those early issues where traditional names have become universally established.

Determining colours. When comparing actual stamps with colour samples in the Stamp Colour Key, view in a good north daylight (or its best substitute; fluorescent "colour matching" light). Sunshine is not recommended. Choose a solid portion of the stamp design; if available, marginal markings such as solid bars of colour or colour check dots are helpful. Shading lines in the design can be misleading as they appear lighter than solid colour. Postmarked portions of a stamp appear darker than normal. If more than one colour is present, mask off the extraneous ones as the eye tends to mix them.

Errors of colour. Major colour errors in stamps or overprints which qualify for listing are: wrong colours; one colour inverted in relation to the rest; albinos (colourless impressions), where these have Expert Committee certificates; colours completely omitted, but only on unused stamps (if found on used stamps the information is footnoted) and with good credentials, missing colours being frequently faked.

Colours only partially omitted are not recognised, Colour shifts, however spectacular, are not listed.

Shades. Shades in philately refer to variations in the intensity of a colour or the presence of differing amounts of other colours. They are particularly significant when they can be linked to specific printings. In general, shades need to be quite marked to fall within the scope of this Catalogue; it does not favour nowadays listing the often numerous shades of a stamp, but chooses a single applicable colour name which will indicate particular groups of outstanding shades. Furthermore, the listings refer to colours as issued; they may deteriorate into something different through the passage of time.

Modern colour printing by lithography is prone to marked differences of shade, even within a single run, and variations can occur within the same sheet. Such shades are not listed.

Aniline colours. An aniline colour meant originally one derived from coal-tar; it now refers more widely to colour of a particular brightness suffused on the surface of a stamp and showing through clearly on the back.

Colours of overprints and surcharges. All overprints and surcharges are in black unless stated otherwise in the heading or after the description of the stamp.

7. Specimen Stamps

Originally, stamps overprinted SPECIMEN were circulated to postmasters or kept in official records, but after the establishment of the Universal Postal Union supplies were sent to Berne for distribution to the postal administrations of member countries.

During the period 1884 to 1928 most of the stamps of British Crown Colonies required for this purpose were overprinted SPECIMEN in various shapes and sizes by their printers from typeset formes. Some locally produced provisionals were handstamped locally, as were sets prepared for presentation. From 1928 stamps were punched with holes forming the word SPECIMEN, each firm of printers using a different machine or machines. From 1948 the stamps supplied for UPU distribution were no longer punctured.

Stamps of some other Commonwealth territories were overprinted or handstamped locally, while stamps of Great Britain and those overprinted for use in overseas postal agencies (mostly of the higher denominations) bore SPECIMEN overprints and handstamps applied by the Inland Revenue or the Post Office.

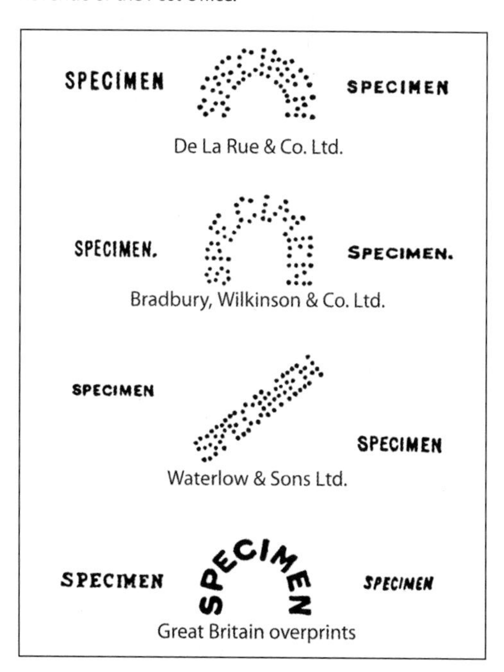

Some of the commoner types of overprints or punctures are illustrated here. Collectors are warned that dangerous forgeries of the punctured type exist.

The *Stanley Gibbons Commonwealth Catalogues* record those Specimen overprints or perforations intended for distribution by the UPU to member countries. In addition the Specimen overprints of Australia and its dependent territories, which were sold to collectors by the Post Office, are also included.

Various Perkins Bacon issues exist obliterated with a "CANCELLED" within an oval of bars handstamp.

Perkins Bacon "CANCELLED" Handstamp

This was applied to six examples of those issues available in 1861 which were then given to members of Sir Rowland Hill's family. 75 different stamps (including four from Chile) are recorded with this handstamp although others may possibly exist. The unauthorised gift of these "CANCELLED" stamps to the Hill family was a major factor in the loss of the Agent General for the Crown Colonies (the forerunner of the Crown Agents) contracts by Perkins Bacon in the following year. Where examples of these scarce items are known to be in private hands the catalogue provides a price.

For full details of these stamps see *CANCELLED by Perkins Bacon* by Peter Jaffé (published by Spink in 1998).

All other Specimens are outside the scope of this volume.

Specimens are not quoted in Great Britain as they are fully listed in the Stanley Gibbons *Great Britain Specialised Catalogue*.

In specifying type of specimen for individual high-value stamps, "H/S" means handstamped, "Optd" is overprinted and "Perf" is punctured. Some sets occur mixed, e.g. "Optd/Perf". If unspecified, the type is apparent from the date or it is the same as for the lower values quoted as a set.

Prices. Prices for stamps up to £1 are quoted in sets; higher values are priced singly. Where specimens exist in more than one type the price quoted is for the cheapest. Specimen stamps have rarely survived even as pairs; these and strips of three, four or five are worth considerably more than singles.

8. Luminescence

Machines which sort mail electronically have been introduced in recent years. In consequence some countries have issued stamps on fluorescent or phosphorescent papers, while others have marked their stamps with phosphor bands.

The various papers can only be distinguished by ultraviolet lamps emitting particular wavelengths. They are separately listed only when the stamps have some other means of distinguishing them, visible without the use of these lamps. Where this is not so, the papers are recorded in footnotes or headings.

For this catalogue we do not consider it appropriate that collectors be compelled to have the use of an ultraviolet lamp before being able to identify stamps by our listings. Some experience will also be found necessary in interpreting the results given by ultraviolet. Collectors using the lamps, nevertheless, should exercise great care in their use as exposure to their light is potentially dangerous to the eyes.

Phosphor bands are listable, since they are visible to the naked eye (by holding stamps at an angle to the light and looking along them, the bands appear dark). Stamps existing with or without phosphor bands or with differing numbers of bands are given separate listings. Varieties such as double bands, bands omitted, misplaced or printed on the back are not listed.

Detailed descriptions appear at appropriate places in the listings in explanation of luminescent papers; see, for example, Australia above No. 363, Canada above Nos. 472 and 611, Cook Is. above 249, etc.

For Great Britain, where since 1959 phosphors have played a prominent and intricate part in stamp issues, the main notes above Nos. 599 and 723 should be studied, as well as the footnotes to individual listings where appropriate. In general the classification is as follows.

Stamps with phosphor bands are those where a separate cylinder applies the phosphor after the stamps are printed. Issues with "all-over" phosphor have the "band" covering the entire stamp. Parts of the stamp covered by phosphor bands, or the entire surface for "all-over" phosphor versions, appear matt. Stamps on phosphorised paper have the phosphor added to the paper coating before the stamps are printed. Issues on this paper have a completely shiny surface.

Further particularisation of phosphor – their methods of printing and the colours they exhibit under ultraviolet – is outside the scope. The more specialised listings should be consulted for this information.

9. Coil Stamps

Stamps issued only in coil form are given full listing. If stamps are issued in both sheets and coils the coil stamps are listed separately only where there is some feature (e.g. perforation or watermark sideways) by which singles can be distinguished. Coil stamps containing different stamps *se-tenant* are also listed.

Coil join pairs are too random and too easily faked to permit of listing; similarly ignored are coil stamps which have accidentally suffered an extra row of perforations from the claw mechanism in a malfunctioning vending machine.

10. Stamp Booklets

Stamp booklets are now listed in this catalogue.

Single stamps from booklets are listed if they are distinguishable in some way (such as watermark or perforation) from similar sheet stamps.

Booklet panes are listed where they contain stamps of different denominations *se-tenant*, where stamp-size labels are included, or where such panes are otherwise identifiable. Booklet panes are placed in the listing under the lowest denomination present.

Particular perforations (straight edges) are covered by appropriate notes.

11. Miniature Sheets and Sheetlets

We distinguish between "miniature sheets" and "sheetlets" and this affects the catalogue numbering. An item in sheet form that is postally valid, containing a single stamp, pair, block or set of stamps, with wide, inscribed and/or decorative margins, is a miniature sheet if it is sold at post offices as an indivisable entity. As such the Catalogue allots a single MS number and describes what stamps make it up. The sheetlet or small sheet differs in that the individual stamps are intended to be purchased separately for postal purposes. For sheetlets, all the component postage stamps are numbered individually and the composition explained in a footnote. Note that the definitions refer to post office sale—not how items may be subsequently offered by stamp dealers.

12. Forgeries and Fakes

Forgeries. Where space permits, notes are considered if they can give a concise description that will permit unequivocal detection of a forgery. Generalised warnings, lacking detail, are not nowadays inserted, since their value to the collector is problematic.

Forged cancellations have also been applied to genuine stamps. This catalogue includes notes regarding those manufactured by "Madame Joseph", together with the cancellation dates known to exist. It should be remembered that these dates also exist as genuine cancellations.

For full details of these see *Madame Joseph Forged Postmarks* by Derek Worboys (published by the Royal Philatelic Society London and the British Philatelic Trust in 1994) or *Madame Joseph Revisited* by Brian Cartwright (published by the Royal Philatelic Society London in 2005).

Fakes. Unwitting fakes are numerous, particularly "new shades" which are colour changelings brought about by exposure to sunlight, soaking in water contaminated with dyes from adherent paper, contact with oil and dirt from a pocketbook, and so on. Fraudulent operators, in addition, can offer to arrange: removal of hinge marks; repairs of thins on white or coloured papers; replacement of missing margins or perforations; reperforating in true or false gauges; removal of fiscal cancellations; rejoining of severed pairs, strips and blocks; and (a major hazard) regumming. Collectors can only be urged to purchase from reputable sources and to insist upon Expert Committee certification where there is any kind of doubt.

The Catalogue can consider footnotes about fakes where these are specific enough to assist in detection.

ACKNOWLEDGEMENTS

We are grateful to individual collectors, members of the philatelic trade and specialist societies and study circles for their assistance in improving and extending the Stanley Gibbons range of catalogues. The addresses of societies and study circles relevant to this volume are:

Ascension Study Circle
Secretary — Dr. R.C.F. Baker
Greys, Tower Road, Whitstable
Kent CT5 3ER

St. Helena, Ascension and Tristan da Cunha Philatelic Society
Secretary — Mr. J. Havill
205 N. Murray Blvd. # 221, Colorado Springs
CO 80916, USA

West Africa Study Circle
Hon Membership Secretary — Mr P Duggan,
75 Alexandra Road, Reading RG1 5PS

Abbreviations

Printers

A.B.N. Co.	American Bank Note Co, New York.
B.A.B.N.	British American Bank Note Co. Ottawa
B.D.T.	B.D.T. International Security Printing Ltd, Dublin, Ireland
B.W.	Bradbury Wilkinson & Co, Ltd.
Cartor	Cartor S.A., La Loupe, France
C.B.N.	Canadian Bank Note Co, Ottawa.
Continental	Continental Bank Note Co. B.N. Co.
Courvoisier	Imprimerie Courvoisier S.A., La-Chaux-de-Fonds, Switzerland.
D.L.R.	De La Rue & Co, Ltd, London.
Enschedé	Joh. Enschedé en Zonen, Haarlem, Netherlands.
Format	Format International Security Printers Ltd., London
Harrison	Harrison & Sons, Ltd. London
J.W.	John Waddington Security Print Ltd., Leeds
P.B.	Perkins Bacon Ltd, London.
Questa	Questa Colour Security Printers Ltd, London
Walsall	Walsall Security Printers Ltd
Waterlow	Waterlow & Sons, Ltd, London.

General Abbreviations

Alph	Alphabet
Anniv	Anniversary
Comp	Compound (perforation)
Des	Designer; designed
Diag	Diagonal; diagonally
Eng	Engraver; engraved
F.C.	Fiscal Cancellation
H/S	Handstamped
Horiz	Horizontal; horizontally
Imp, Imperf	Imperforate
Inscr	Inscribed
L	Left
Litho	Lithographed
mm	Millimetres
MS	Miniature sheet
N.Y.	New York
Opt(d)	Overprint(ed)
P or P-c	Pen-cancelled
P, Pf or Perf	Perforated
Photo	Photogravure
Pl	Plate
Pr	Pair
Ptd	Printed
Ptg	Printing
R	Right
R.	Row
Recess	Recess-printed
Roto	Rotogravure
Roul	Rouletted
S	Specimen (overprint)
Surch	Surcharge(d)
T.C.	Telegraph Cancellation
T	Type
Typo	Typographed
Un	Unused
Us	Used
Vert	Vertical; vertically
W or wmk	Watermark
Wmk s	Watermark sideways

(†) = Does not exist

(–) (or blank price column) = Exists, or may exist, but no market price is known.

/ between colours means "on" and the colour following is that of the paper on which the stamp is printed.

Colours of Stamps

Bl (blue); blk (black); brn (brown); car, carm (carmine); choc (chocolate); clar (claret); emer (emerald); grn (green); ind (indigo); mag (magenta); mar (maroon); mult (multicoloured); mve (mauve); ol (olive); orge (orange); pk (pink); pur (purple); scar (scarlet); sep (sepia); turq (turquoise); ultram (ultramarine); verm (vermilion); vio (violet); yell (yellow).

Colour of Overprints and Surcharges

(B.) = blue, (Blk.) = black, (Br.) = brown, (C.) = carmine, (G.) = green, (Mag.) = magenta, (Mve.) = mauve, (Ol.) = olive, (O.) = orange, (P.) = purple, (Pk.) = pink, (R.) = red, (Sil.) = silver, (V.) = violet, (Vm.) or (Verm.) = vermilion, (W.) = white, (Y.) = yellow.

Arabic Numerals

As in the case of European figures, the details of the Arabic numerals vary in different stamp designs, but they should be readily recognised with the aid of this illustration.

International Philatelic Glossary

English	French	German	Spanish	Italian
Agate	Agate	Achat	Agata	Agata
Air stamp	Timbre de la poste aérienne	Flugpostmarke	Sello de correo aéreo	Francobollo per posta aerea
Apple Green	Vert-pomme	Apfelgrün	Verde manzana	Verde mela
Barred	Annulé par barres	Balkenentwertung	Anulado con barras	Sbarrato
Bisected	Timbre coupé	Halbiert	Partido en dos	Frazionato
Bistre	Bistre	Bister	Bistre	Bistro
Bistre-brown	Brun-bistre	Bisterbraun	Castaño bistre	Bruno-bistro
Black	Noir	Schwarz	Negro	Nero
Blackish Brown	Brun-noir	Schwärzlichbraun	Castaño negruzco	Bruno nerastro
Blackish Green	Vert foncé	Schwärzlichgrün	Verde negruzco	Verde nerastro
Blackish Olive	Olive foncé	Schwärzlicholiv	Oliva negruzco	Oliva nerastro
Block of four	Bloc de quatre	Viererblock	Bloque de cuatro	Bloco di quattro
Blue	Bleu	Blau	Azul	Azzurro
Blue-green	Vert-bleu	Blaugrün	Verde azul	Verde azzuro
Bluish Violet	Violet bleuâtre	Bläulichviolett	Violeta azulado	Violtto azzurrastro
Booklet	Carnet	Heft	Cuadernillo	Libretto
Bright Blue	Bleu vif	Lebhaftblau	Azul vivo	Azzurro vivo
Bright Green	Vert vif	Lebhaftgrün	Verde vivo	Verde vivo
Bright Purple	Mauve vif	Lebhaftpurpur	Púrpura vivo	Porpora vivo
Bronze Green	Vert-bronze	Bronzegrün	Verde bronce	Verde bronzo
Brown	Brun	Braun	Castaño	Bruno
Brown-lake	Carmin-brun	Braunlack	Laca castaño	Lacca bruno
Brown-purple	Pourpre-brun	Braunpurpur	Púrpura castaño	Porpora bruno
Brown-red	Rouge-brun	Braunrot	Rojo castaño	Rosso bruno
Buff	Chamois	Sämisch	Anteado	Camoscio
Cancellation	Oblitération	Entwertung	Cancelación	Annullamento
Cancelled	Annulé	Gestempelt	Cancelado	Annullato
Carmine	Carmin	Karmin	Carmín	Carminio
Carmine-red	Rouge-carmin	Karminrot	Rojo carmín	Rosso carminio
Centred	Centré	Zentriert	Centrado	Centrato
Cerise	Rouge-cerise	Kirschrot	Color de ceresa	Color Ciliegia
Chalk-surfaced paper	Papier couché	Kreidepapier	Papel estucado	Carta gessata
Chalky Blue	Bleu terne	Kreideblau	Azul turbio	Azzurro smorto
Charity stamp	Timbre de bienfaisance	Wohltätigkeitsmarke	Sello de beneficenza	Francobollo di beneficenza
Chestnut	Marron	Kastanienbraun	Castaño rojo	Marrone
Chocolate	Chocolat	Schokolade	Chocolate	Cioccolato
Cinnamon	Cannelle	Zimtbraun	Canela	Cannella
Claret	Grenat	Weinrot	Rojo vinoso	Vinaccia
Cobalt	Cobalt	Kobalt	Cobalto	Cobalto
Colour	Couleur	Farbe	Color	Colore
Comb-perforation	Dentelure en peigne	Kammzähnung, Reihenzähnung	Dentado de peine	Dentellatura e pettine
Commemorative stamp	Timbre commémoratif	Gedenkmarke	Sello conmemorativo	Francobollo commemorativo
Crimson	Cramoisi	Karmesin	Carmesí	Cremisi
Deep Blue	Blue foncé	Dunkelblau	Azul oscuro	Azzurro scuro

English	French	German	Spanish	Italian
Deep bluish Green	Vert-bleu foncé	Dunkelbläulichgrün	Verde azulado oscuro	Verde azzurro scuro
Design	Dessin	Markenbild	Diseño	Disegno
Die	Matrice	Urstempel. Type, Platte	Cuño	Conio, Matrice
Double	Double	Doppelt	Doble	Doppio
Drab	Olive terne	Trüboliv	Oliva turbio	Oliva smorto
Dull Green	Vert terne	Trübgrün	Verde turbio	Verde smorto
Dull purple	Mauve terne	Trübpurpur	Púrpura turbio	Porpora smorto
Embossing	Impression en relief	Prägedruck	Impresión en relieve	Impressione a relievo
Emerald	Vert-eméraude	Smaragdgrün	Esmeralda	Smeraldo
Engraved	Gravé	Graviert	Grabado	Inciso
Error	Erreur	Fehler, Fehldruck	Error	Errore
Essay	Essai	Probedruck	Ensayo	Saggio
Express letter stamp	Timbre pour lettres par exprès	Eilmarke	Sello de urgencia	Francobollo per espresso
Fiscal stamp	Timbre fiscal	Stempelmarke	Sello fiscal	Francobollo fiscale
Flesh	Chair	Fleischfarben	Carne	Carnicino
Forgery	Faux, Falsification	Fälschung	Falsificación	Falso, Falsificazione
Frame	Cadre	Rahmen	Marco	Cornice
Granite paper	Papier avec fragments de fils de soie	Faserpapier	Papel con filamentos	Carto con fili di seta
Green	Vert	Grün	Verde	Verde
Greenish Blue	Bleu verdâtre	Grünlichblau	Azul verdoso	Azzurro verdastro
Greenish Yellow	Jaune-vert	Grünlichgelb	Amarillo verdoso	Giallo verdastro
Grey	Gris	Grau	Gris	Grigio
Grey-blue	Bleu-gris	Graublau	Azul gris	Azzurro grigio
Grey-green	Vert gris	Graugrün	Verde gris	Verde grigio
Gum	Gomme	Gummi	Goma	Gomma
Gutter	Interpanneau	Zwischensteg	Espacio blanco entre dos grupos	Ponte
Imperforate	Non-dentelé	Geschnitten	Sin dentar	Non dentellato
Indigo	Indigo	Indigo	Azul indigo	Indaco
Inscription	Inscription	Inschrift	Inscripción	Dicitura
Inverted	Renversé	Kopfstehend	Invertido	Capovolto
Issue	Émission	Ausgabe	Emisión	Emissione
Laid	Vergé	Gestreift	Listado	Vergato
Lake	Lie de vin	Lackfarbe	Laca	Lacca
Lake-brown	Brun-carmin	Lackbraun	Castaño laca	Bruno lacca
Lavender	Bleu-lavande	Lavendel	Color de alhucema	Lavanda
Lemon	Jaune-citron	Zitrongelb	Limón	Limone
Light Blue	Bleu clair	Hellblau	Azul claro	Azzurro chiaro
Lilac	Lilas	Lila	Lila	Lilla
Line perforation	Dentelure en lignes	Linienzähnung	Dentado en linea	Dentellatura lineare
Lithography	Lithographie	Steindruck	Litografía	Litografia
Local	Timbre de poste locale	Lokalpostmarke	Emisión local	Emissione locale
Lozenge roulette	Percé en losanges	Rautenförmiger Durchstich	Picadura en rombos	Perforazione a losanghe
Magenta	Magenta	Magentarot	Magenta	Magenta
Margin	Marge	Rand	Borde	Margine
Maroon	Marron pourpré	Dunkelrotpurpur	Púrpura rojo oscuro	Marrone rossastro
Mauve	Mauve	Malvenfarbe	Malva	Malva
Multicoloured	Polychrome	Mehrfarbig	Multicolores	Policromo
Myrtle Green	Vert myrte	Myrtengrün	Verde mirto	Verde mirto
New Blue	Bleu ciel vif	Neublau	Azul nuevo	Azzurro nuovo

English	French	German	Spanish	Italian
Newspaper stamp	Timbre pour journaux	Zeitungsmarke	Sello para periódicos	Francobollo per giornali
Obliteration	Oblitération	Abstempelung	Matasello	Annullamento
Obsolete	Hors (de) cours	Ausser Kurs	Fuera de curso	Fuori corso
Ochre	Ocre	Ocker	Ocre	Ocra
Official stamp	Timbre de service	Dienstmarke	Sello de servicio	Francobollo di
Olive-brown	Brun-olive	Olivbraun	Castaño oliva	Bruno oliva
Olive-green	Vert-olive	Olivgrün	Verde oliva	Verde oliva
Olive-grey	Gris-olive	Olivgrau	Gris oliva	Grigio oliva
Olive-yellow	Jaune-olive	Olivgelb	Amarillo oliva	Giallo oliva
Orange	Orange	Orange	Naranja	Arancio
Orange-brown	Brun-orange	Orangebraun	Castaño naranja	Bruno arancio
Orange-red	Rouge-orange	Orangerot	Rojo naranja	Rosso arancio
Orange-yellow	Jaune-orange	Orangegelb	Amarillo naranja	Giallo arancio
Overprint	Surcharge	Aufdruck	Sobrecarga	Soprastampa
Pair	Paire	Paar	Pareja	Coppia
Pale	Pâle	Blass	Pálido	Pallido
Pane	Panneau	Gruppe	Grupo	Gruppo
Paper	Papier	Papier	Papel	Carta
Parcel post stamp	Timbre pour colis postaux	Paketmarke	Sello para paquete postal	Francobollo per pacchi postali
Pen-cancelled	Oblitéré à plume	Federzugentwertung	Cancelado a pluma	Annullato a penna
Percé en arc	Percé en arc	Bogenförmiger Durchstich	Picadura en forma de arco	Perforazione ad arco
Percé en scie	Percé en scie	Bogenförmiger Durchstich	Picado en sierra	Foratura a sega
Perforated	Dentelé	Gezähnt	Dentado	Dentellato
Perforation	Dentelure	Zähnung	Dentar	Dentellatura
Photogravure	Photogravure, Heliogravure	Rastertiefdruck	Fotograbado	Rotocalco
Pin perforation	Percé en points	In Punkten durchstochen	Horadado con alfileres	Perforato a punti
Plate	Planche	Platte	Plancha	Lastra, Tavola
Plum	Prune	Pflaumenfarbe	Color de ciruela	Prugna
Postage Due stamp	Timbre-taxe	Portomarke	Sello de tasa	Segnatasse
Postage stamp	Timbre-poste	Briefmarke, Freimarke, Postmarke	Sello de correos	Francobollo postale
Postal fiscal stamp	Timbre fiscal-postal	Stempelmarke als Postmarke verwendet	Sello fiscal-postal	Fiscale postale
Postmark	Oblitération postale	Poststempel	Matasello	Bollo
Printing	Impression, Tirage	Druck	Impresión	Stampa, Tiratura
Proof	Épreuve	Druckprobe	Prueba de impresión	Prova
Provisionals	Timbres provisoires	Provisorische Marken. Provisorien	Provisionales	Provvisori
Prussian Blue	Bleu de Prusse	Preussischblau	Azul de Prusia	Azzurro di Prussia
Purple	Pourpre	Purpur	Púrpura	Porpora
Purple-brown	Brun-pourpre	Purpurbraun	Castaño púrpura	Bruno porpora
Recess-printing	Impression en taille douce	Tiefdruck	Grabado	Incisione
Red	Rouge	Rot	Rojo	Rosso
Red-brown	Brun-rouge	Rotbraun	Castaño rojizo	Bruno rosso
Reddish Lilac	Lilas rougeâtre	Rötlichlila	Lila rojizo	Lilla rossastro
Reddish Purple	Poupre-rouge	Rötlichpurpur	Púrpura rojizo	Porpora rossastro
Reddish Violet	Violet rougeâtre	Rötlichviolett	Violeta rojizo	Violetto rossastro
Red-orange	Orange rougeâtre	Rotorange	Naranja rojizo	Arancio rosso
Registration stamp	Timbre pour lettre chargée (recommandée)	Einschreibemarke	Sello de certificado lettere	Francobollo per raccomandate

ATLANTIC ISLANDS

Muscotts have been prime sellers of all three Atlantic Island areas for very many years. Many wonderful pieces, some unique, have passed through our hands such as –

ASCENSION 1817 cover to UK plus many early QV covers, so many of the popular 1924–33 'Badge' series plate flaws, lovely coloured die proofs of the 1934 set, 1938 2/6d frame double one albino, mint & used, QEII varieties including the 1978 Volcanoes miniature sheet with 'ASCENSION ISLAND' omitted (2 known).

ST. HELENA The rare 1873 2d with blue-black surcharge, Boer war covers, 1916 1d+1d WAR TAX double opt (6 known) & among the 1922–37 flaws was the 15/- with TORN MAST plus QEII errors.

TRISTAN DA CUNHA has included all the early cachet cover types through to QEII varieties plus rare 1972 die proof of the £1.

Apart from these spectacular pieces much of our stock bears prices from £50 upwards and we are especially helpful to clients who wish to pay over a period of time. Listed below are just a few fine pieces available at time of publication.

ASCENSION.

Great Britain 1913 1/- used in Ascension. A fine block of 4 SG Z51. Rare multiple Cat £ 900+ **£550**

1924–33 ½d SG 10 with damaged 'P' of 'POSTAGE' similar to the St. Helena flaw & fresh u/m **£175**

1933 Scarce 1d Grey-black & bright blue-green SG 11d in gorgeous lower right corner plate No. block of 4 superb mint. Rare in this form **£475**

1924–33 Script wmk 4d 'TORN FLAG' SG 15b v.f.mint. Cat £475 .... **£330**

ST. HELENA.

1922–37 MCA wmk 5/- 'TORN FLAG' SG 95b in v.f.mint pair with normal Cat £990 .... **£725**

1922–37 ½d. Two positional blocks of 4, both with scarce inverted wmk, one corner block with 'CLEFT ROCK', the other lower marginal with 'TORN FLAG', SG 97b/fw & 97c/fw all superb u/m. A wonderful pair. Only four of each printed **£10,750**

1937 The scarce 1½d deep carmine-red SG 99e with popular 'Madam Joseph' forged canc **£60**

1922–37 1/6d Script wmk with 'BROKEN MAINMAST' SG 107a v.f.mint. Cat £ 425 .... **£295**

1961 Tristan Relief Fund set of 4, SG 172–175 superb u/m. Cat £7,500. Certificate **£5,500**

1976 Aquatints £1 GOLD OMITTED SG 330Aa unique with plate No. 1D fresh u/m **£1,500**

TRISTAN DA CUNHA.

1908 Type 1 cachet. A magnificent strike in deep violet SG C1 on p/c written by J.C.Keytel who supplied this handstamp. Only two recorded of this first useage. The most important cachet of them all and used on Xmas day **£6,500**

1929 Cover to Montreal bearing two GB 1½d each cancelled by a superb strike of the rare type 1Va cachet in bright red SG C5 The best we have seen. Cat from £5,500 for a single strike **£4,950**

1935 Cover to Montivideo bearing special cachet of the Dutch submarine plus type V cachet. Both superb. Rare **£1,800**

1966 Churchill 1d VALUE OMITTED SG 89a cat £1,300. Certificate **£1,200**

1969 Clipper Ships. The set of 4 each opt SPECIMEN by local h/s & affixed to advertising card used outside local post office. Unique & attractive. The only, known, specimen **£475**

If you are a serious collector of these territories you need to be on our books.
Be assured of a friendly & helpful personal service.

MUSCOTT'S

P.O.BOX 5319, UPLYME, LYME REGIS, DEVON DT7 3ZJ
TEL: 01297 444128 • FAX: 01297 444129
muscotts@btinternet.com

English	French	German	Spanish	Italian
Reprint	Réimpression	Neudruck	Reimpresión	Ristampa
Reversed	Retourné	Umgekehrt	Invertido	Rovesciato
Rose	Rose	Rosa	Rosa	Rosa
Rose-red	Rouge rosé	Rosarot	Rojo rosado	Rosso rosa
Rosine	Rose vif	Lebhaftrosa	Rosa vivo	Rosa vivo
Roulette	Percage	Durchstich	Picadura	Foratura
Rouletted	Percé	Durchstochen	Picado	Forato
Royal Blue	Bleu-roi	Königblau	Azul real	Azzurro reale
Sage green	Vert-sauge	Salbeigrün	Verde salvia	Verde salvia
Salmon	Saumon	Lachs	Salmón	Salmone
Scarlet	Écarlate	Scharlach	Escarlata	Scarlatto
Sepia	Sépia	Sepia	Sepia	Seppia
Serpentine roulette	Percé en serpentin	Schlangenliniger Durchstich	Picado a serpentina	Perforazione a serpentina
Shade	Nuance	Tönung	Tono	Gradazione de colore
Sheet	Feuille	Bogen	Hoja	Foglio
Slate	Ardoise	Schiefer	Pizarra	Ardesia
Slate-blue	Bleu-ardoise	Schieferblau	Azul pizarra	Azzurro ardesia
Slate-green	Vert-ardoise	Schiefergrün	Verde pizarra	Verde ardesia
Slate-lilac	Lilas-gris	Schierferlila	Lila pizarra	Lilla ardesia
Slate-purple	Mauve-gris	Schieferpurpur	Púrpura pizarra	Porpora ardesia
Slate-violet	Violet-gris	Schieferviolett	Violeta pizarra	Violetto ardesia
Special delivery stamp	Timbre pour exprès	Eilmarke	Sello de urgencia	Francobollo per espressi
Specimen	Spécimen	Muster	Muestra	Saggio
Steel Blue	Bleu acier	Stahlblau	Azul acero	Azzurro acciaio
Strip	Bande	Streifen	Tira	Striscia
Surcharge	Surcharge	Aufdruck	Sobrecarga	Soprastampa
Tête-bêche	Tête-bêche	Kehrdruck	Tête-bêche	Tête-bêche
Tinted paper	Papier teinté	Getöntes Papier	Papel coloreado	Carta tinta
Too-late stamp	Timbre pour lettres en retard	Verspätungsmarke	Sello para cartas retardadas	Francobollo per le lettere in ritardo
Turquoise-blue	Bleu-turquoise	Türkisblau	Azul turquesa	Azzurro turchese
Turquoise-green	Vert-turquoise	Türkisgrün	Verde turquesa	Verde turchese
Typography	Typographie	Buchdruck	Tipografia	Tipografia
Ultramarine	Outremer	Ultramarin	Ultramar	Oltremare
Unused	Neuf	Ungebraucht	Nuevo	Nuovo
Used	Oblitéré, Usé	Gebraucht	Usado	Usato
Venetian Red	Rouge-brun terne	Venezianischrot	Rojo veneciano	Rosso veneziano
Vermilion	Vermillon	Zinnober	Cinabrio	Vermiglione
Violet	Violet	Violett	Violeta	Violetto
Violet-blue	Bleu-violet	Violettblau	Azul violeta	Azzurro violetto
Watermark	Filigrane	Wasserzeichen	Filigrana	Filigrana
Watermark sideways	Filigrane couché	Wasserzeichen liegend	Filigrana acostado	Filigrana coricata
Wove paper	Papier ordinaire, Papier uni	Einfaches Papier	Papel avitelado	Carta unita
Yellow	Jaune	Gelb	Amarillo	Giallo
Yellow-brown	Brun-jaune	Gelbbraun	Castaño amarillo	Bruno giallo
Yellow-green	Vert-jaune	Gelbgrün	Verde amarillo	Verde giallo
Yellow-olive	Olive-jaunâtre	Gelboliv	Oliva amarillo	Oliva giallastro
Yellow-orange	Orange jaunâtre	Gelborange	Naranja amarillo	Arancio giallastro
Zig-zag roulette	Percé en zigzag	Sägezahnartiger Durchstich	Picado en zigzag	Perforazione a zigzag

Guide to Entries

A **Country of Issue** – When a country changes its name, the catalogue listing changes to reflect the name change, for example Namibia was formerly known as South West Africa, the stamps in Southern Africa are all listed under Namibia, but split into South West Africa and then Namibia.

B **Country Information** – Brief geographical and historical details for the issuing country.

C **Currency** – Details of the currency, and dates of earliest use where applicable, on the face value of the stamps.

D **Illustration** – Generally, the first stamp in the set. Stamp illustrations are reduced to 75%, with overprints and surcharges shown actual size.

E **Illustration or Type Number** – These numbers are used to help identify stamps, either in the listing, type column, design line or footnote, usually the first value in a set. These type numbers are in a bold type face – **123**; when bracketed (**123**) an overprint or a surcharge is indicated. Some type numbers include a lower-case letter – **123a**, this indicates they have been added to an existing set.

F **Date of issue** – This is the date that the stamp/set of stamps was issued by the post office and was available for purchase. When a set of definitive stamps has been issued over several years the Year Date given is for the earliest issue. Commemorative sets are listed in chronological order. Stamps of the same design, or issue are usually grouped together, for example some of the New Zealand landscapes definitive series were first issued in 2003 but the set includes stamps issued to May 2007.

G **Number Prefix** – Stamps other than definitives and commemoratives have a prefix letter before the catalogue number.
Their use is explained in the text: some examples are A for airmail, D for postage due and O for official stamps.

H **Footnote** – Further information on background or key facts on issues.

I **Stanley Gibbons Catalogue number** – This is a unique number for each stamp to help the collector identify stamps in the listing. The Stanley Gibbons numbering system is universally recognized as definitive.

Where insufficient numbers have been left to provide for additional stamps to a listing, some stamps will have a suffix letter after the catalogue number (for example 214a). If numbers have been left for additions to a set and not used they will be left vacant.

The separate type numbers (in bold) refer to illustrations (see **E**).

J **Colour** – If a stamp is printed in three or fewer colours then the colours are listed, working from the centre of the stamp outwards (see **R**).

K **Design line** – Further details on design variations

L **Key Type** – Indicates a design type on which the stamp is based. These are the bold figures found below each illustration, for example listed in Cameroon, in the West Africa catalogue, is the Key type A and B showing the ex-Kaiser's yacht *Hohenzollern*. The type numbers are also given in bold in the second column of figures alongside the stamp description to indicate the design of each stamp. Where an issue comprises stamps of similar design, the corresponding type number should be taken as indicating the general design. Where there are blanks in the type number column it means that the type of the corresponding stamp is that shown by the number in the type column of the same issue. A dash (–) in the type column means that the stamp is not illustrated. Where type numbers refer to stamps of another country, e.g. where stamps of one country are overprinted for use in another, this is always made clear in the text.

M **Coloured Papers** – Stamps printed on coloured paper are shown – e.g. "brown/*yellow*" indicates brown printed on yellow paper.

N **Surcharges and Overprints** – Usually described in the headings. Any actual wordings are shown in bold type. Descriptions clarify words and figures used in the overprint. Stamps with the same overprints in different colours are not listed separately. Numbers in brackets after the descriptions are the catalogue numbers of the non-overprinted stamps. The words "inscribed" or "inscription" refer to the wording incorporated in the design of a stamp and not surcharges or overprints.

O **Face value** – This refers to the value of each stamp and is the price it was sold for at the Post Office when issued. Some modern stamps do not have their values in figures but instead it is shown as a letter, for example Great Britain use 1st or 2nd on their stamps as opposed to the actual value.

P **Catalogue Value** – Mint/Unused. Prices quoted for Queen Victoria to King George V stamps are for lightly hinged examples.

Q **Catalogue Value** – Used. Prices generally refer to fine postally used examples. For certain issues they are for cancelled-to-order.

Prices
Prices are given in pence and pounds. Stamps worth £100 and over are shown in whole pounds:

Shown in Catalogue as	Explanation
10	10 pence
1.75	£1.75
15.00	£15
£150	£150
£2300	£2300

Prices assume stamps are in 'fine condition'; we may ask more for superb and less for those of lower quality. The minimum catalogue price quoted is 10p and is intended as a guide for catalogue users. The lowest price for individual stamps purchased from Stanley Gibbons is £1.

Prices quoted are for the cheapest variety of that particular stamp. Differences of watermark, perforation, or other details, often increase the value. Prices quoted for mint issues are for single examples, unless otherwise stated. Those in *se-tenant* pairs, strips, blocks or sheets may be worth more. Where no prices are listed it is either because the stamps are not known to exist (usually shown by a †) in that particular condition, or, more usually, because there is no reliable information on which to base their value.
All prices are subject to change without prior notice and we cannot guarantee to supply all stamps as priced. Prices quoted in advertisements are also subject to change without prior notice.

R **Multicoloured** – Nearly all modern stamps are multicoloured (more than three colours); this is indicated in the heading, with a description of the stamp given in the listing.

S **Perforations** – Please see page xiii for a detailed explanation of perforations.

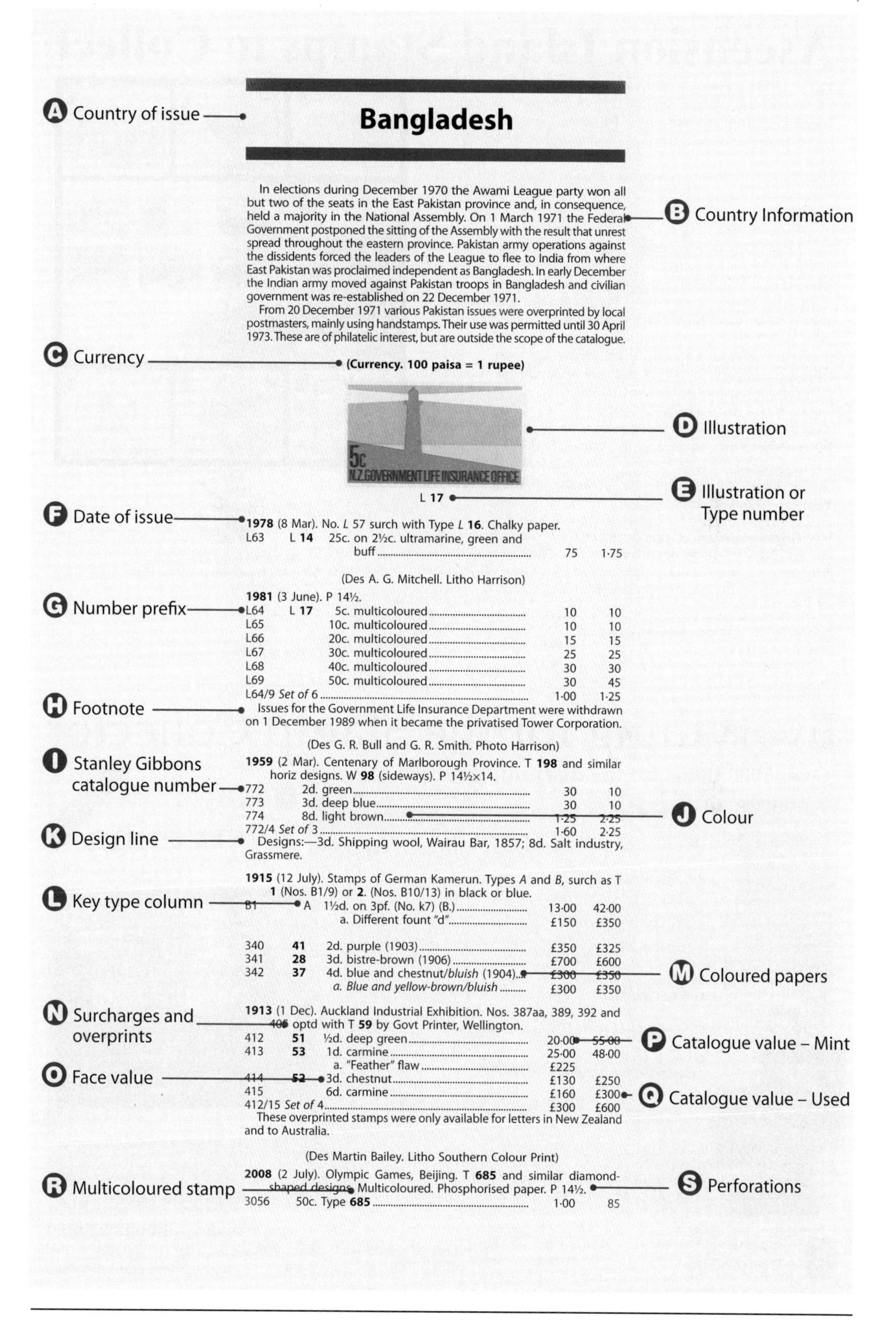

Bangladesh

In elections during December 1970 the Awami League party won all but two of the seats in the East Pakistan province and, in consequence, held a majority in the National Assembly. On 1 March 1971 the Federal Government postponed the sitting of the Assembly with the result that unrest spread throughout the eastern province. Pakistan army operations against the dissidents forced the leaders of the League to flee to India from where East Pakistan was proclaimed independent as Bangladesh. In early December the Indian army moved against Pakistan troops in Bangladesh and civilian government was re-established on 22 December 1971.

From 20 December 1971 various Pakistan issues were overprinted by local postmasters, mainly using handstamps. Their use was permitted until 30 April 1973. These are of philatelic interest, but are outside the scope of the catalogue.

(Currency. 100 paisa = 1 rupee)

L 17

1978 (8 Mar). No. *L* 57 surch with Type *L* **16**. Chalky paper.

L63	L **14**	25c. on 2½c. ultramarine, green and buff	75	1·75

(Des A. G. Mitchell. Litho Harrison)

1981 (3 June). P 14½.

L64	L **17**	5c. multicoloured	10	10
L65		10c. multicoloured	10	10
L66		20c. multicoloured	15	15
L67		30c. multicoloured	25	25
L68		40c. multicoloured	30	30
L69		50c. multicoloured	30	45
L64/9 *Set of 6*			1·00	1·25

Issues for the Government Life Insurance Department were withdrawn on 1 December 1989 when it became the privatised Tower Corporation.

(Des G. R. Bull and G. R. Smith. Photo Harrison)

1959 (2 Mar). Centenary of Marlborough Province. T **198** and similar horiz designs. W **98** (sideways). P 14½×14.

772	2d. green	30	10
773	3d. deep blue	30	10
774	8d. light brown	1·25	2·25
772/4 *Set of 3*		1·60	2·25

Designs:—3d. Shipping wool, Wairau Bar, 1857; 8d. Salt industry, Grassmere.

1915 (12 July). Stamps of German Kamerun. Types *A* and *B*, surch as T **1** (Nos. B1/9) or **2**. (Nos. B10/13) in black or blue.

B1	A	1½d. on 3pf. (No. k7) (B.)	13·00	42·00
		a. Different fount "d"	£150	£350

340	**41**	2d. purple (1903)	£350	£325
341	**28**	3d. bistre-brown (1906)	£700	£600
342	**37**	4d. blue and chestnut/*bluish* (1904)	£300	£350
		a. Blue and yellow-brown/bluish	£300	£350

1913 (1 Dec). Auckland Industrial Exhibition. Nos. 387aa, 389, 392 and 405 optd with T **59** by Govt Printer, Wellington.

412	**51**	½d. deep green	20·00	55·00
413	**53**	1d. carmine	25·00	48·00
		a. "Feather" flaw	£225	
414	**52**	3d. chestnut	£130	£250
415		6d. carmine	£160	£300
412/15 *Set of 4*			£300	£600

These overprinted stamps were only available for letters in New Zealand and to Australia.

(Des Martin Bailey. Litho Southern Colour Print)

2008 (2 July). Olympic Games, Beijing. T **685** and similar diamond-shaped designs. Multicoloured. Phosphorised paper. P 14½.

3056	50c. Type **685**	1·00	85

Ascension

DEPENDENCY OF ST. HELENA

Ascension, first occupied in 1815, was retained as a Royal Navy establishment from 1816 until 20 October 1922 when it became a dependency of St. Helena by Letters Patent.

Under Post Office regulations of 1850 (ratings) and 1854 (officers) mail from men of the Royal Navy serving abroad had the postage prepaid in Great Britain stamps, supplies of which were issued to each ship. Great Britain stamps used on Ascension before 1860 may have been provided by the naval officer in charge of the postal service.

The British G.P.O. assumed responsibility for such matters in 1860, but failed to send any stamps to the island until January 1867.

Until about 1880 naval mail, which made up most early correspondence, did not have the stamps cancelled until arrival in England. The prices quoted for Nos. Z1/3 and Z6 are for examples on cover showing the Great Britain stamps cancelled on arrival and an Ascension postmark struck elsewhere on the front of the envelope.

The use of British stamps ceased in December 1922.

The following postmarks were used on Great Britain stamps from Ascension:

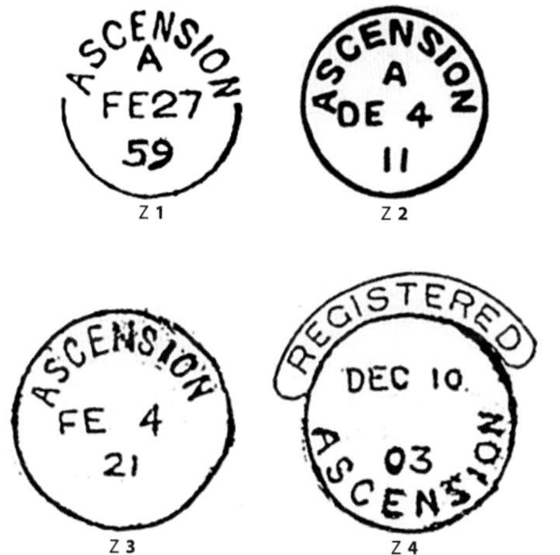

Z 1 Z 2

Z 3 Z 4

Z 5

Postmark Type	Approx Period of Use	Diameter	Index Letter
Z **1**	1862	20 mm	A
Z **2**	1864–1872	20 mm	A
	1872–1878	21½ mm	A
	1879–1889	19½ mm	A
	1891–1894	21½ mm	C
	1894–1902	22 mm	A
	1903–1907	20½ mm	A
	1908–1920	21 mm	A or none
	1909–1920	23 mm	C sideways (1909), none (1910–11), B (1911–20)
Z **3**	1920–1922	24 mm	none
Z **4**	1897–1903 Reg'd	23 mm	none
Z **5**	1900–1902 Reg'd	28 mm	C
	1903–1904 Reg'd	29 mm	A

Postmark Type Z **1** appears in the G.P.O. proof book for 1858, but the first recorded use is 3 November 1862.

Forged postmarks exist. Those found most frequently are genuine postmarks of the post-1922 period with earlier date slugs fraudulently inserted, namely a 20 mm postmark as Type Z **2** (because of the shape of the "O" in "ASCENSION" this is often known as the "Square O" postmark) and a 24 mm postmark as Type Z **3** but with the index letter A.

Stamps of GREAT BRITAIN cancelled with Types Z **2/5**. Prices quoted for Nos. Z1/6 are for complete covers.

Line-engraved issues.

Z1	1d. red-brown (1855)	£8000
Z2	1d. rose-red (1864–79) From	£3250
	Plate Nos. 71, 74, 76, 78, 83, 85, 96, 100, 102, 103, 104, 122, 134, 138, 154, 155, 157, 160, 168, 178	

Surface-printed issues (1856–1883)

Z2*a*	6d. lilac (1856)	
Z3	6d. lilac (1865) (Plate No. 5)	£8000
Z4	1s. green (1865) (Plate No. 4)	
Z5	1s. green (1867) (Plate No. 7)	
Z6	6d. grey (1874) (Plate Nos. 15, 16)	£6500
Z6*a*	6d. on 6d. lilac (1883)	
Z7	1d. lilac (1881) (16 dots)	90·00

1887–92.

Z8	½d. vermilion	£130
Z9	1½d. purple and green	£850
Z10	2d. green and carmine	£325
Z11	2½d. purple/*blue*	£150
Z12	3d. purple/*yellow*	£650
Z13	4d. green and brown	£450
Z14	4½d. green and carmine	£1200
Z15	5d. dull purple and blue	£475
Z16	6d. purple/*rose-red*	£375
Z17	9d. purple and blue	£1000
Z17*a*	10d. dull purple and carmine	£1200
Z18	1s. green	£1100

1900.

Z19	½d. blue-green	£150
Z20	1s. green and carmine	£1200

1902–11. King Edward VII issues.

Z21	½d. green	95·00
Z22	1d. red	32·00
Z23	1½d. purple and green	£400
Z24	2d. green and carmine	£200
Z25	2½d. blue	£225
Z26	3d. purple/*yellow*	£400
Z27	4d. green and brown	£1000
Z28	4d. orange (1909)	£400
Z29	5d. purple and ultramarine	£400
Z30	6d. purple	£350
Z31	7d. grey-black (1910)	£475
Z32	9d. purple and ultramarine (1910)	£600
Z32*a*	10d. dull purple and scarlet	£800
Z33	1s. green and carmine	£200
Z33*a*	2s.6d. dull reddish purple (1911)	£1600
Z34	5s. carmine	£2250
Z35	10s. ultramarine	£3250
Z35*a*	£1 green	£8000

1911–12. T **98/9** of Great Britain.

Z36	½d. green (Die A)	£225
Z37	½d. yellow-green (Die B)	£100
Z38	1d. scarlet (Die B)	£100

1912. T **101/2** of Great Britain.

Z38*a*	½d. green	£100
Z38*b*	1d. scarlet	95·00

1912–22.

Z39	½d. green (1913)	80·00
Z40	1d. scarlet	38·00
Z41	1½d. red-brown	£100
Z42	2d. orange (Die I)	90·00
Z42*a*	2d. orange (Die II) (1921)	£900
Z43	2½d. blue	£130
Z44	3d. violet	£180
Z45	4d. grey-green (1913)	£225
Z46	5d. brown (1913)	£325
Z47	6d. purple (1913)	£180
Z47*a*	7d. green (1913)	£750
Z47*b*	8d. black/*yellow* (1913)	£800
Z48	9d. agate (1913)	£700
Z49	9d. olive-green (1922)	£1600
Z50	10d. turquoise-blue (1913)	£750
Z51	1s. bistre (1913)	£225
Z52	2s.6d. brown (1918)	£2000
Z53	5s. rose-red (1919)	£3500

Supplies of some values do not appear to have been sent to the island and known examples originate from maritime or, in the case of high values, philatelic mail.

PRICES FOR STAMPS ON COVER

Nos. 1/34	*from* × 5
Nos. 35/7	*from* × 10
Nos. 38/47	*from* × 6

ASCENSION
(**1**)

2d. Line through "P" of "POSTAGE" (R. 3/6)

2d. Blot on scroll (R. 3/10)

1922 (2 Nov). Stamps of St. Helena, showing Government House or the Wharf, optd with T **1** by D.L.R.

	(a) Wmk Mult Script CA		
1	½d. black and green	6·50	26·00
	x. Wmk reversed	£1200	
2	1d. green	6·50	25·00
3	1½d. rose-scarlet	17·00	48·00
4	2d. black and grey	17·00	13·00
	a. Line through "P" of "POSTAGE"	£450	£500
	b. Blot on scroll	£450	£500
5	3d. bright blue	13·00	26·00
6	8d. black and dull purple	27·00	50·00
7	2s. black and blue/*blue*	£110	£130
8	3s. black and violet	£140	£160
	(b) Wmk Mult Crown CA		
9	1s. black/*green* (R.)	28·00	48·00
1/9 *Set of 9*		£325	£475
1s/9s Optd "SPECIMEN" *Set of 9*		£800	

Nos. 1, 4 and 6/8 are on special printings which were not issued without overprint.

Examples of all values are known showing a forged Ascension postmark dated "MY 24 23".

PLATE FLAWS ON THE 1924–33 ISSUE. Many constant plate varieties exist on both the vignette and duty plates of this issue.

The three major varieties are illustrated and listed below.

This issue utilised the same vignette plate as the St. Helena 1922–37 set so that these flaws occur there also.

2 Badge of St. Helena

Broken mainmast. Occurs on R. 2/1 of all values.

Torn flag. Occurs on R. 4/6 of all values except the 5d. Retouched on sheets of ½d., 1d. and 2d. printed after 1927.

Cleft rock. Occurs on R. 5/1 of all values.

Broken scroll. (R. 1/4)

1½d. line through "c" (R. 1/6)

8d. "Shamrock" flaw (R. 4/1)

(Typo D.L.R.)

1924 (20 Aug)–**33**. Wmk Mult Script CA. Chalk-surfaced paper. P 14.

10	**2**	½d. grey-black and black	6·00	18·00
		a. Broken mainmast	£130	£275
		b. Torn flag	£200	£350
		c. Cleft rock	£110	£250
11		1d. grey-black and deep blue-green	6·00	13·00
		a. Broken mainmast	£140	£225
		b. Torn flag	£150	£250
		c. Cleft rock	£130	£225
11*d*		1d. grey-black and bright blue-green (1933)	£110	£500
		da. Broken mainmast	£850	
		dc. Cleft rock	£850	
12		1½d. rose-red	10·00	42·00
		a. Broken mainmast	£150	£350
		b. Torn flag	£150	£350
		c. Cleft rock	£140	£350
		d. Broken scroll	£170	£350
		e. line through "c"	£170	£350
13		2d. grey-black and grey	20·00	12·00
		a. Broken mainmast	£250	£250
		b. Torn flag	£325	£325
		c. Cleft rock	£200	£225
14		3d. blue	8·00	18·00
		a. Broken mainmast	£160	£275
		b. Torn flag	£160	£275
		c. Cleft rock	£150	£250
15		4d. grey-black and black/*yellow*	50·00	95·00
		a. Broken mainmast	£475	£750
		b. Torn flag	£475	£750
		c. Cleft rock	£450	£700
15*d*		5d. purple and olive-green (8.27)	19·00	26·00
		da. Broken mainmast	£325	£425
		dc. Cleft rock	£300	£425
16		6d. grey-black and bright purple	60·00	£120
		a. Broken mainmast	£550	£850
		b. Torn flag	£550	£850
		c. Cleft rock	£550	£850
17		8d. grey-black and bright violet	17·00	45·00
		a. Broken mainmast	£300	£475
		b. Torn flag	£300	£475
		c. Cleft rock	£275	£450
		d. "Shamrock" flaw	£300	£475
18		1s. grey-black and brown	21·00	55·00
		a. Broken mainmast	£375	£500
		b. Torn flag	£375	£500
		c. Cleft rock	£350	£475
19		2s. grey-black and blue/*blue*	75·00	£100
		a. Broken mainmast	£650	£800
		b. Torn flag	£650	£800
		c. Cleft rock	£600	£750
20		3s. grey-black and black/*blue*	£100	£100
		a. Broken mainmast	£800	£850
		b. Torn flag	£800	£850
		c. Cleft rock	£750	£900
10/20 *Set of 12*			£350	£600
10s/20s Optd "SPECIMEN" *Set of 12*			£1000	

3 Georgetown

4 Ascension Island

5 The Pier

6 Long Beach

7 Three Sisters

8 Sooty Tern and Wideawake Fair

9 Green Mountain

"Teardrops" flaw (R. 4/5)

(Des and recess D.L.R.)

1934 (2 July). T **3/4** and similar designs. Wmk Mult Script CA. P 14.

21	**3**	½d. black and violet	90	80
22	**4**	1d. black and emerald	1·75	1·50
		a. Teardrops flaw	£130	£130
23	**5**	1½d. black and scarlet	1·75	2·25
24	**4**	2d. black and orange	1·75	2·50
		a. Teardrops flaw	£225	£250
25	**6**	3d. black and ultramarine	2·50	1·50
26	**7**	5d. black and blue	2·25	3·25
27	**4**	8d. black and sepia	4·25	5·50
		a. Teardrops flaw	£400	£450
28	**8**	1s. black and carmine	18·00	11·00
29	**4**	2s.6d. black and bright purple	45·00	48·00
		a. Teardrops flaw	£1200	£1300
30	**9**	5s. black and brown	55·00	60·00
21/30 *Set of* 10			£120	£120
21s/30s Perf "SPECIMEN" *Set of* 10			£500	

9a Windsor Castle

Kite and vertical log (Plate "2A" R. 10/6)

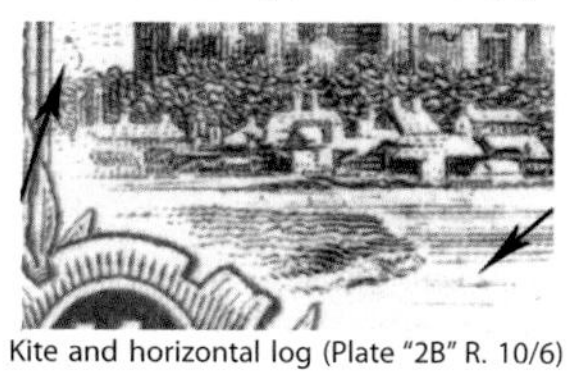

Kite and horizontal log (Plate "2B" R. 10/6)

(Des H. Fleury. Recess Waterlow)

1935 (6 May). Silver Jubilee. Wmk Mult Sript CA. P 11×12.

31	**9a**	1½d. deep blue and scarlet	3·50	14·00
		l. Kite and horizontal log	£425	£550
32		2d. ultramarine and grey	11·00	38·00
		l. Kite and horizontal log	£650	
33		5d. green and indigo	23·00	32·00
		k. Kite and vertical log	£375	£475
		l. Kite and horizontal log	£700	£800
34		1s. slate and purple	23·00	40·00
		l. Kite and horizontal log	£850	£1000
31/4 *Set of* 4			55·00	£110
31s/4s Perf "SPECIMEN" *Set of* 4			£425	

9b King George VI and Queen Elizabeth

(Des and recess D.L.R)

1937 (19 May). Coronation. Wmk Mult Script CA. P 14.

35	**9b**	1d. green	50	1·40
36		2d. orange	1·00	60
37		3d. bright blue	1·00	50
35/37 *Set of* 3			2·25	2·25
35s/7s Perf "SPECIMEN" *Set of* 3			£450	

10 Georgetown

11 Green Mountain

12 Three Sisters

13 The Pier

14 Long Beach

½d. Long centre bar to "E" in "GEORGETOWN" (R. 2/3)

"Mountaineer" flaw (R. 4/4)

"Davit" flaw (R. 5/1) (all ptgs of 1½d. and 2s.6d.)

"Cut mast and railings" (R. 3/1)

(Recess D.L.R.)

1938 (12 May)–**53**. T **10/14**. Wmk Mult Script CA. P 13½.

No.	Type	Description	Unused	Used
38	**10**	½d. black and violet	6·50	3·25
		a. Long centre bar to E	£300	£250
		b. Perf 13. *Black and bluish violet* (17.5.44)	1·40	3·25
		ba. Long centre bar to E	90·00	
39	**11**	1d. black and green	45·00	13·00
39*a*		1d. black and yellow-orange (8.7.40)	14·00	9·00
		b. Perf 13 (5.42)	45	60
		ba. Mountaineer flaw	£250	
		c. Perf 14 (17.2.49)	70	16·00
		ca. Mountaineer flaw	£190	
39*d*	**12**	1d. black and green, P 13 (1.6.49)	60	1·50
40	**13**	1½d. black and vermilion	6·00	1·40
		a. Davit flaw	£375	£200
		b. Perf 13 (17.5.44)	1·00	80
		ba. Davit flaw	£140	£170
		bb. Cut mast and railings	£200	
		c. Perf 14 (17.2.49)	3·00	13·00
		ca. Davit flaw	£325	£475
		cb. Cut mast and railings	£325	
40*d*		1½d. black and rose-carmine, P 14 (1.6.49)	1·50	1·00
		da. Davit flaw	£130	£170
		db. Cut mast and railings	£130	£170
		e. *Black and carmine*	12·00	5·00
		ea. Davit flaw	£450	£400
		eb. Cut mast and railings	£450	£400
		f. Perf 13 (25.2.53)	45	6·50
		fa. Davit flaw	£140	
		fb. Cut mast and railings	£140	
41	**11**	2d. black and red-orange	7·00	1·00
		a. Perf 13 (17.5.44)	80	40
		aa. Mountaineer flaw	£400	£300
		b. Perf 14 (17.2.49)	2·75	35·00
		ba. Mountaineer flaw	£325	
41*c*		2d. black and scarlet, P 14 (1.6.49)	1·25	1·75
		ca. Mountaineer flaw	£275	£375
42	**14**	3d. black and ultramarine	£100	29·00
42*a*		3d. black and grey (8.7.40)	20·00	3·50
		b. Perf 13 (17.5.44)	70	80
42*c*	**11**	4d. black and ultramarine (8.7.40)	17·00	3·25
		d. Perf 13 (17.5.44)	5·00	3·00
		da. Mountaineer flaw	£850	£600
43	**12**	6d. black and blue	10·00	2·25
		a. Perf 13 (17.5.44)	12·00	7·00
44	**10**	1s. black and sepia	22·00	2·25
		a. Perf 13 (17.5.44)	4·75	2·00
45	**13**	2s.6d. black and deep carmine	42·00	9·50
		a. Frame printed double, one albino	£5000	
		b. Davit flaw	£1600	£750
		c. Perf 13 (17.5.44)	27·00	32·00
		ca. Davit flaw	£1400	£1700
		cb. Cut mast and railings	£1600	£1800
46	**14**	5s. black and yellow-brown	95·00	9·50
		a. Perf 13 (17.5.44)	38·00	40·00
47	**12**	10s. black and bright purple	£110	48·00
		a. Perf 13 (17.5.44)	48·00	60·00
38b/47a *Set of* 16			£250	£110
38s/47s Perf "SPECIMEN" *Set of* 13			£1000	

14a Houses of Parliament, London

(Des and recess D.LR.)

1946 (21 Oct). Victory. Wmk Mult Script CA. P 13½×14.

No.	Type	Description	Unused	Used
48	**14a**	2d. red-orange	40	1·00
49		4d. blue	40	60
48s/9s Perf "SPECIMEN" *Set of* 2			£450	

14b King George VI and Queen Elizabeth

14c

(Des and photo Waterlow (T **14b**). Design recess; name typo B.W. (T **14c**))

1948 (20 Oct). Royal Silver Wedding. Wmk Mult Script CA.

No.	Type	Description	Unused	Used
50	**14b**	3d. black (P 14×15)	50	30
51	**14c**	10s. bright purple (P 11½×11)	55·00	50·00

14d Hermes, Globe and Forms of Transport

14e Hemispheres, Jet-powered Vickers Viking Airliner and Steamer

14f Hermes and Globe

14g U.P.U. Monument

(Recess Waterlow (T **14d**, **14g**). Designs recess, name typo B.W. (T **14e/14f**)

1949 (10 Oct). 75th Anniv of Universal Postal Union. Wmk Mult Script CA.

No.	Type	Description	Unused	Used
52	**14d**	3d. carmine (P 13½–14)	1·00	2·00
53	**14e**	4d. deep blue (P 11×11½)	4·00	1·50
54	**14f**	6d. olive (P 11×11½)	2·00	3·50
55	**14g**	1s. blue-black (P 13½–14)	2·00	1·50
		a. "A" of "CA" missing from Wmk	—	£1500
52/55 *Set of* 4			8·00	7·75

14h Queen Elizabeth II

(Des and eng B.W. Recess D.L.R)

1953 (2 June). Coronation. Wmk Mult Script CA. P 13½×13.

No.	Type	Description	Unused	Used
56	**14h**	3d. black and grey-black	1·00	2·25

15 Water Catchment

16 Map of Ascension

17 View of Georgetown

18 Map showing cable network

19 Mountain road

20 White-tailed Tropic Bird ("Boatswain Bird")

21 Yellow-finned Tuna

22 Rollers on the seashore

23 Young turtles

24 Land Crab

25 Sooty Tern ("Wideawake")

26 Perfect Crater

27 View of Ascension from North-west

(Recess B.W.)

1956 (19 Nov). T **19/27**. Wmk Mult Script CA. P 13.

57	**15**	½d. black and brown	10	50
58	**16**	1d. black and magenta	4·25	2·50
59	**17**	1½d. black and orange	1·00	1·00
60	**18**	2d. black and carmine-red	5·50	3·25
61	**19**	2½d. black and orange-brown	2·00	3·00
62	**20**	3d. black and blue	5·50	1·25
63	**21**	4d. black and deep turquoise-green	1·25	2·00
64	**22**	6d. black and indigo	1·50	2·50
65	**23**	7d. black and deep olive	3·75	1·50
66	**24**	1s. black and vermilion	1·00	1·25
67	**25**	2s.6d. black and deep dull purple	29·00	8·50
68	**26**	5s. black and blue-green	40·00	18·00
69	**27**	10s. black and purple	50·00	40·00
57/69 *Set of* 13			£130	75·00

28 Brown Booby

29 Protein Foods

(Des after photos by N. P. Ashmole. Photo Harrison)

1963 (23 May). T **28** and similar horiz designs. W w **12**. P 14×14½.

70	1d. black, lemon and new blue	1·50	30
71	1½d. black, cobalt and ochre	2·00	1·00
	a. Cobalt omitted	£120	
72	2d. black, grey and bright blue	1·25	30
73	3d. black, magenta and turquoise-blue	1·75	30
74	4½d. black, bistre-brown and new blue	1·75	30
	w. Wmk inverted	£500	
75	6d. bistre, black and yellow-green	1·25	30
76	7d. black, brown and reddish violet	1·25	30
77	10d. black, greenish yellow and blue-green	1·25	50
78	1s. multicoloured	1·25	30
79	1s.6d. multicoloured	4·50	1·75
80	2s.6d. multicoloured	8·50	11·00
81	5s. multicoloured	10·00	11·00
82	10s. multicoloured	13·00	14·00
83	£1 multicoloured	20·00	16·00
70/83 *Set of* 14		60·00	50·00

Designs:—1½d. White-capped Noddy; 2d. White Tern; 3d. Red billed Tropic Bird; 4½d. Common Noddy; 6d. Sooty Tern; 7d. Ascension Frigate Bird; 10d. Blue-faced Booby; 1s. White-tailed Tropic Bird; 1s.6d. Red-billed Tropic Bird; 2s.6d. Madeiran Storm Petrel; 5s. Red-footed Booby (brown phase); 10s. Ascension Frigate Birds; £1 Red-footed Booby (white phase).

(Des M. Goaman. Photo Harrison)

1963 (4 June). Freedom from Hunger. W w **12**. P 14×14½.

84	**29**	1s.6d. carmine	75	40

30 Red Cross Emblem

31 I.T.U. Emblem

(Des V. Whiteley. Litho B.W.)

1963 (2 Sept). Red Cross Centenary. W w **12**. P 13½.

85	**30**	3d. red and black	1·00	1·25
86		1s.6d. red and blue	1·50	2·25

(Des M. Goaman. Litho Enschedé)

1965 (17 May). I.T.U. Centenary. W w **12**. P 11×11½.

87	**31**	3d. magenta and bluish violet	50	65
88		6d. turquoise-blue and light chestnut	75	65

32 I.C.Y. Emblem

33 Sir Winston Churchill and St. Paul's Cathedral in Wartime

(Des V. Whiteley. Litho Harrison)

1965 (25 Oct). International Co-operation Year. W w **12**. P 14½.

89	**32**	1d. reddish purple and turquoise-green	40	60
90		6d. deep bluish green and lavender	60	90

(Des Jennifer Toombs. Photo Harrison)

1966 (24 Jan). Churchill Commemoration. Printed in black, cerise and gold with background in colours stated. W w **12**. P 14.

91	**33**	1d. new blue	50	75
92		3d. deep green	1·75	1·00
93		6d. brown	2·00	1·25
94		1s.6d. bluish violet	2·50	1·50
91/94 *Set of* 4			6·00	4·00

34 Footballer's Legs, Ball and Jules Rimet Cup

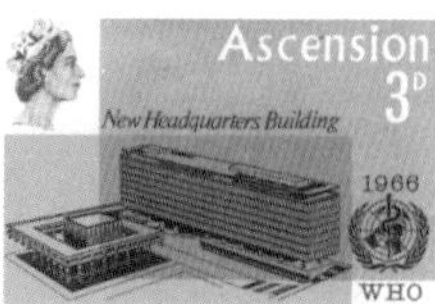

35 W.H.O. Building

(Des V. Whiteley. Litho Harrison)

1966 (1 July). World Cup Football Championship. W w **12** (sideways). P 14.

95	**34**	3d. violet, yellow-green, lake and yell-brown	1·50	60
96		6d. chocolate, blue-green, lake and yellow-brown	1·50	80

(Des M. Goaman. Litho Harrison)

1966 (20 Sept). Inauguration of W.H.O. Headquarters, Geneva. W w **12** (sideways). P 14.

97	**35**	3d. black, yellow-green and light blue	1·75	1·00
98		1s.6d. black, light purple and yellow-brown	4·75	2·00

36 Satellite Station

37 B.B.C. Emblem

(Des V. Whiteley. Photo Harrison)

1966 (7 Nov). Opening of Apollo Communications Satellite Earth Station. W w **12**. (sideways). P 14×14½.

99	**36**	4d. black and reddish violet	10	10
100		8d. black and deep bluish green	15	15
101		1s.3d. black and olive-brown	15	20
102		2s.6d. black and turquoise-blue	15	20
99/102 *Set of 4*			50	60

(Des B.B.C. staff. Photo, Queen's head and emblem die-stamped, Harrison)

1966 (1 Dec). Opening of B.B.C. Relay Station. W w **12**. P 14½.

103	**37**	1d. gold and ultramarine	10	10
104		3d. gold and myrtle-green	15	15
		w. Wmk inverted	50	1·25
105		6d. gold and reddish violet	15	15
106		1s.6d. gold and red	15	15
103/106 *Set of 4*			50	50

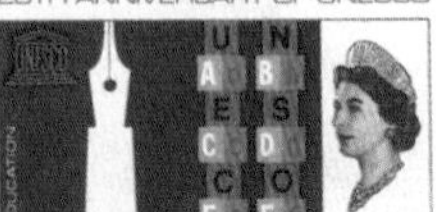

38 "Education"

39 "Science"

20TH ANNIVERSARY OF UNESCO

ASCENSION 1/6

40 "Culture"

(Des Jennifer Toombs. Litho Harrison)

1967 (1 Jan). 20th Anniv of U.N.E.S.C.O. W w **12** (sideways). P 14.

107	**38**	3d. slate-violet, red, yellow and orange	2·25	1·50
108	**39**	6d. orange-yellow, violet and deep olive	3·00	2·00
109	**40**	1s.6d. black, bright purple and orange	4·75	2·50
107/109 *Set of 3*			9·00	5·50

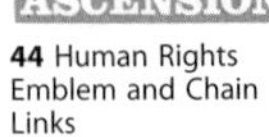
44 Human Rights Emblem and Chain Links

45 Black Durgon ("Ascension Black-Fish")

(Des and litho Harrison)

1968 (8 July). Human Rights Year. W w **12** (sideways*). P 14½×14.

110	**44**	6d. light orange, red and black	30	15
111		1s.6d. light grey-blue, red and black	40	25
112		2s.6d. light green, red and black	40	30
		w. Wmk Crown to right of CA	£650	
110/112 *Set of 3*			1·00	65

*The normal sideways watermark shows Crown to left of CA, *as seen from the back of the stamp.*

(Des M. Farrar Bell. Litho D.L.R.)

1968 (23 Oct). Fish (1st series). T **45** and similar horiz designs. W w **12** (sideways*). P 13.

113	4d. black, slate and turquoise-blue	30	35
114	8d. multicoloured	35	60
	w. Wmk Crown to right of CA	£450	
115	1s.9d. multicoloured	40	65
116	2s.3d. multicoloured	40	65
113/116 *Set of 4*		1·25	2·00

Designs:—8d. Scribbled Filefish ("Leather-jacket"); 1s.9d. Yellow-finned Tuna; 2s.3d. Short-finned Mako.

*The normal sideways watermark shows Crown to left of CA, *as seen from the back of the stamp.*

See also Nos. 117/20 and 126/9.

(Des M. Farrar Bell. Litho D.L.R.)

1969 (3 Mar). Fish (2nd series). Horiz designs as T **45**. Multicoloured. W w **12** (sideways). P 13½×13.

117	4d. Sailfish	65	80
118	6d. White Seabream ("Old Wife")	80	1·00
119	1s.6d. Yellowtail	1·00	2·25
120	2s.11d. Rock Hind ("Jack")	1·25	2·50
117/120 *Set of 4*		3·25	6·00

46 H.M.S. *Rattlesnake*

50 Early Chinese Rocket

(Des L. Curtis. Photo Harrison)

1969 (1 Oct). Royal Naval Crests (1st series). T **46** and similar vert designs. W w **12** (sideways*). P 14×14½.

121	4d. multicoloured	60	30
122	9d. multicoloured	75	35
123	1s.9d. deep blue, pale blue and gold	1·10	45
124	2s.3d. multicoloured	1·25	55
121/124 *Set of 4*		3·25	1·50
MS125	165×105 mm. Nos. 121/4. P 14½	6·50	13·00
	w. Wmk Crown to right of CA	£1000	

Designs:—9d. H.M.S. *Weston*; 1s.9d. H.M.S. *Undaunted*; 2s.3d. H.M.S. *Eagle*.

*The normal sideways watermark shows Crown to left of CA, *as seen from the back of the stamp.*

See also Nos. 130/4.

(Des M. Farrar Bell. Litho D.L.R.)

1970 (6 Apr). Fish (3rd series). Horiz designs as T **45**. Multicoloured. W w **12** (sideways*). P 14.

126	4d. Wahoo	4·50	2·75
	w. Wmk Crown to right of CA	£475	
127	9d. Ascension Jack ("Coalfish")	5·00	2·75
	w. Wmk Crown to right of CA	3·00	1·25
128	1s.9d. Pompano Dolphin	5·50	3·50
129	2s.3d. Squirrelfish ("Soldier")	5·50	3·50
	w. Wmk Crown to right of CA	3·00	1·50
126/129w *Set of 4*		14·00	8·00

*The normal sideways watermark shows Crown to left of CA, *as seen from the back of the stamp.*

(Des L. Curtis. Photo D.L.R.)

1970 (7 Sept). Royal Naval Crests (2nd series). Designs as T **46**. Multicoloured. W w **12**. P 12½.

130	4d. H.M.S. *Penelope*	1·00	1·00
131	9d. H.M.S. *Carlisle*	1·25	1·50
132	1s.6d. H.M.S. *Amphion*	1·75	2·00
133	2s.6d. H.M.S. *Magpie*	1·75	2·00
130/133 *Set of 4*		5·25	6·00
MS134	153×96 mm. Nos. 130/3	9·00	15·00

(Des V. Whiteley. Litho Format)

1971 (15 Feb). Decimal Currency. The Evolution of Space Travel. T **50** and similar multicoloured designs. W w **12** (sideways on horiz designs). P 14.

135	½p. Type **50**	15	20
136	1p. Medieval Arab astronomers	20	20
137	1½p. Tycho Brahe's Observatory, quadrant and Supernova	30	30
138	2p. Galileo, Moon and telescope	40	30
139	2½p. Isaac Newton, instruments and apple	1·75	1·00
140	3½p. Harrison's Chronometer and H.M.S. *Deptford* (frigate), 1735	2·50	1·50
141	4½p. Space Rocket taking-off	1·25	1·00

142	5p. World's largest telescope, Palomar	1·00	1·00
143	7½p. World's largest radio telescope, Jodrell Bank	4·00	1·75
144	10p. "Mariner 7" and Mars	3·50	1·75
145	12½p. "Sputnik 2" and Space dog, Laika	5·00	2·00
146	25p. Walking in Space	6·00	2·25
147	50p. "Apollo 11" crew on Moon	5·00	2·75
148	£1 Future Space Research Station	5·00	4·50
135/48	*Set of* 14	32·00	18·00

The ½p., 1p., 4½p. and 25p. are vertical, and the remainder are horizontal.

(Des L. Curtis. Photo D.L.R.)

1971 (15 Nov). Royal Naval Crests (3rd series). Designs as T **46**. Multicoloured. W w **12**. P 13.

149	2p. H.M.S. *Phoenix*	1·00	30
150	4p. H.M.S. *Milford*	1·00	55
151	9p. H.M.S. *Pelican*	1·25	80
152	15p. H.M.S. *Oberon*	1·25	1·00
149/52	*Set of* 4	4·25	2·40
MS153	151×104 mm. Nos. 149/52	4·00	15·00

(Des L. Curtis. Litho Questa)

1972 (29 May). Royal Naval Crests (4th series). Multicoloured designs as T **46**. W w **12** (sideways*). P 14.

154	1½p. H.M.S. *Lowestoft*	50	50
155	3p. H.M.S. *Auckland*	55	75
156	6p. H.M.S. *Nigeria*	60	1·25
157	17½p. H.M.S. *Bermuda*	90	2·50
154/7	*Set of* 4	2·25	4·50
MS158	157×93 mm. Nos. 154/7	2·25	7·50
	w. Wmk Crown to right of CA	£300	

*The normal sideways watermark shows Crown to left of CA, *as seen from the back of the stamp.*

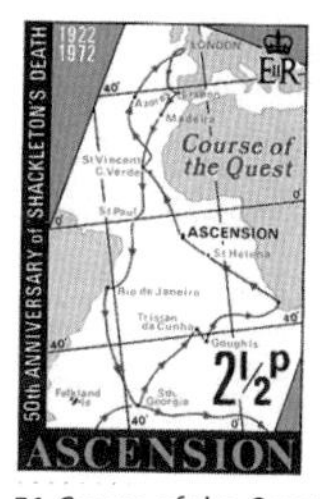

51 Course of the *Quest*

52 Land Crab and Short-finned Mako

(Des J. Cooter. Litho Questa)

1972 (2 Aug). 50th Anniv of Shackleton's Death. T **51** and similar multicoloured designs. W w **12** (sideways on 4 and 7½p.). P 14.

159	2½p. Type **51**	30	60
160	4p. Shackleton and *Quest* (*horiz*)	35	60
161	7½p. Shackleton's cabin and *Quest* (*horiz*)	35	65
162	11p. Shackleton's statue and memorial	40	80
159/62	*Set of* 4	1·25	2·40
MS163	139×114 mm. Nos. 159/62 (wmk sideways)	1·25	6·00

(Des (from photograph by D. Groves) and photo Harrison)

1972 (20 Nov). Royal Silver Wedding. Multicoloured; background colour given. W w **12**. P 14×14½.

164	**52**	2p. bright bluish violet	15	10
165		16p. rose-carmine	35	30

(Des L. Curtis. Litho J.W.)

1973 (28 May). Royal Naval Crests (5th series). Multicoloured designs as T **46**. W w **12** (sideways*). P 14.

166	2p. H.M.S. *Birmingham*	1·50	1·50
167	4p. H.M.S. *Cardiff*	1·75	1·50
168	9p. H.M.S. *Penzance*	2·25	1·75
169	13p. H.M.S. *Rochester*	2·75	1·75
	w. Wmk Crown to right of CA	16·00	
166/9	*Set of* 4	7·50	5·75
MS170	109×152 mm. Nos. 166/9	28·00	10·00

*The normal sideways watermark shows Crown to left of CA on 2, 4, 13p. and **MS**170, or Crown to right of CA on 9p., *as seen from the back of the stamp.*

53 Green Turtle

(Des V. Whiteley Studio. Litho Enschedé)

1973 (28 Aug). Turtles. T **53** and similar triangular designs. Multicoloured. W w **12**. P 13½.

171	4p. Type **53**	2·25	1·75
172	9p. Loggerhead turtle	2·50	2·00
173	12p. Hawksbill turtle	2·75	2·25
171/3	*Set of* 3	6·75	5·50

54 Sergeant, R.M. Light Infantry, 1900

54a Princess Anne and Captain Mark Phillips

(Des G. Drummond from paintings by C. Stadden. Litho Walsall)

1973 (31 Oct). 50th Anniv of Departure of Royal Marines from Ascension. T **54** and similar vert designs. Multicoloured. W w **12** (sideways*). P 14.

174	2p. Type **54**	1·25	1·50
175	6p. R.M. Private, 1816	2·00	1·50
176	12p. R.M. Light Infantry Officer, 1880	2·25	2·25
	w. Wmk Crown to right of CA	38·00	
177	20p. R.M. Artillery Colour Sergeant, 1910	2·25	2·50
174/7	*Set of* 4	7·00	7·00

The normal sideways watermark shows Crown to left of CA, *as seen from the back of the stamp.*

(Des PAD Studio. Litho Questa)

1973 (14 Nov). Royal Wedding. Centre multicoloured. W w **12** (sideways). P 13½.

178	**54a**	2p. ochre	15	10
179		18p. dull blue-green	20	20

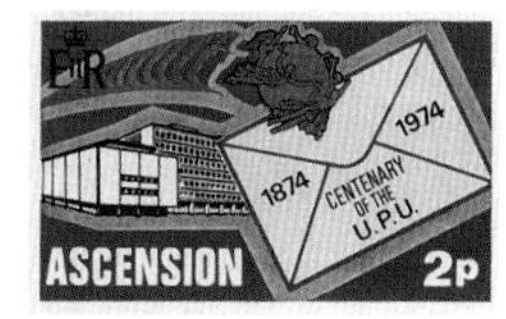

55 Letter and H.Q., Berne

(Des PAD Studio. Litho Questa)

1974 (27 Mar). Centenary of U.P.U.T **55** and similar horiz design. Multicoloured. W w **12**. P 14½×14.

180	2p. Type **55**	20	30
181	9p. Hermes and U.P.U monument	30	45

56 Churchill as a Boy, and Birthplace, Blenheim Palace

(Des J.W. Litho Questa)

1974 (30 Nov). Birth Centenary of Sir Winston Churchill. T **56** and similar horiz design. Multicoloured. No wmk. P 14.

182	5p. Type **56**	20	35
183	25p. Churchill as statesman, and U.N. Building	30	75
MS184	93×87 mm. Nos. 182/3	1·00	2·50

57 "Skylab 3" and Photograph of Ascension

(Des PAD Studio. Litho Questa)

1975 (20 Mar). Space Satellites. T **57** and similar horiz design. Multicoloured. W w **12** (sideways). P 14.

185 2p. Type **57** ... 20 30
186 18p. "Skylab 4" command module and photograph ... 30 40

The date "11.1.73" given on the 2p. is incorrect, "Skylab 3" was launched in July 1973 and returned to Earth in September 1973.

The date on the 18p. is also incorrect. The photograph was taken on 6 January 1974, three days later than the date given in the caption.

58 U.S.A.F. Lockheed C-141A Starlifter

APOLLO-SOYUZ LINK 1975

(**59**)

(Des R. Granger Barrett. Litho Questa)

1975 (19 June). Wideawake Airfield. T **58** and similar horiz designs. Multicoloured. W w **12** (sideways*). P 13½.

187 2p. Type **58** ... 60 65
188 5p. R.A.F. Lockheed C-130 Hercules ... 60 85
189 9p. Vickers Super VC-10 ... 60 1·10
190 24p. U.S.A.F. Lockheed C-5A Galaxy ... 1·00 2·00
w. Wmk Crown to right of CA ...
187/90 *Set of 4* ... 2·50 4·25
MS191 144×99 mm. Nos 187/90 ... 14·00 22·00

*The normal sideways watermark shows Crown to left of CA, *as seen from the back of the stamp.*

1975 (18 Aug). "Apollo-Soyuz" Space Link. Nos. 141 and 145/6 optd with T **59**.

192 4½p. Space rocket taking-off ... 15 20
193 12½p. Sputnik II and Space Dog, Laika ... 15 25
194 25p. Walking in Space ... 25 40
192/4 *Set of 3* ... 50 75

60 Arrival of Royal Navy, 1815

(Des J.W. from paintings by Isabel McManus. Litho Walsall)

1975 (22 Oct). 160th Anniv of Occupation. T **60** and similar horiz designs. Multicoloured. W w **14** (sideways*). P 14.

195 2p. Type **60** ... 25 25
w. Wmk Crown to right of CA ... £275
196 5p. Water Supply, Dampiers Drip ... 25 40
197 9p. First landing, 1815 ... 25 60
198 15p. The garden on Green Mountain ... 35 85
195/8 *Set of 4* ... 1·00 1·90

*The normal sideways watermark shows Crown to left of CA, *as seen from the back of the stamp.*

61 Yellow Canary

62 Boatswain Bird Island Sanctuary

(Des J.W. Litho Questa)

1976 (26 Apr). Birds. Multicoloured designs as T **61** and T **62**. W w **14** (sideways on horiz designs*). P 13½ (£2) or 14 (others).

199 1p. Type **61** ... 40 1·50
200 2p. White Tern (*vert*) ... 50 1·50
w. Wmk inverted ... £550
201 3p. Common Waxbill ... 50 1·50
202 4p. White-capped Noddy (*vert*) ... 50 1·50
203 5p. Common Noddy ... 70 1·50
204 6p. Common Mynah ... 70 1·50
205 7p. Madeiran Storm Petrel (*vert*) ... 1·00 1·50
206 8p. Sooty Tern ... 70 1·50
w. Wmk Crown to right of CA ... £450
207 9p. Blue-faced Booby (*vert*) ... 70 1·50
208 10p. Red-footed Booby ... 70 1·50
209 15p. Red-necked Spurfowl ("Red-throated Francolin") (*vert*) ... 85 1·50
210 18p. Brown Booby (*vert*) ... 85 1·50
211 25p. Red-billed Tropicbird ("Bos'un Bird") ... 90 1·50
212 50p. White-tailed Tropic Bird ... 1·00 1·75
213 £1 Ascension Frigate Bird (*vert*) ... 1·00 2·25
214 £2 Type **62** ... 2·00 5·00
199/214 *Set of 16* ... 11·50 26·00

*The normal sideways watermark shows Crown to left of CA, *as seen from the back of the stamp.*

63 G.B. Penny Red with Ascension Postmark

(Des C. Abbott. Litho J.W.)

1976 (4 May). Festival of Stamps, London. T **63** and similar designs. W w **14** (sideways on 5 and 25p.). P 13½.

215 5p. rose-red, black and cinnamon ... 15 15
216 9p. green, black and greenish stone ... 15 20
217 25p. multicoloured ... 25 45
215/17 *Set of 3* ... 65 70
MS218 133×121 mm. No. 217 with St. Helena 318 and Tristan da Cunha 206 (wmk sideways*). P 13 ... 1·75 2·00
w. Wmk Crown to left of CA ... £600

Designs: *Vert*—9p. ½d. stamp of 1922. *Horiz*—25p. *Southampton Castle* (liner).

*The normal sideways watermark shows Crown to right of CA, *as seen from the back of the stamp.*

No. **MS**218 was postally valid on each island to the value of 25p.

64 U.S. Base, Ascension

65 Visit of Prince Philip, 1957

(Des V. Whiteley Studio. Litho J.W.)

1976 (4 July). Bicentenary of American Revolution. T **64** and similar horiz designs. Multicoloured. W w **14** (sideways). P 13.

219 8p. Type **64** ... 30 40
220 9p. NASA Station at Devils Ashpit ... 30 45
221 25p. "Viking" landing on Mars ... 50 80
219/21 *Set of 3* ... 1·00 1·50

(Des J. Cooter. Litho Walsall)

1977 (7 Feb). Silver Jubilee. T **65** and similar horiz designs. Multicoloured. W w **14** (sideways on 12 and 25p.). P 13½.

222 8p. Type **65** ... 15 15
w. Wmk inverted ... £225
223 12p. Coronation Coach leaving Buckingham Palace ... 20 20
224 25p. Coronation Coach ... 35 40
222/4 *Set of 3* ... 60 65

66 Tunnel carrying Water Pipe

67 Mars Bay Location, 1877

(Des G. Drummond. Litho Harrison)

1977 (27 June). Water Supplies. T **66** and similar multicoloured designs. W w **14** (sideways on 12 and 25p.). P 14.

225 3p. Type **66** ... 15 15
226 5p. Breakneck Valley wells ... 20 20
227 12p. Break tank (*horiz*) ... 30 35
228 25p. Water catchment (*horiz*) ... 45 65
225/8 *Set of* 4 ... 1·00 1·25

(Des J.W. Litho Questa)

1977 (3 Oct). Centenary of Visit of Professor Gill (astronomer). T **67** and similar horiz designs. Multicoloured. W w **14** (sideways). P 13½.

229 3p. Type **67** ... 15 20
230 8p. Instrument sites, Mars Bay ... 15 25
231 12p. Sir David and Lady Gill ... 20 40
232 25p. Maps of Ascension ... 60 70
229/32 *Set of* 4 ... 1·00 1·40

68 Lion of England

69 Queen Elizabeth II

(Des C. Abbott. Litho Questa)

1978 (2 June). 25th Anniv of Coronation. T **68/9** and similar vert design. P 15.

233 **68** 25p. yellow, sepia and silver ... 35 50
a. Sheetlet. Nos. 233/5×2 ... 1·75
234 **69** 25p. multicoloured ... 35 50
235 – 25p. yellow, sepia and silver ... 35 50
233/5 *Set of* 3 ... 95 1·40

Design:—No. 235, Green Turtle.

Nos. 233/5 were printed together in small sheets of 6, containing two *se-tenant* strips of 3 with horizontal gutter margin between.

70 Flank of Sisters, Sisters' Red Hill and East Crater

71 *"The Resolution"* (H. Roberts)

(Des J.W. Litho Questa)

1978 (4 Sept). Volcanic Rock Formations of Ascension. T **70** and similar horiz designs. Multicoloured. W w **14**. P 14½.

236 3p. Type **70** ... 15 20
a. Horiz strip of 5. Nos. 236/40 ... 1·10 1·60
237 5p. Holland's Crater (Hollow Tooth) ... 20 30
238 12p. Street Crater, Lower Valley Crater and Bear's Back ... 25 40
239 15p. Butt Crater, Weather Post and Green Mountain ... 30 45
240 25p. Flank of Sisters, Thistle Hill and Two Boats Village ... 35 50
236/40 *Set of* 5 ... 1·10 1·60
MS241 185×100 mm. Nos. 236/40, each×2 ... 1·50 5·00
a. Blue ("Ascension Island") omitted ... £5500 £5500

Nos. 236/40 were printed together, *se-tenant*, in horizontal strips of 5 throughout the sheet forming a composite design.

(Des and litho (25p. also embossed) Walsall)

1979 (19 Feb*). Bicentenary of Captain Cook's Voyages, 1768–79. T **71** and similar vert designs. Multicoloured. P 11.

242 3p. Type **71** ... 30 25
243 8p. Chronometer ... 25 40
244 12p. Green Turtle ... 30 50
245 25p. Flaxman/Wedgwood medallion of Captain Cook ... 30 70
242/5 *Set of* 4 ... 1·00 1·75

*This is the local date of issue; the stamps were released in London on 8 January.

72 St. Mary's Church, Georgetown

73 Landing Cable, Comfortless Cove

(Des Walsall. Litho Format)

1979 (24 May). Ascension Day. T **72** and similar vert designs. Multicoloured. W w **14**. P 14.

246 8p. Type **72** ... 10 30
247 12p. Map of Ascension ... 15 40
248 50p. "The Ascension" (painting by Rembrandt) ... 30 90
246/8 *Set of* 3 ... 50 1·40

(Des G. Vasarhelyi. Litho Walsall)

1979 (15 Sept). 80th Anniv of Eastern Telegraph Company's Arrival on Ascension. T **73** and similar designs. W w **14** (inverted on 12p. or sideways on others*). P 14.

249 3p. black and carmine ... 10 10
250 8p. black and yellowish green ... 15 15
251 12p. black and yellow ... 20 20
252 15p. black and bright violet ... 20 25
w. Wmk Crown to right of CA ... 75·00
253 25p. black and orange-brown ... 25 35
249/53 *Set of* 5 ... 80 95

Designs: *Horiz*—8p. C.S. *Anglia*; 15p. C.S. *Seine*; 25p Cable and Wireless earth station. *Vert*—12p. Map of Atlantic cable network.

*The normal sideways watermark shows Crown to left of CA, *as seen from the back of the stamp.*

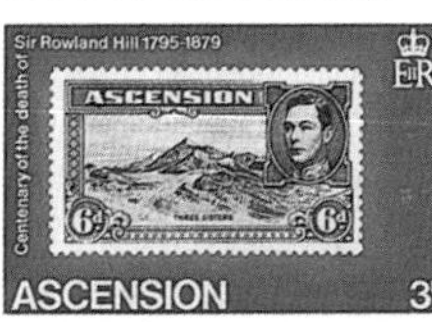

74 1938 6d. Stamp

75 *Anogramma ascensionis*

(Des BG Studio. Litho Questa)

1979 (12 Dec). Death Centenary of Sir Rowland Hill. T **74** and similar designs. W w **14** (sideways on 3 and 8p.). P 14.

254 3p. black, new blue & deep turquoise-blue ... 10 10
255 8p. black, blue-green and light green ... 15 20
256 12p. black, bright blue and turquoise-blue ... 15 25
w. Wmk inverted ... £190
257 50p. black, brownish grey and red ... 40 90
254/7 *Set of* 4 ... 70 1·25

Designs: *Horiz*—8p. 1956 5s. definitive stamp. *Vert*—12p. 1924 3s. stamp; 50p. Sir Rowland Hill.

(Des J. Cooter. Litho Format)

1980 (18 Feb). Ferns and Grasses. T **75** and similar multicoloured designs. W w **14** (sideways on 12 to 24p.). P 14½×14 (3 to 8p.) or 14×14½ (12 to 24p.).

258 3p. Type **75** ... 10 15
259 6p. *Xiphopteris ascensionense* ... 10 20
260 8p. *Sporobolus caespitosus* ... 10 20
261 12p. *Sporobolus durus (vert)* ... 15 30

No.	Description		
262	18p. *Dryopteris ascensionis (vert)*	15	40
	a. Brown (thorns) omitted	£300	
263	24p. *Marattia purpurascens (vert)*	20	55
258/63	*Set of 6*	70	1·60

76 17th-century Bottle Post

77 Queen Elizabeth the Queen Mother

(Des L. Curtis. Litho Format)

1980 (1 May). "London 1980" International Stamp Exhibition. T **76** and similar horiz designs. Multicoloured. W w **14** (sideways). P 13½.

No.	Description		
264	8p. Type **76**	15	20
265	12p. 19th-century chance calling ship	20	25
266	15p. *Garth Castle* (regular mail service from 1863)	20	30
267	50p. *St. Helena* (mail services, 1980)	60	90
264/7	*Set of 4*	1·00	1·50
MS268	102×154 mm. Nos. 264/7	1·00	2·40

(Des Harrison. Litho Questa)

1980 (11 Aug*). 80th Birthday of Queen Elizabeth the Queen Mother. W w **14** (sideways). P 14.

No.	Type	Description		
269	**77**	15p. multicoloured	40	40

*This was the local release date. The Crown Agents placed stocks on sale in London on 4 August.

78 Lubbock's Yellowtail

79 H.M.S. *Tortoise*

(Des G. Drummond. Litho Enschedé)

1980 (15 Sept). Fish. T **78** and similar horiz designs. Multicoloured. W w **14** (sideways*). P 13×13½.

No.	Description		
270	3p. Type **78**	20	25
271	10p. Resplendent Angelfish	20	25
272	25p. Bicoloured Butterflyfish	30	55
	w. Wmk Crown to right of CA	1·25	
273	40p. Marmalade Razorfish	40	75
	w. Wmk Crown to right of CA	1·75	
270/3	*Set of 4*	1·00	1·60

*The normal sideways watermark shows Crown to left of CA, *as seen from the back of the stamp.*

(Des D. Bowen. Litho Rosenbaum Bros, Vienna)

1980 (17 Nov). 150th Anniv of Royal Geographical Society. T **79** and similar multicoloured designs. W w **14** (sideways*). P 14 (60p.) or 13½ (others).

No.	Description		
274	10p. Type **79**	20	40
	w. Wmk Crown to left of CA	1·00	
275	15p. "Wideawake Fair"	25	45
	w. Wmk Crown to left of CA	1·50	
276	60p. Mid-Atlantic Ridge (38×48 *mm*)	65	1·25
	w. Wmk Crown to left of CA	3·00	
274/6	*Set of 3*	1·00	2·00

*The normal sideways watermark shows Crown to right of CA, *as seen from the back of the stamp.*

80 Green Mountain Farm, 1881

(Des C. Abbott. Litho Format)

1981 (15 Feb). Green Mountain Farm. T **80** and similar horiz designs. Multicoloured. W w **14** (sideways). P 13½×14.

No.	Description		
277	12p. Type **80**	15	35
278	15p. Two Boats, 1881	15	40
279	20p. Green Mountain and Two Boats, 1981	20	50
280	30p. Green Mountain Farm, 1981	30	70
277/80	*Set of 4*	70	1·75

81 Cable and Wireless Earth Station

(Des G. Vasarhelyi and Walsall. Litho Walsall)

1981 (27 Apr). "Space Shuttle" Mission and Opening of 2nd Earth Station. W w **14** (sideways). P 14.

No.	Type	Description		
281	**81**	15p. black, bright blue and pale blue	30	35

82 Poinsettia

83 Solanum

(Des J. Cooter. Litho J.W.)

1981 (11 May)–**82**. Flowers. Designs as T **82** (1 to 40p) or vert as T **83** (50p. to £2). Multicoloured. W w **14** (sideways* on 1, 2, 4, 5, 8, 15, 20, 40, 50p., £1 and £2). P 13½.

A. Without imprint date

No.	Description		
282A	1p. Type **82**	70	1·25
283A	2p. Clustered Wax Flower	80	1·25
284A	3p. Kolanchoe (*vert*)	80	1·25
285A	4p. Yellow Pops	80	1·25
286A	5p. Camels Foot Creeper	80	1·25
287A	8p. White Oleander	80	1·25
288A	10p. Ascension Lily (*vert*)	1·40	1·25
289A	12p. Coral Plant (*vert*)	1·50	1·10
290A	15p. Yellow Allamanda	1·25	85
291A	20p. Ascension Euphorbia	1·25	1·00
	w. Wmk Crown to left of CA	2·50	
292A	30p. Flame of the Forest (*vert*)	1·25	1·25
293A	40p. Bougainvillea "King Leopold"	1·25	3·00
294A	50p. Type **83**	1·75	3·25
295A	£1 Ladies Petticoat	2·00	4·00
296A	£2 Red Hibiscus	3·50	6·00
282A/96A	*Set of 15*	17·00	25·00

B. With imprint date ("1982") (27.8.82)

No.	Description		
283B	2p. Clustered Wax Flower	50	1·25
284B	3p. Kolanchoe (*vert*)	50	1·25
288B	10p. Ascension Lily (*vert*)	45	75
290B	15p. Yellow Allamanda	50	75
291B	20p. Ascension Euphorbia	1·00	75
295B	£1 Ladies Petticoat	2·00	3·00
	w. Wmk Crown to left of CA	10·00	
283B/95B	*Set of 6*	4·50	6·00

*The normal sideways watermark shows Crown to right of CA, *as seen from the back of the stamp.*

Nos. 283B/95B had the imprint dates printed on the stamps by typography.

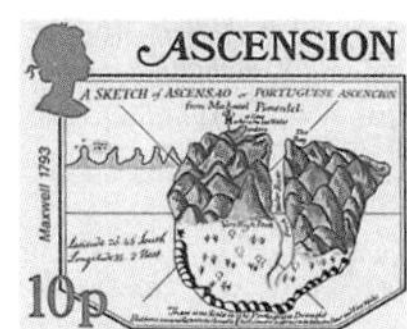

84 Map by Maxwell, 1793

(Des L. Curtis. Litho Walsall)

1981 (22 May). Early Maps of Ascension. T **84** and similar horiz designs. W w **14** (sideways). P 14×14½.

297	10p. black, gold and pale blue	20	35
298	12p. black, gold and apple-green	20	35
299	15p. black, gold and stone	20	35
300	40p. black, gold and pale greenish yellow	50	70
297/300	*Set of* 4	1·00	1·60
MS301	79×64 mm. 5p.×4, multicoloured	60	75

Designs:—12p. Maxwell, 1793 (*different*); 15p. Ekeberg and Chapman, 1811; 40p. Campbell, 1819; miniature sheet, Linschoten, 1599.

Stamps from No. **MS**301 form a composite design.

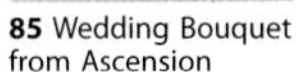

85 Wedding Bouquet from Ascension

86 Prince Charles and Lady Diana Spencer

(Des J.W. Litho Questa)

1981 (22 July). Royal Wedding. T **85/6** and similar vert design. Multicoloured. W w **14**. P 14.

302	10p. Type **85**	15	15
303	15p. Prince Charles in Fleet Air Arm flying kit	30	30
304	50p. Type **86**	65	90
302/4	*Set of* 3	1·00	1·25

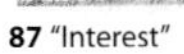

87 "Interest"

88 Scout crossing Rope Bridge

(Des BG Studio. Litho Questa)

1981 (14 Sept). 25th Anniv of Duke of Edinburgh Award Scheme. T **87** and similar vert designs. Multicoloured. W w **14**. P 14.

305	5p. Type **87**	15	15
306	10p. "Physical activities"	15	15
307	15p. "Service"	20	20
308	40p. Duke of Edinburgh	45	45
	w. Wmk inverted	28·00	
305/8	*Set of* 4	85	85

(Des A. Theobald. Litho Format)

1982 (22 Feb). 75th Anniv of Boy Scout Movement. T **88** and similar designs. W w **14** (sideways). P 14.

309	10p. black, bright blue and azure	15	35
310	15p. black, orange-brown and greenish yellow	15	50
311	25p. black, bright mauve and pale mauve	20	60
312	40p. black, rosine and pale orange	30	85
309/12	*Set of* 4	1·00	2·10
MS313	121×121 mm. 10p., 15p., 25p., 40p As Nos. 309/12 (*each diamond*, 40×40 *mm*). P 14½	1·00	2·50

Designs:—15p. 1st Ascension Scout Group flag; 25p. Scouts learning to use radio; 40p. Lord Baden-Powell.

Stamps from No. **MS**313 have an overall design showing a flag printed on the reverse beneath the gum.

89 Charles Darwin

90 Fairey Swordfish Torpedo Bomber

(Des L. Curtis. Litho Questa)

1982 (19 Apr). 150th Anniv of Charles Darwin's Voyage. T **89** and similar horiz designs. Multicoloured. W w **14** (sideways). P 14.

314	10p. Type **89**	20	40
315	12p. Darwin's pistols	20	50
316	15p. Rock Crab	25	55
317	40p. H.M.S. *Beagle*	60	95
314/17	*Set of* 4	1·10	2·25

(Des A. Theobald. Litho Walsall)

1982 (15 June). 40th Anniv of Wideawake Airfield. T **90** and similar horiz designs. Multicoloured. W w **14** (sideways). P 14.

318	5p. Type **90**	60	35
319	10p. North American B-25C Mitchell	75	40
320	15p. Boeing EC-135N Aria	90	55
321	50p. Lockheed C-130 Hercules	1·25	1·10
318/21	*Set of* 4	3·25	2·25

91 Ascension Coat of Arms

92 Formal Portrait

(Des Jennifer Toombs. Litho Questa)

1982 (1 July). 21st Birthday of Princess of Wales. T **91/2** and similar vert designs. Multicoloured. W w **14**. P 14×14½.

322	12p. Type **91**	20	20
323	15p. Lady Diana Spencer in Music Room, Buckingham Palace	20	20
324	25p. Bride and Earl Spencer leaving Clarence House	30	30
325	50p. Type **92**	65	65
322/5	*Set of* 4	1·25	1·25

1st PARTICIPATION
COMMONWEALTH GAMES 1982
(**93**)

1982 (29 Oct). Commonwealth Games, Brisbane. Nos. 290B/1B optd with T **93**.

326	15p. Yellow Allamanda	30	40
327	20p. Ascension Euphorbia	40	45

94 Bush House, London

95 *Marasmius thwaitesii* ("*Marasmius echinosphaerus*")

(Des A. Theobald. Litho Questa)

1982 (1 Dec). Christmas. 50th Anniv of B.B.C. External Broadcasting. T **94** and similar horiz designs. Multicoloured. W w **14** (sideways*). P 14.

328	5p. Type **94**	15	20
329	10p. Atlantic relay station	20	30
330	25p. Lord Reith, first director-general	30	60
	w. Wmk Crown to right of CA	1·75	
331	40p. King George V making his first Christmas broadcast, 1932	45	75
328/31	*Set of* 4	1·00	1·60

*The normal sideways watermark shows Crown to left of CA, *as seen from the back of the stamp.*

(Des Harrison. Litho Questa)

1983 (1 Mar). Fungi. T **95** and similar vert designs. Multicoloured. W w **14**. P 14.

332	7p. Type **95**	25	30
333	12p. *Chlorophyllum molybdites*	35	45
334	15p. *Leucocoprinus cepaestripes*	40	50
335	20p. *Lycoperdon marginatum*	45	65
336	50p. *Marasmiellus distantifolius*	55	1·25
332/6	*Set of* 5	1·75	2·75

96 Aerial View of Georgetown

(Des Jennifer Toombs. Litho Format)

1983 (12 May). Island Views (1st series). T **96** and similar horiz designs. Multicoloured. W w **14** (sideways*). P 14×13½.

337	12p. Type **96**	15	25
338	15p. Green Mountain farm	15	25
	w. Wmk Crown to right of CA		
339	20p. Boatswain Bird Island	20	40
340	60p. Telemetry Hill by night	40	80
337/40	*Set of 4*	80	1·50

*The normal sideways watermark shows Crown to left of CA, *as seen from the back of the stamp.*

See also Nos. 367/70.

97 Westland Wessex 5 Helicopter of No. 845 Naval Air Squadron

(Des D. Hartley-Marjoram. Litho Questa)

1983 (1 Aug). Bicentenary of Manned Flight. British Military Aircraft. T **97** and similar horiz designs. Multicoloured. W w **14** (sideways). P 13½.

341	12p. Type **97**	30	50
342	15p. Avro Vulcan B.2 of No. 44 Squadron	30	60
343	20p. Hawker Siddeley H.S.801 Nimrod M.R. 2P of No. 120 Squadron	30	75
344	60p. Handley Page H.P.80 Victor K2 of No. 55 Squadron	50	1·75
341/4	*Set of 4*	1·25	3·25

98 Iguanid

(Des D. Nockles. Litho Questa)

1983 (20 Sept). Introduced Species. T **98** and similar horiz designs. Multicoloured. W w **14** (sideways). P 14.

345	12p. Type **98**	20	30
346	15p. Rabbit	25	35
347	20p. Cat	30	45
348	60p. Donkey	60	1·40
345/8	*Set of 4*	1·25	2·25

99 Speckled Tellin (*Tellina listeri*)

100 1922 1½d. Stamp

(Des G. Wilby. Litho Format)

1983 (28 Nov). Sea Shells. T **99** and similar horiz designs. Multicoloured. W w **14** (sideways). P 14½×14.

349	7p. Type **99**	15	20
350	12p. Lion's Paw Scallop (*Lyropecten nodosa*)	15	30
351	15p. Lurid Cowrie (*Cypraea lurida oceanica*)	20	35
352	20p. Ascension Nerite (*Nerita ascensionis*)	20	45
353	50p. Miniature Melo (*Micromelo undatus*)	40	1·10
349/53	*Set of 5*	1·00	2·25

(Des C. Abbott. Litho Questa)

1984 (3 Jan). 150th Anniv of St. Helena as a British Colony. T **100** and similar vert designs showing stamps of the 1922 issue overprinted on St. Helena. Multicoloured. W w **14**. P 14.

354	12p. Type **100**	20	45
355	15p. 1922 2d. stamp	20	50
356	20p. 1922 8d. stamp	20	55
357	60p. 1922 1s. stamp	50	1·40
354/7	*Set of 4*	1·00	2·50

101 Prince Andrew

102 Naval Semaphore

(Des L. Curtis. Litho Questa)

1984 (10 Apr). Visit of Prince Andrew. Sheet, 124×90 mm, containing vert designs as T **101**. W w **14**. P 14½×14.

MS358	12p. Type **101**; 70p. Prince Andrew in naval uniform	1·00	1·60

(Des D. Hartley-Marjoram. Litho Questa)

1984 (28 May). 250th Anniv of "Lloyd's List" (newspaper). T **102** and similar vert designs. Multicoloured. W w **14**. P 14½×14.

359	12p. Type **102**	50	30
360	15p. *Southampton Castle* (liner)	50	35
361	20p. Pier Head	55	45
362	70p. *Dane* (screw steamer)	1·25	1·50
359/62	*Set of 4*	2·50	2·40

103 Penny Coin and Yellow-finned Tuna

104 Bermuda Cypress

(Des G. Drummond. Litho Questa)

1984 (26 July). New Coinage. T **103** and similar horiz designs. Multicoloured. W w **14** (sideways). P 14.

363	12p. Type **103**	35	35
364	15p. Twopenny coin and donkey	40	40
365	20p. Fifty pence coin and Green Turtle	45	50
366	70p. Pound coin and Sooty Tern	80	1·75
363/6	*Set of 4*	1·75	2·75

(Des Jennifer Toombs. Litho B.D.T.)

1984 (26 Oct). Island Views (2nd series). Horiz designs as T **96**. Multicoloured. W w **14** (sideways). P 13½.

367	12p. The Devil's Riding-school	20	30
368	15p. St. Mary's Church	25	35
369	20p. Two Boats Village	25	45
370	70p. Ascension from the sea	80	1·50
367/70	*Set of 4*	1·25	2·40

(Des N. Shewring. Litho Questa)

1985 (8 Mar). Trees. T **104** and similar vert designs. Multicoloured. W w **14**. P 14½.

371	7p. Type **104**	20	20
372	12p. Norfolk Island Pine	25	30
373	15p. Screwpine	25	35
374	20p. Eucalyptus	25	45
375	65p. Spore Tree	70	1·40
371/5	*Set of 5*	1·50	2·40

105 The Queen Mother with Prince Andrew at Silver Jubilee Service

106 32 Pdr. Smooth Bore Muzzle-loader, *c* 1820, and Royal Marine Artillery Hat Plate, *c* 1816

(Des A. Theobald (75p.), C. Abbott (others). Litho Questa)

1985 (7 June). Life and Times of Queen Elizabeth the Queen Mother. T **105** and similar vert designs. Multicoloured. W w **16**. P 14½×14.

376	12p. With the Duke of York at Balmoral, 1924	25	35
	w. Wmk inverted	12·00	
377	15p. Type **105**	25	40
	w. Wmk inverted	1·00	
378	20p. The Queen Mother at Ascot	30	55
	w. Wmk inverted	30·00	
379	70p. With Prince Henry at his christening (from photo by Lord Snowdon)	80	1·75
376/9	*Set of 4*	1·40	2·75
MS380	91×73 mm. 75p. Visiting the *Queen Elizabeth 2* at Southampton, 1968. Wmk sideways	1·10	1·60

(Des W. Fenton. Litho Walsall)

1985 (19 July). Guns on Ascension Island. T **106** and similar horiz designs. Multicoloured. W w **14** (sideways). P 14×14½.

381	12p. Type **106**	40	90
382	15p. 7 inch rifled muzzle-loader, *c* 1866, and Royal Cypher on barrel	40	1·00
383	20p. 7 pdr. rifled muzzle-loader, *c* 1877, and Royal Artillery badge	40	1·25
384	70p. 5.5 inch gun, 1941, and crest from H.M.S. *Hood*	80	3·00
381/4	*Set of 4*	1·75	5·50

107 Guide Flag

108 *Clerodendrum fragrans*

(Des N. Shewring. Litho Questa)

1985 (4 Oct). 75th Anniv of Girl Guide Movement and International Youth Year. T **107** and similar vert designs. Multicoloured. W w **14**. P 14½×14.

385	12p. Type **107**	30	70
	w. Wmk inverted	1·50	
386	15p. Practising first aid	30	80
	w. Wmk inverted	1·50	
387	20p. Camping	30	90
388	70p. Lady Baden-Powell	80	2·50
385/8	*Set of 4*	1·50	4·50

(Des Josephine Martin. Litho Questa)

1985 (6 Dec). Wild Flowers. T **108** and similar vert designs. Multicoloured. W w **16**. P 14.

389	12p. Type **108**	30	75
390	15p. Shell Ginger	30	90
391	20p. Cape Daisy	35	90
392	70p. Ginger Lily	70	2·50
389/92	*Set of 4*	1·50	4·50

109 Newton's Reflector Telescope

110 Princess Elizabeth in 1926

(Des D. Hartley. Litho B.D.T.)

1986 (7 Mar). Appearance of Halley's Comet. T **109** and similar vert designs. Multicoloured. W w **16**. P 14.

393	12p. Type **109**	40	1·10
394	15p. Edmond Halley and Old Greenwich Observatory	40	1·25
395	20p. Short's Gregorian telescope and comet, 1759	40	1·25
396	70p. Ascension satellite tracking station and ICE spacecraft	1·10	3·50
393/6	*Set of 4*	2·10	6·00

(Des A. Theobald. Litho Format)

1986 (21 Apr). 60th Birthday of Queen Elizabeth II. T **110** and similar vert designs. Multicoloured. W w **16**. P 14×14½.

397	7p. Type **110**	15	25
398	15p. Queen making Christmas broadcast, 1952	15	40
399	20p. At Garter ceremony, Windsor Castle, 1983	20	50
400	35p. In Auckland, New Zealand, 1981	30	80
401	£1 At Crown Agents' Head Office, London, 1983	75	2·25
397/401	*Set of 5*	1·40	3·75

111 1975 Space Satellites 2p. Stamp

112 Prince Andrew and Miss Sarah Ferguson

(Des L. Curtis. Litho Walsall)

1986 (22 May). "Ameripex '86" International Stamp Exhibition, Chicago. T **111** and similar horiz designs showing previous Ascension stamps. Multicoloured. W w **16** (sideways*). P 14×14½.

402	12p. Type **111**	25	60
403	15p. 1980 "London 1980" International Stamp Exhibition 50p.	20	70
404	20p. 1976 Bicentenary of American Revolution 8p.	25	90
	w. Wmk Crown to right of CA	70·00	
405	70p 1982 40th Anniv of Wideawake Airfield 10p.	70	2·00
402/5	*Set of 4*	1·25	3·75
MS406	60×75 mm. 75p. Statue of Liberty	1·50	2·75

*The normal sideways watermark shows Crown to left of CA, *as seen from the back of the stamp.*

(Des D. Miller. Litho Questa)

1986 (23 July). Royal Wedding. T **112** and similar square design. Multicoloured. W w **16**. P 14.

407	15p. Type **112**	25	50
408	35p. Prince Andrew aboard H.M.S. *Brazen*	50	1·00

113 H.M.S. *Ganymede* (*c* 1811)

(Des E. Nisbet. Litho Questa)

1986 (14 Oct). Ships of the Royal Navy. T **113** and similar horiz designs. Multicoloured. W w **16** (sideways*). P 14½.

409	1p. Type **113**	55	1·50

410	2p. H.M.S. *Kangaroo* (*c* 1811)	60	1·50
	w. Wmk Crown to right of CA		
411	4p. H.M.S. *Trinculo* (*c* 1811)	60	1·75
412	5p. H.M.S. *Daring* (*c* 1811)	60	1·75
413	9p. H.M.S. *Thais* (*c* 1811)	70	1·50
414	10p. H.M.S. *Pheasant* (1819)	70	1·50
415	15p. H.M.S. *Myrmidon* (1819)	80	1·75
416	18p. H.M.S. *Atholl* (1825)	1·00	1·75
417	20p. H.M.S. *Medina* (1830)	90	1·75
418	25p. H.M.S. *Saracen* (1840)	1·00	2·00
419	30p. H.M.S. *Hydra* (*c* 1845)	1·00	2·00
420	50p. H.M.S. *Sealark* (1849)	1·00	2·50
421	70p. H.M.S. *Rattlesnake* (1868)	1·00	3·00
422	£1 H.M.S. *Penelope* (1889)	1·25	3·75
423	£2 H.M.S. *Monarch* (1897)	2·50	6·50
409/23 *Set of 15*		12·50	30·00

*The normal sideways watermark shows Crown to left of CA, *as seen from the back of the stamp.*

114 Cape Gooseberry

115 Ignition of Rocket Motors

(Des R. Gorringe. Litho Walsall)

1987 (29 Jan). Edible Bush Fruits. T **114** and similar horiz designs. Multicoloured. W w **16** (sideways). P 14.

424	12p. Type **114**	50	70
425	15p. Prickly Pear	50	80
426	20p. Guava	55	90
427	70p. Loquat	90	2·50
424/7 *Set of 4*		2·25	4·50

(Des D. Hartley. Litho Questa)

1987 (30 Mar). 25th Anniv of First American Manned Earth Orbit. T **115** and similar vert designs. Multicoloured. W w **16**. P 14.

428	15p. Type **115**	55	75
429	18p. Lift-off	60	80
430	25p. Re-entry	75	95
431	£1 Splashdown	2·50	3·25
428/31 *Set of 4*		4·00	5·25
MS432 92×78 mm. 70p. "Friendship 7" capsule		1·25	2·00

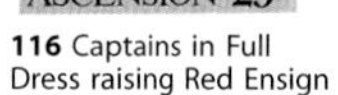

116 Captains in Full Dress raising Red Ensign

117 *Cynthia cardui*

(Des C. Collins. Litho Format)

1987 (29 June). 19th-century Uniforms (1st series). Royal Navy, 1815–20. T **116** and similar vert designs. Multicoloured. W w **16**. P 14.

433	25p. Type **116**	40	50
	a. Horiz strip of 5. Nos. 433/7	1·75	2·25
434	25p. Surgeon and seamen	40	50
435	25p. Seaman with water-carrying donkey	40	50
436	25p. Midshipman and gun	40	50
437	25p. Commander in undress uniform surveying	40	50
433/7 *Set of 5*		1·75	2·25

Nos. 433/7 were printed together, *se-tenant*, in horizontal strips of five throughout the sheet.

See also Nos. 478/82.

(Des I. Loe. Litho Questa)

1987 (10 Aug). Insects (1st series). Butterflies. T **117** and similar horiz designs. Multicoloured. W w **16** (sideways). P 14×14½.

438	15p. Type **117**	45	50
439	18p. *Danaus chrysippus*	50	60
440	25p. *Hypolimnas misippus*	60	70
441	£1 *Lampides boeticus*	1·25	2·00
438/41 *Set of 4*		2·50	3·50

See also Nos. 452/5 and 483/6.

118 Male Ascension Frigate Birds

40TH WEDDING ANNIVERSARY
(**119**)

(Des N. Arlott. Litho B.D.T.)

1987 (8 Oct). Sea Birds (1st series). T **118** and similar vert designs. Multicoloured. W w **16**. P 14.

442	25p. Type **118**	1·60	2·00
	a. Horiz strip of 5. Nos. 442/6	7·00	9·00
443	25p. Juvenile Ascension Frigate Bird, Brown Booby and Blue-faced Boobies	1·60	2·00
444	25p. Male Ascension Frigate Bird and Blue-faced Boobies	1·60	2·00
445	25p. Female Ascension Frigate Bird	1·60	2·00
446	25p. Adult male feeding juvenile Ascension Frigate Bird	1·60	2·00
442/6 *Set of 5*		7·00	9·00

Nos. 442/6 were printed together, *se-tenant*, in horizontal strips of five throughout the sheet, forming a composite design.

See also Nos. 469/73.

1987 (9 Dec). Royal Ruby Wedding. Nos. 397/401 optd with T **119** in silver.

447	7p. Type **110**	15	15
448	15p. Queen making Christmas broadcast, 1952	20	20
449	20p. At Garter ceremony, Windsor Castle, 1983	25	25
	a. Opt double	60·00	
450	35p. In Auckland, New Zealand, 1981	40	45
451	£1 At Crown Agents' Head Office, London, 1983	1·00	1·10
447/51 *Set of 5*		1·75	1·90

(Des I. Loe. Litho Questa)

1988 (18 Jan). Insects (2nd series). Horiz designs as T **117**. Multicoloured. W w **16** (sideways). P 14×14½.

452	15p. *Gryllus bimaculatus* (field cricket)	30	30
453	18p. *Ruspolia differeus* (bush cricket)	35	35
454	25p. *Chilomenus lunata* (ladybird)	40	40
455	£1 *Diachrysia orichalcea* (moth)	1·50	1·50
452/5 *Set of 4*		2·25	2·25

120 Bate's Memorial, St. Mary's Church

121 H.M.S. *Resolution* (ship of the line), 1667

(Des S. Noon. Litho Questa)

1988 (14 Apr). 150th Death Anniv of Captain William Bate (garrison commander, 1828–38). T **120** and similar horiz designs. Multicoloured. W w **16** (sideways). P 14.

456	9p. Type **120**	20	20
457	15p. Commodore's Cottage	25	25
458	18p. North East Cottage	25	25
459	25p. Map of Ascension	40	40
460	70p. Captain Bate and marines	90	90
456/60 *Set of 5*		1·75	1·75

(Des E. Nisbet. Litho Questa)

1988 (23 June). Bicentenary of Australian Settlement. Ships of the Royal Navy. T **121** and similar diamond-shaped designs. Multicoloured. W w **16** (sideways*). P 14.

461	9p. Type **121**	1·25	45
	w. Wmk Crown to left of CA	80·00	
462	18p. H.M.S. *Resolution* (Captain Cook), 1772.	1·75	70
	w. Wmk Crown to left of CA	80·00	
463	25p. H.M.S. *Resolution* (battleship), 1892	1·75	85
464	65p. H.M.S. *Resolution* (battleship), 1916	2·50	1·50
461/4	*Set of 4*	6·50	3·25

*The normal sideways watermark shows Crown to right of CA, *as seen from the back of the stamp positioned with the Royal cypher in the top left corner.*

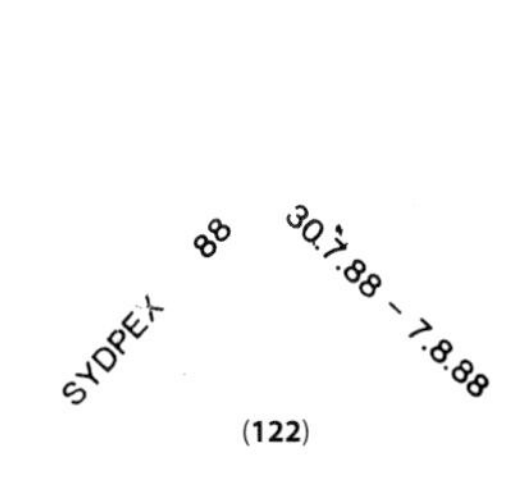

(**122**)

123 Lloyd's Coffee House, London, 1688

1988 (30 July). "Sydpex '88" National Stamp Exhibition, Sydney. Nos. 461/4 optd with T **122**.

465	9p. Type **121**	40	30
466	18p. H.M.S. *Resolution* (Captain Cook), 1772.	65	50
467	25p. H.M.S. *Resolution* (battleship), 1892	70	60
468	65p. H.M.S. *Resolution* (battleship), 1916	1·25	1·00
465/8	*Set of 4*	2·75	2·25

(Des N. Arlott. Litho Questa)

1988 (15 Aug). Sea Birds (2nd series). Sooty Tern. Vert designs as T **118**. Multicoloured. W w **16**. P 14.

469	25p. Pair displaying	1·25	90
	a. Horiz strip of 5. Nos. 469/73	5·50	4·00
470	25p. Turning egg	1·25	90
471	25p. Incubating egg	1·25	90
472	25p. Feeding chick	1·25	90
473	25p. Immature Sooty Tern	1·25	90
469/73	*Set of 5*	5·50	4·00

Nos. 469/73 were printed together, *se-tenant*, in horizontal strips of five throughout the sheet, forming a composite design of a nesting colony.

(Des E. Nisbet and D. Miller (8p., 25p.), D. Miller (others). Litho Questa)

1988 (17 Oct). 300th Anniv of Lloyd's of London. T **123** and similar multicoloured designs. W w **14** (sideways on 18, 25p.). P 14.

474	8p. Type **123**	25	25
475	18p. *Alert IV* (cable ship) (*horiz*)	65	65
476	25p. Satellite recovery in space (*horiz*)	80	80
477	65p. *Good Hope Castle* (cargo liner) on fire off Ascension, 1973	1·75	1·75
474/7	*Set of 4*	3·00	3·00

(Des C. Collins. Litho B.D.T.)

1988 (21 Nov). 19th-century Uniforms (2nd series). Royal Marines, 1821–34. Vert designs as T **116**. Multicoloured. W w **14**. P 14.

478	25p. Marines landing on Ascension, 1821	85	1·25
	a. Horiz strip of 5. Nos. 478/82	3·75	5·50
479	25p. Officer and Marine at semaphore station, 1829	85	1·25
480	25p. Sergeant and Marine at Octagonal Tank, 1831	85	1·25
481	25p. Officers at water pipe tunnel, 1833	85	1·25
482	25p. Officer supervising construction of barracks, 1834	85	1·25
478/82	*Set of 5*	3·75	5·50

Nos. 478/82 were printed together, *se-tenant*, in horizontal strips of five throughout the sheet.

(Des I. Loe. Litho Questa)

1989 (16 Jan). Insects (3rd series). Horiz designs as T **117**. Multicoloured. W w **16** (sideways). P 14×14½.

483	15p. *Trichoptilus wahlbergi* (moth)	75	50
484	18p. *Lucilia sericata* (fly)	80	55
485	25p. *Alceis ornatus* (weevil)	1·10	70
486	£1 *Polistes fuscatus* (wasp)	3·00	2·40
483/6	*Set of 4*	5·00	3·75

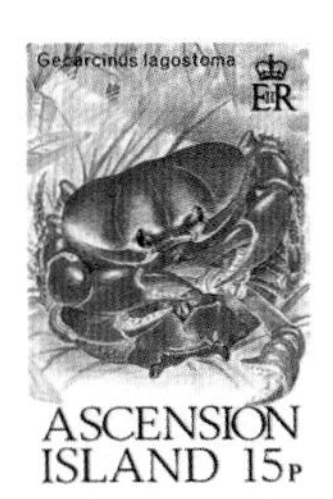

124 Two Land Crabs

125 1949 75th Anniversary of U.P.U. 1s. Stamp

(Des Doreen McGuiness. Litho Questa)

1989 (17 Apr). Ascension Land Crabs (*Gecarcinus lagostoma*). T **124** and similar vert designs. Multicoloured. W w **16**. P 14.

487	15p. Type **124**	40	45
488	18p. Crab with claws raised	45	50
489	25p. Crab on rock	60	70
490	£1 Crab in surf	1·40	2·00
487/90	*Set of 4*	2·50	3·25
MS491	98×101 mm. Nos. 487/90	2·50	3·25

(Des D. Miller. Litho Walsall)

1989 (7 July). "Philexfrance 89" International Stamp Exhibition, Paris, and "World Stamp Expo '89", Washington (1st issue). Sheet 104×86 mm. W w **16**. P 14×13½.

MS492	**125** 75p. multicoloured	1·25	1·40

See also Nos. 498/503.

126 "Apollo 7" Tracking Station, Ascension

127 *Queen Elizabeth 2* (liner) and U.S.S. *John F. Kennedy* (aircraft carrier) in New York Harbour

(Des A. Theobald (£1), D. Miller (others). Litho Questa)

1989 (20 July). 20th Anniv of First Manned Landing on Moon. T **126** and similar multicoloured designs. W w **16** (sideways on 18, 25p). P 14×13½ (15, 70p.) or 14 (others).

493	15p. Type **126**	50	35
494	18p. Launch of "Apollo 7" (30×30 *mm*)	55	40
495	25p. "Apollo 7" emblem (30×30 *mm*)	70	60
496	70p. "Apollo 7" jettisoning expended Saturn rocket	1·25	1·50
493/6	*Set of 4*	2·75	2·50
MS497	101×83 mm. £1 Diagram of "Apollo 11" mission. P 14×13½	2·00	2·10

(Des D. Miller. Litho Walsall)

1989 (21 Aug). "Philexfrance 89" International Stamp Exhibition, Paris, and "World Stamp Expo '89", Washington (2nd issue). T **127** and similar vert designs showing Statue of Liberty and Centenary celebrations. Multicoloured. W w **14**. P 14×13½.

498	15p. Type **127**	50	50
	a. Sheetlet. Nos. 498/503	2·75	2·75
499	15p. Cleaning Statue	50	50
500	15p. Statue of Liberty	50	50
501	15p. Crown of Statue	50	50
502	15p. Warships and New York skyline	50	50
503	15p. *Jean de Vienne* (French destroyer) and skyscrapers	50	50
498/503	*Set of 6*	2·75	2·75

Nos. 498/503 were printed, *se-tenant*, in sheetlets of 6.

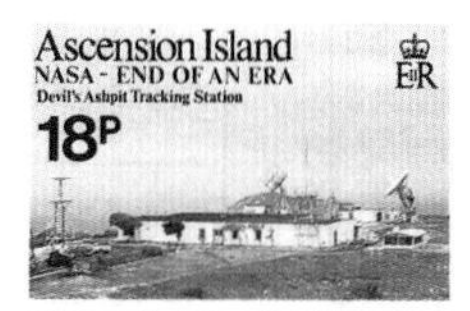

128 Devil's Ashpit Tracking Station

(Des D. Miller. Litho Questa)

1989 (30 Sept). Closure of Devil's Ashpit Tracking Station, Ascension. T **128** and similar horiz design. Multicoloured. W w **16** (sideways). P 14.

504	18p. Type **128**	80	50
	a. Sheetlet. Nos. 504/5, each×5	7·00	
505	25p. Launch of shuttle *Atlantis*	80	55

Nos. 504/5 were issued in sheetlets of ten containing vertical strips of five of each design, separated by a central inscribed gutter.

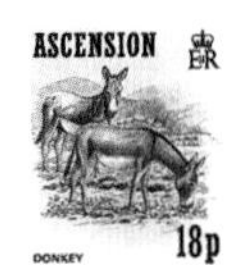

129 Bubonian Conch (*Strombus latus*) **130** Donkeys

(Des I. Loe. Litho Questa)

1989 (2 Nov). Sea Shells. T **129** and similar horiz designs. Multicoloured. W w **16** (sideways). P 14.

506	8p. Type **129**	35	30
507	18p. Giant Tun (*Tonna galea*)	55	50
508	25p. Doris Harp (*Harpa doris*)	65	55
509	£1 Atlantic Trumpet Triton (*Charonia variegata*)	2·00	1·75
506/9	*Set of 4*	3·25	2·75

(Des G. Drummond, adapted N. Harvey. Litho Walsall)

1989 (17 Nov). Ascension Wildlife. T **130** and similar vert design. Multicoloured. W w **16** (sideways). P 14.

510	18p. Type **130**	1·10	1·50
	a. Booklet pane. No. 510×6	6·00	
511	25p. Green Turtle	1·25	1·50
	a. Booklet pane. No. 511×4	4·50	

Nos. 510/11 were only issued in £1 stamp booklets, Nos. SB 5/6, and come with either the left or right-hand side imperforate.

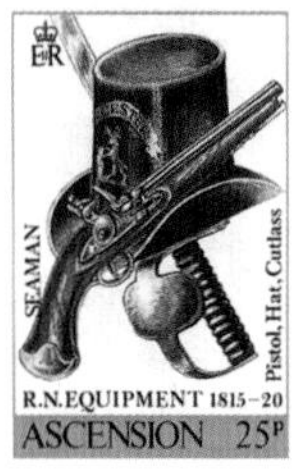

131 Seaman's Pistol, Hat and Cutlass **132** Pair of Ascension Frigate Birds with Young

(Des C. Collins. Litho Questa)

1990 (12 Feb). Royal Navy Equipment, 1815–20. T **131** and similar vert designs. Multicoloured. W w **16**. P 14.

512	25p. Type **131**	80	70
	a. Horiz strip of 5. Nos. 512/16	3·50	3·25
513	25p. Midshipman's belt plate, button, sword and hat	80	70
514	25p. Surgeon's hat, sword and instrument chest	80	70
515	25p. Captain's hat, telescope and sword	80	70
516	25p. Admiral's epaulette, megaphone, hat and pocket	80	70
512/16	*Set of 5*	3·50	3·25

Nos. 512/16 were printed together, *se-tenant*, in horizontal strips of 5 throughout the sheet.

See also Nos. 541/5.

(Des W. Oliver. Litho Questa)

1990 (5 Mar). Endangered Species. Ascension Frigate Bird. T **132** and similar vert designs. Multicoloured. W w **14**. P 14½×14.

517	9p. Type **132**	1·25	75
518	10p. Fledgeling	1·25	75
519	11p. Adult male in flight	1·25	75
520	15p. Female and immature birds in flight	1·50	1·00
517/20	*Set of 4*	4·75	3·00

133 Penny Black and Twopence Blue

(Des D. Miller. Litho Walsall)

1990 (3 May). "Stamp World London 90" International Stamp Exhibition, London. T **133** and similar horiz designs. Multicoloured. W w **14** (sideways). P 14.

521	9p. Type **133**	50	40
522	18p. Ascension postmarks used on G.B. stamps	70	60
523	25p. Unloading mail at Wideawake Airfield	95	85
524	£1 Mail van and Main Post Office	2·25	2·75
521/4	*Set of 4*	4·00	4·25

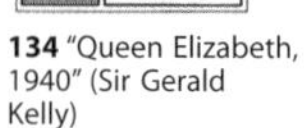

134 "Queen Elizabeth, 1940" (Sir Gerald Kelly) **135** King George VI and Queen Elizabeth with Bren-gun Carrier

(Des D. Miller. Litho Questa)

1990 (4 Aug). 90th Birthday of Queen Elizabeth the Queen Mother. W w **16**. P 14×15 (25p.) or 14½ (£1).

525	**134**	25p. multicoloured	75	75
526	**135**	£1 black and deep lilac	2·25	2·25

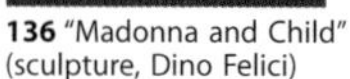

136 "Madonna and Child" (sculpture, Dino Felici) **137** *Garth Castle* (mail steamer), 1910

(Des D. Miller. Litho B.D.T.)

1990 (24 Oct). Christmas. Works of Art. T **136** and similar vert designs. Multicoloured. W w **14**. P 13½.

527	8p. Type **136**	60	70
528	18p. "Madonna and Child" (anon)	1·00	1·25
529	25p. "Madonna and Child with St. John" (Johann Gebhard)	1·40	1·75
530	65p. "Madonna and Child" (Giacomo Gritti)	2·50	4·00
527/30	*Set of 4*	5·00	7·00

(Des L. Curtis. Litho Walsall)

1990 (27 Nov). Maiden Voyage of *St. Helena II*. T **137** and similar horiz designs. Multicoloured. W w **14** (sideways). P 14×14½.

531	9p. Type **137**	90	90
532	18p. *St. Helena I* during Falkland Islands campaign, 1982	1·25	1·25
533	25p. Launch of *St. Helena II*	1·75	1·75
534	70p. Duke of York launching *St. Helena II*	3·00	4·25
531/4	*Set of 4*	6·25	7·25
MS535	100×100 mm. £1 *St. Helena II* and outline map of Ascension	3·50	5·50

No. **MS**535 also contains two imperforate designs of similar stamps from St. Helena and Tristan da Cunha without face values.

BRITISH FOR 175 YEARS

(**138**)

1991 (5 Feb). 175th Anniv of Occupation. Nos. 418, 420 and 422 optd with T **138** in silver by Cartor.

536	25p. H.M.S. *Saracen* (1840)	1·75	2·50
537	50p. H.M.S. *Sealark* (1849)	2·25	3·50
538	£1 H.M.S. *Penelope* (1889)	3·25	5·00
536/8	*Set of 3*	6·50	10·00

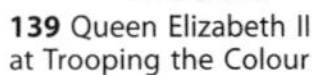

139 Queen Elizabeth II at Trooping the Colour

140 B.B.C. World Service Relay Station

(Des D. Miller. Litho Questa)

1991 (18 June). 65th Birthday of Queen Elizabeth II and 70th Birthday of Prince Philip. T **139** and similar vert design. Multicoloured. W w **16** (sideways). P 14½×14.

No.	Description	Unused	Used
539	25p. Type **139**	1·25	1·60
	a. Horiz pair. Nos. 539/40 separated by label	2·50	3·00
540	25p. Prince Philip in naval uniform	1·25	1·60

Nos. 539/40 were printed together, *se-tenant*, in sheetlets of 10 (2×5) with designs alternating and the vertical rows separated by inscribed labels.

(Des C. Collins. Litho Questa)

1991 (1 Aug). Royal Marines Equipment, 1821–44 .Vert designs as T **131**. Multicoloured. W w **14**. P 14.

No.	Description	Unused	Used
541	25p. Officer's shako, epaulettes, belt plate and button	1·25	1·60
	a. Horiz strip of 5. Nos. 541/5	5·50	7·25
542	25p. Officer's cap, sword, epaulettes and belt plate	1·25	1·60
543	25p. Drum major's shako and staff	1·25	1·60
544	25p. Sergeant's shako, chevrons, belt plate and canteen	1·25	1·60
545	25p. Drummer's shako and side-drum	1·25	1·60
541/5	*Set of* 5	5·50	7·25

Nos. 541/5 were printed together, *se-tenant*, in horizontal strips of 5 throughout the sheet.

(Des D. Miller. Litho Questa)

1991 (17 Sept). 25th Anniv of B.B.C. Atlantic Relay Station. T **140** and similar multicoloured designs. W w **16** (sideways on 15, 18p). P 14½.

No.	Description	Unused	Used
546	15p. Type **140**	90	1·10
547	18p. Transmitters at English Bay	1·00	1·25
548	25p. Satellite receiving station (*vert*)	1·25	1·40
549	70p. Antenna support tower (*vert*)	2·50	4·00
546/9	*Set of* 4	5·00	7·00

141 St. Mary's Church

142 Black Durgon ("Blackfish")

(Des D. Miller. Litho Questa)

1991 (1 Oct). Christmas. Ascension Churches. T **141** and similar horiz designs. Multicoloured. W w **16** (sideways). P 14.

No.	Description	Unused	Used
550	8p. Type **141**	55	55
551	18p. Interior of St. Mary's Church	1·00	1·00
552	25p. Our Lady of Ascension Grotto	1·25	1·25
553	65p. Interior of Our Lady of Ascension Grotto	2·75	5·00
550/3	*Set of* 4	5·00	7·00

(Des G. Drummond. Litho Walsall)

1991 (10 Dec). Fish. T **142** and similar horiz designs. Multicoloured. W w **14** (sideways). P 14.

No.	Description	Unused	Used
554	1p. Type **142**	1·25	60
555	2p. Sergeant Major ("Five Finger")	1·25	60
556	4p. Resplendent Angelfish	1·50	70
557	5p. Derbio ("Silver Fish")	1·50	70
558	9p. Spotted Scorpionfish ("Gurnard")	1·75	80
559	10p. St Helena Parrotfish ("Blue Dad")	1·75	80
560	15p. St. Helena Butterflyfish ("Cunning Fish")	2·25	1·00
561	18p. Rock Hind ("Grouper")	2·25	1·00
562	20p. Spotted Moray	2·25	1·25
563	25p. Squirrelfish ("Hardback Soldierfish")	2·25	1·25
564	30p. Blue Marlin	2·25	1·40
565	50p. Wahoo	3·00	2·00
566	70p. Yellow-finned Tuna	3·00	2·75
567	£1 Blue Shark	3·25	3·50
568	£2.50 Bottlenose Dolphin	7·00	7·00
554/68	*Set of* 15	32·00	23·00

143 Holland's Crater

(Des D. Miller. Litho Questa (70p.), Walsall (others))

1992 (6 Feb). 40th Anniv of Queen Elizabeth II's Accession. T **143** and similar horiz designs. W w **14** (sideways). P 14.

No.	Description	Unused	Used
569	9p. Type **143**	30	30
570	15p. Green Mountain	50	50
571	18p. Boatswain Bird Island	60	60
572	25p. Three portraits of Queen Elizabeth	80	80
573	70p. Queen Elizabeth II	2·00	2·00
569/73	*Set of* 5	3·75	3·75

The portraits shown on the 25p. are repeated from the three lower values of the set.

144 Compass Rose and *Eye of the Wind* (cadet brig)

145 Control Tower, Wideawake Airfield

(Des R. Watton. Litho Walsall)

1992 (18 Feb). 500th Anniv of Discovery of America by Columbus and Re-enactment Voyages. T **144** and similar horiz designs. Multicoloured. W w **14** (sideways). P 13½×14.

No.	Description	Unused	Used
574	9p. Type **144**	1·25	80
575	18p. Map of re-enactment voyages and *Soren Larsen* (cadet brigantine)	1·75	1·25
576	25p. *Santa Maria, Pinta* and *Nina*	2·25	1·50
577	70p. Columbus and *Santa Maria*	3·75	3·50
574/7	*Set of* 4	8·00	6·25

(Des N. Shewring. Litho Questa)

1992 (5 May). 50th Anniv of Wideawake Airfield. T **145** and similar square designs. Multicoloured. W w **14** (sideways). P 14.

No.	Description	Unused	Used
578	15p. Type **145**	65	65
579	18p. Nose hangar	70	70
580	25p. Site preparation by U.S. Army engineers	90	90
581	70p. Laying fuel pipeline	2·25	2·25
578/81	*Set of* 4	4·00	4·00

146 Hawker Siddeley H.S.801 Nimrod

147 "Christmas in Great Britain and Ascension"

(Des N. Shewring. Litho Questa)

1992 (12 June). 10th Anniv of Liberation of Falkland Islands. Aircraft. T **146** and similar square designs. Multicoloured. W w **14** (sideways). P 14.

No.	Description	Unused	Used
582	15p. Type **146**	1·50	1·75
583	18p. Vickers VC-10 landing at Ascension	1·50	1·75
584	25p. Westland Wessex HU Mk 5 helicopter lifting supplies	2·00	1·75
585	65p. Avro Vulcan B.2 over Ascension	3·25	4·75
582/5	*Set of* 4	7·50	9·00
MS586	116×116 mm. 15p.+3p. Type **146**; 18p.+4p As No. 583; 25p.+5p. As No. 584; 65p.+13p. As No. 585	4·00	6·50

The premiums on No. **MS**586 were for the S.S.A.F.A.

(Adapted G. Vasarhelyi. Litho Walsall)

1992 (13 Oct). Christmas. Children's Paintings. T **147** and similar horiz designs. Multicoloured. W w **16** (sideways). P 14.

No.	Description	Unused	Used
587	8p. Type **147**	80	1·00
588	18p. "Santa Claus riding turtle"	1·25	1·50
589	25p. "Nativity"	1·50	1·75
590	65p. "Nativity with rabbit"	2·75	5·00
587/90	*Set of* 4	5·50	8·25

148 Male Canary singing **149** Sopwith Snipe

(Des N. Arlott. Litho Questa)

1993 (12 Jan). Yellow Canary. T **148** and similar vert designs. Multicoloured. W w **14**. P 14½×14.

591	15p. Type **148**	75	80
592	18p. Adult male and female	85	90
593	25p. Young birds calling for food	95	1·10
594	70p. Adults and young birds on the wing	2·50	4·00
591/4	*Set of 4*	4·50	6·00

(Des A. Theobald. Litho Questa)

1993 (1 Apr). 75th Anniv of Royal Air Force. T **149** and similar horiz designs. Multicoloured. W w **14** (sideways). P 14.

595	20p. Type **149**	2·00	1·75
596	25p. Supermarine Southampton	2·00	1·75
597	30p. Avro Type 652 Anson	2·00	1·90
598	70p. Vickers-Armstrong Wellington	3·25	4·50
595/8	*Set of 4*	8·25	9·00
MS599	110×77 mm. 25p. Westland Lysander; 25p. Armstrong-Whitworth Meteor ("Gloster Meteor"); 25p. de Havilland DH.106 Comet; 25p. Hawker Siddeley H.S.801 Nimrod	3·00	4·00

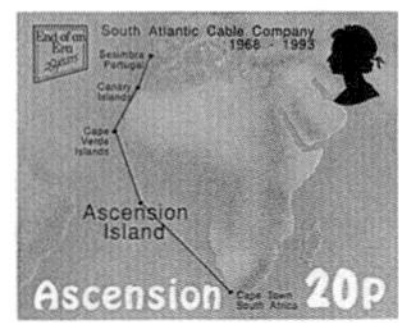

150 Map of South Atlantic Cable **151** Lantana Camara

(Des D. Miller. Litho Questa)

1993 (8 June). 25th Anniv of South Atlantic Cable Company. T **150** and similar horiz designs. Multicoloured. W w **16** (sideways). P 14½.

600	20p. Type **150**	80	1·00
601	25p. *Sir Eric Sharpe* laying cable	90	1·10
602	30p. Map of Ascension	1·00	1·25
603	70p. *Sir Eric Sharpe* (cable ship) off Ascension	2·25	3·00
600/3	*Set of 4*	4·50	5·75

(Des N. Shewring. Litho Questa)

1993 (3 Aug). Local Flowers. T **151** and similar horiz designs. Multicoloured. W w **16** (sideways). P 14×14½.

604	20p. Type **151**	1·50	1·10
605	25p. Moonflower	1·60	1·25
606	30p. Hibiscus	1·60	1·40
607	70p. Frangipani	3·00	4·00
604/7	*Set of 4*	7·00	7·00

152 Posting Christmas Card to Ascension **153** Ichthyosaurus

(Des N. Shewring. Litho Walsall)

1993 (19 Oct). Christmas. T **152** and similar vert designs. Multicoloured. W w **14**. P 14½×14.

608	12p. Type **152**	60	55
609	20p. Loading mail onto R.A.F. Lockheed L-1011 TriStar at Brize Norton	1·40	80
610	25p. Tristar over South Atlantic	1·50	90
611	30p. Unloading mail at Wideawake Airfield	1·50	1·10
612	65p. Receiving card and Georgetown Post Office	1·75	3·50
608/12	*Set of 5*	6·00	6·25
MS613	161×76 mm. Nos. 608/12	10·00	10·00

(Des N. Shewring. Litho B.D.T.)

1994 (25 Jan). Prehistoric Aquatic Reptiles. T **153** and similar vert designs. Multicoloured. W w **14**. P 14.

614	12p. Type **153**	70	1·10
615	20p. Metriorhynchus	85	1·25
616	25p. Mosasaurus	90	1·40
617	30p. Elasmosaurus	90	1·50
618	65p. Plesiosaurus	1·75	2·75
614/18	*Set of 5*	4·50	7·25

(**154**) **155** Young Green Turtles heading towards Sea

1994 (18 Feb). "Hong Kong '94" International Stamp Exhibition. Nos. 614/18 optd with T **154**.

619	12p. Type **153**	1·00	1·50
620	20p. Metriorhynchus	1·25	1·60
621	25p. Mosasaurus	1·25	1·90
622	30p. Elasmosaurus	1·40	2·00
623	65p. Plesiosaurus	2·50	4·00
619/23	*Set of 5*	6·75	10·00

(Des A. Robinson. Litho Questa)

1994 (22 Mar). Green Turtles. T **155** and similar horiz designs. Multicoloured. W w **14** (sideways). P 14.

624	20p. Type **155**	2·25	2·25
625	25p. Turtle digging nest	2·25	2·25
626	30p. Turtle leaving sea	2·25	2·25
627	65p. Turtle swimming	3·75	6·00
624/7	*Set of 4*	9·50	11·50
MS628	116×90 mm. 30p. Turtle leaving sea (*different*); 30p. Turtle digging nest (*different*); 30p. Young turtles heading towards sea (*different*); 30p. Young turtle leaving nest	12·00	12·00

156 *Yorkshireman* (tug)

(Des R. Walton. Litho Walsall)

1994 (14 June). Civilian Ships used in Liberation of Falkland Islands,1982. T **156** and similar horiz designs. Multicoloured. W w **16** (sideways). P 14.

629	20p. Type **156**	2·75	2·25
630	25p. *St. Helena I* (minesweeper support ship)	2·75	2·25
631	30p. *British Esk* (tanker)	2·75	2·50
632	65p. *Uganda* (hospital ship)	5·00	6·00
629/32	*Set of 4*	12·00	11·50

157 Sooty Tern Chick

(Des N. Arlott. Litho Walsall)

1994 (16 Aug). Sooty Tern. T **157** and similar horiz designs. Multicoloured. W w **14** (sideways). P 14½.

633	20p. Type **157**	90	1·50
634	25p. Juvenile bird	95	1·50
635	30p. Brooding adult	1·10	1·60
636	65p. Adult male performing courting display	1·75	2·75
633/6	*Set of 4*	4·25	6·50
MS637	77×58 mm. £1 Flock of Sooty Terns	3·75	6·00

158 Donkey Mare with Foal

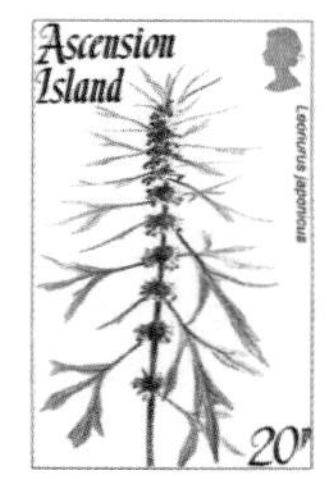
159 *Leonurus japonicus*

(Des Josephine Martin. Litho Questa)

1994 (11 Oct). Christmas. Donkeys. T **158** and similar horiz designs. Multicoloured. W w **16** (sideways). P 14½.

638	12p. Type **158**	1·60	1·40
639	20p. Juvenile	1·90	1·75
640	25p. Foal	1·90	1·75
641	30p. Adult and Cattle Egrets	1·90	1·90
642	65p. Adult	3·75	5·00
638/42	*Set of* 5	10·00	10·50

(Des Jennifer Toombs. Litho Walsall)

1995 (10 Jan). Flowers. T **159** and similar multicoloured designs. W w **16** (sideways on horiz designs). P 14.

643	20p. Type **159**	2·75	2·25
644	25p. *Catharanthus roseus* (*horiz*)	2·75	2·25
645	30p. *Mirabilis jalapa*	3·00	2·50
646	65p. *Asclepias curassavica* (*horiz*)	3·75	5·50
643/6	*Set of* 4	11·00	11·00

160 Two Boats and Green Mountain

161 5.5-inch Coastal Battery

(Des S. Noon. Litho Questa)

1995 (7 Mar). Late 19th-century Scenes. T **160** and similar horiz designs, each in cinnamon and reddish brown. W w **16** (sideways). P 14×14½.

647	12p. Type **160**	50	80
648	20p. Island Stewards' Store	70	90
649	25p. Navy headquarters and barracks	90	1·10
650	30p. Police office	1·75	1·75
651	65p. Pierhead	2·00	3·50
647/51	*Set of* 5	5·25	7·25

(Des R. Watton. Litho Questa)

1995 (8 May). 50th Anniv of End of Second World War. T **161** and similar multicoloured designs. W w **16** (sideways). P 14.

652	20p. Type **161**	1·75	2·00
653	25p. Fairey Swordfish aircraft	2·00	2·00
654	50p. H.M.S. *Dorsetshire* (cruiser)	2·25	3·25
655	65p. H.M.S. *Devonshire* (cruiser)	3·75	4·50
652/5	*Set of* 4	8·75	10·50
MS656	75×85 mm. £1 Reverse of 1939–45 War Medal (*vert*). W w **14**	2·00	3·25

162 Male and Female *Lampides boeticus*

163 "Santa Claus on Boat" (Phillip Stephens)

(Des K. McGee. Litho B.D.T.)

1995 (1 Sept). Butterflies. T **162** and similar vert designs. Multicoloured. W w **16**. P 14.

657	20p. Type **162**	1·50	1·50
658	25p. *Vanessa cardui*	1·75	1·75
659	30p. Male *Hypolimnas misippus*	1·75	1·75
660	65p. *Danaus chrysippus*	2·75	3·50
657/60	*Set of* 4	7·00	7·75
MS661	114×85 mm. £1 *Vanessa atalanta*	6·00	6·50

No. **MS**661 includes the "Singapore '95" International Stamp Exhibition logo on the sheet margin.

(Des B. Dare. Litho Walsall)

1995 (10 Oct). Christmas. Children's Drawings. T **163** and similar horiz designs. Multicoloured. W w **14** (sideways). P 14.

662	12p. Type **163**	1·75	1·25
663	20p. "Santa sitting on Wall" (Kelly Lemon)	2·00	1·75
664	25p. "Santa in Chimney" (Mario Anthony)	2·00	1·75
665	30p. "Santa riding Dolphin" (Verena Benjamin)	2·00	1·75
666	65p. "Santa in Sleigh over Ascension" (Tom Butler)	3·50	5·00
662/6	*Set of* 5	10·00	10·50

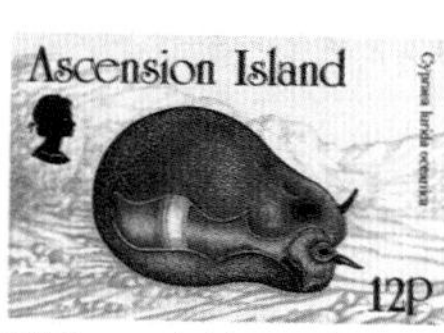
164 *Cypraea lurida oceanica*

165 Queen Elizabeth II and St. Mary's Church

(Des I. Loe. Litho B.D.T.)

1996 (10 Jan). Molluscs. T **164** and similar horiz designs. Multicoloured. W w **16** (sideways). P 14.

667	12p. Type **164**	2·75	3·00
	a. Horiz strip of 4. Nos. 667/70	11·50	12·00
668	25p. *Cypraea spurca sanctaehelenae*	3·00	3·25
669	30p. *Harpa doris*	3·00	3·25
670	65p. *Umbraculum umbraculum*	3·75	4·00
667/70	*Set of* 4	11·50	12·00

Nos. 667/70 were printed together, *se-tenant*, in horizontal strips of 4 throughout the sheet with the backgrounds forming a composite design.

(Des D. Miller. Litho B.D.T.)

1996 (22 Apr). 70th Birthday of Queen Elizabeth II. T **165** and similar vert designs. W w **16**. P 13½.

671	20p. Type **165**	55	60
672	25p. The Residency	60	60
673	30p. The Roman Catholic Grotto	70	75
674	65p. The Exiles' Club	1·75	2·00
671/4	*Set of* 4	3·25	3·50

166 American Army Jeep

167 Madeiran Storm Petrel

(Des B. Dare. Litho Walsall)

1996 (8 June). "CAPEX '96" International Stamp Exhibition, Toronto. Island Transport. T **166** and similar horiz designs. Multicoloured. W w **16** (sideways). P 14.

675	20p. Type **166**	1·75	1·75
676	25p. Citroen 7.5hp two-seater car, 1924	1·75	1·75
677	30p. Austin ten tourer car, 1930	1·75	1·75
678	65p. Series 1 Land Rover	2·75	3·25
675/8	*Set of* 4	7·25	7·75

(Des N. Arlott. Litho Walsall)

1996 (12 Aug). Birds and their Young. T **167** and similar vert designs. Multicoloured. W w **14**. P 13½×13.

679	1p. Type **167**	85	1·25
680	2p. Red-billed Tropic Bird	85	1·25
681	4p. Common Mynah	85	1·25
682	5p. House Sparrow	1·00	1·25
683	7p. Common Waxbill	1·25	1·50

684	10p. White Tern	1·50	1·75
685	12p. Bare-throated Francolin	1·75	1·50
686	15p. Common Noddy	1·75	1·75
687	20p. Yellow Canary	2·00	1·50
688	25p. Lesser Noddy	2·00	1·50
689	30p. Red-footed Booby	2·00	1·50
690	40p. White-tailed Tropic Bird	2·50	2·25
691	65p. Brown Booby	3·50	3·50
692	£1 Blue-faced Booby	4·75	5·00
693	£2 Sooty Tern	7·00	7·50
694	£3 Ascension Frigate Bird	9·00	10·00
679/94	*Set of* 16	38·00	40·00

For 65p. and £1 (with "1997" imprint date) used in miniature sheets see Nos. **MS** 708 and **MS** 718.

For 15p. and 35p. in designs of 7p and 20p, but 20×24 mm from booklets see Nos. 726/7.

168 Pylons

169 Santa Claus on Dish Aerial

(Des D. Miller. Litho Walsall)

1996 (9 Sept). 30th Anniv of B.B.C. Atlantic Relay Station. T **168** and similar horiz designs. Multicoloured. W w **16** (sideways). P 14×14½.

695	20p. Type **168**	75	75
696	25p. Pylons (*different*)	80	80
697	30p. Pylons and station buildings	90	90
698	65p. Dish aerial, pylon and beach	1·90	2·50
695/8	*Set of* 4	4·00	4·50

(Des B. Dare. Litho Questa)

1996 (23 Sept). Christmas. T **169** and similar horiz designs showing Santa Claus. Multicoloured. W w **14** (sideways). P 14×14½.

699	12p. Type **169**	50	50
700	20p. Playing golf	75	75
701	25p. In deck chair	75	75
702	30p. On top of aircraft	85	85
703	65p. On funnel of *St. Helena II* (mail ship)	1·90	2·25
699/703	*Set of* 5	4·25	4·50

170 Date Palm

171 Red Ensign and *Maersk Ascension* (tanker)

(Des R. Watton. Litho Walsall)

1997 (7 Jan). "HONG KONG '97" International Stamp Exhibition. Trees. T **170** and similar vert designs. Multicoloured. W w **14**. P 14½×14.

704	20p. Type **170**	75	75
705	25p. Mauritius Hemp	85	85
706	30p. Norfolk Island Pine	95	95
707	65p. Dwarf Palm	2·00	2·50
704/7	*Set of* 4	4·00	4·50

(Des D. Miller. Litho Questa)

1997 (3 Feb). "HONG KONG '97" International Stamp Exhibition. Sheet 130×90 mm containing design as No. 691. Multicoloured. W w **14**. P 14.

MS708	65p. Brown Booby	1·50	1·75

(Des A. Theobald. Litho Walsall)

1997 (1 Apr). Flags. T **171** and similar vert designs. Multicoloured. W w **14**. P 14½.

709	12p. Type **171**	1·25	80
710	25p. R.A.F. flag and Tristar airliner	1·60	1·10
711	30p. N.A.S.A. emblem and Space Shuttle *Atlantis* landing	1·60	1·25
712	65p. White Ensign and H.M.S. *Northumberland* (frigate)	3·25	2·75
709/12	*Set of* 4	7·00	5·25

172 *Solanum sodomaeum*

173 Queen Elizabeth II

(Des I. Loe. Litho Questa)

1997 (2 June). Wild Herbs. T **172** and similar horiz designs. Multicoloured. W w **14** (sideways). P 14½.

713	30p. Type **172**	1·50	1·60
	a. Horiz strip of 5. Nos. 713/17	6·75	7·25
714	30p. *Ageratum conyzoides*	1·50	1·60
715	30p. *Leonurus sibiricus*	1·50	1·60
716	30p. *Cerastium vulgatum*	1·50	1·60
717	30p. *Commelina diffusa*	1·50	1·60
713/17	*Set of* 5	6·75	7·25

Nos. 713/17 were printed together, *se-tenant*, in horizontal strips of 5 with the backgrounds forming a composite design.

(Des. D. Miller. Litho Questa)

1997 (20 June). Return of Hong Kong to China. Sheet 130×90 mm containing design as No. 692, but with "1997" imprint date. W w **14** (inverted). P 13½×13.

MS718	£1 Blue-faced Booby	1·50	2·10

(Des N. Shewring (No. **MS**725), D. Miller (others). Litho Questa (No. **MS**725), B.D.T. (others))

1997 (10 July). Golden Wedding of Queen Elizabeth and Prince Philip. T **173** and similar vert designs. Multicoloured. W w **16**. P 13½.

719	20p. Type **173**	1·50	2·00
	a. Horiz pair. Nos. 719/20	3·00	4·00
720	20p. Prince Philip on horseback	1·50	2·00
721	25p. Queen Elizabeth with polo pony	1·50	2·00
	a. Horiz pair. Nos. 721/2	3·00	4·00
722	25p. Prince Philip in Montserrat	1·50	2·00
723	30p. Queen Elizabeth and Prince Philip	1·50	2·00
	a. Horiz pair. Nos. 723/4	3·00	4·00
724	30p. Prince William and Prince Harry on horseback	1·50	2·00
719/24	*Set of* 6	8·00	11·00
MS725	110×70 mm. $1.50 Queen Elizabeth and Prince Philip in landau (*horiz*). W w **14** (sideways). P 14×14½	3·50	3·50

Nos. 719/20, 721/2 and 723/4 were each printed together, *se-tenant*, in horizontal pairs throughout the sheets with the backgrounds forming composite designs.

(Des N. Arlott. Litho Walsall)

1997 (1 Sept). Birds and their Young. Designs as Nos. 683 and 687, but smaller, size 20×24 mm. W w **14** (sideways). P 14.

726	15p. Common Waxbill	2·40	2·75
	a. Booklet pane. Nos. 726/7, each×2	8·50	
727	35p. Yellow Canary	2·40	2·75

Nos. 726/7 were only issued in £1 stamp booklets, No. SB9, with the vertical edges of the booklet pane imperforate so that they exist imperforate at left or right.

174 Black Marlin

175 Interior of St. Mary's Church

(Des R. Watton. Litho Walsall)

1997 (3 Sept). Gamefish. T **174** and similar horiz designs. Multicoloured. W w **16** (sideways). P 14×14½.

728	12p. Type **174**	75	75
729	20p. Atlantic Sailfish	1·00	1·00
730	25p. Swordfish	1·10	1·10
731	30p. Wahoo	1·25	1·25
732	£1 Yellowfin Tuna	3·00	4·00
728/32	*Set of* 5	6·25	7·25

(Des G. Vasarhelyi. Litho Walsall)

1997 (1 Oct). Christmas. T **175** and similar vert designs. W w **16**. P 14.

No.	Description	Unused	Used
733	15p. Type **175**	1·00	1·00
734	35p. Falklands memorial window showing Virgin and Child	1·60	1·60
735	40p. Falklands memorial window showing Archangel	1·75	1·90
736	50p. Pair of stained glass windows	2·00	2·25
733/6	*Set of 4*	5·75	6·00

176 *Cactoblastis cactorum* (caterpillar and moth)

177 Diana, Princess of Wales, 1985

(Des I. Loe. Litho B.D.T.)

1998 (10 Feb). Biological Control using Insects. T **176** and similar vert designs. W w **14**. P 14.

No.	Description	Unused	Used
737	15p. Type **176**	2·00	1·75
738	35p. *Teleonemia scrupulosa* (lace-bug)	2·50	2·25
739	40p. *Neltumius arizonensis* (beetle)	2·50	2·75
740	50p. *Algarobius prosopis* (beetle)	2·75	3·25
737/40	*Set of 4*	8·75	9·00

(Des D. Miller. Litho Questa)

1998 (31 Mar). Diana, Princess of Wales Commemoration. Sheet, 145×70 mm, containing T **177** and similar vert designs. Multicoloured. W w **14** (sideways). P 14½×14.

No.	Description	Unused	Used
MS741	35p. Type **177**; 35p. Wearing yellow blouse, 1992; 35p. Wearing grey jacket, 1984; 35p. Carrying bouquets (*sold at* £1.40+20p. *charity premium*)	2·00	3·25

178 Fairey Fawn

179 Barn Swallow

(Des A. Theobald. Litho Questa)

1998 (1 Apr). 80th Anniv of Royal Air Force. T **178** and similar horiz designs. Multicoloured. W w **16** (sideways). P 14.

No.	Description	Unused	Used
742	15p. Type **178**	1·50	1·25
743	35p. Vickers Vernon	2·25	2·25
744	40p. Supermarine Spitfire F.22	2·25	2·50
745	50p. Bristol Britannia C.2	2·50	3·00
742/5	*Set of 4*	7·75	8·00
MS746	110×77 mm. 50p. Blackburn Kangaroo; 50p. S.E.5a; 50p Curtiss Kittyhawk III; 50p. Boeing Fortress II	4·75	4·75

(Des N. Arlott. Litho Walsall)

1998 (15 June). Migratory Birds. T **179** and similar vert designs. Multicoloured. W w **14**. P 14.

No.	Description	Unused	Used
747	15p. Type **179**	1·50	1·50
748	25p. House Martin	1·75	1·75
749	35p. Cattle Egret	2·00	2·00
750	40p. Common Swift	2·00	2·00
751	50p. Allen's Gallinule	2·25	2·25
747/51	*Set of 5*	8·50	8·50

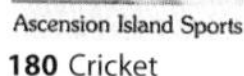

180 Cricket

181 Children in Nativity Play

(Des S. Noon. Litho Walsall)

1998 (17 Aug). Sporting Activities. T **180** and similar vert designs. Multicoloured. W w **14**. P 14.

No.	Description	Unused	Used
752	15p. Type **180**	3·00	2·00
753	35p. Golf	4·00	2·50
754	40p. Football	2·50	2·75
755	50p. Shooting	2·50	2·75
752/5	*Set of 4*	11·00	9·00

(Des N. Shewring. Litho Questa)

1998 (1 Oct). Christmas. T **181** and similar horiz designs. Multicoloured. W w **14** (sideways). P 14.

No.	Description	Unused	Used
756	15p. Type **181**	1·25	1·50
757	35p. Santa Claus arriving on Ascension	1·75	2·00
758	40p. Santa Claus on carnival float	1·75	2·00
759	50p. Carol singers	1·75	2·00
756/9	*Set of 4*	6·00	6·75

182 Curtiss C-46 Commando

(Des A. Theobald. Litho Questa)

1999 (20 Jan). Aircraft. T **182** and similar horiz designs. Multicoloured. W w **14** (sideways). P 14.

No.	Description	Unused	Used
760	15p. Type **182**	1·75	1·75
761	35p. Douglas C-47 Dakota	2·25	2·50
762	40p. Douglas C-54 Skymaster	2·25	2·50
763	50p. Consolidated Liberator Mk. V	2·25	2·75
760/3	*Set of 4*	7·75	8·50
MS764	120×85 mm. £1.50 Consolidated Liberator LB-30	12·00	12·00

No. **MS**764 also commemorates the 125th birth anniversary of Sir Winston Churchill.

183 *Glengorm Castle* (mail ship), 1929

184 Pair of White Terns ("Fairy Terns")

(Des J. Batchelor. Litho Questa)

1999 (5 Mar). "Australia '99" World Stamp Exhibition, Melbourne. Ships. T **183** and similar horiz designs. Multicoloured. W w **14** (sideways). P 15×14.

No.	Description	Unused	Used
765	15p. Type **183**	2·00	2·00
766	35p. *Gloucester Castle* (mail ship), 1930	2·50	2·50
767	40p. *Durham Castle* (mail ship), 1930	2·50	2·50
768	50p. *Garth Castle* (mail ship), 1930	2·50	2·75
765/8	*Set of 4*	8·50	8·75
MS769	121×82 mm. £1 H.M.S. *Endeavour* (Cook)	4·00	5·00

(Des Doreen McGuiness. Litho Questa)

1999 (27 Apr). Endangered Species. White Tern ("Fairy Tern"). T **184** and similar vert designs. Multicoloured. W w **16**. P 14½.

No.	Description	Unused	Used
770	10p. Type **184**	45	55
	a. Strip of 4. Nos. 770/3	1·60	2·00
771	10p. On branch	45	55
772	10p. Adult and fledgling	45	55
773	10p. In flight	45	55

770/3	*Set of 4*	1·60	2·00

Nos. 770/3 were printed in sheets of individual designs, or in sheets of 16 containing the four designs *se-tenant*, both horizontally and vertically.

185 Prince Edward and Miss Sophie Rhys-Jones

186 Command and Service Modules

(Des D. Miller. Litho Walsall)

1999 (19 June). Royal Wedding. T **185** and similar vert design. Multicoloured. W w **16**. P 14.

774	50p. Type **185**	1·25	1·50
775	£1 Engagement photograph	2·25	2·75

(Des N. Shewring. Litho Walsall)

1999 (20 July). 30th Anniv of First Manned Landing on Moon. T **186** and similar multicoloured designs. W w **16**. P 14×13½.

776	15p. Type **186**	75	1·10
777	35p. Moon from "Apollo 11"	1·25	1·60
778	40p. Devil's Ashpit Tracking Station and command module	1·25	1·60
779	50p. Lunar module leaving Moon	1·25	1·60
776/9	*Set of 4*	4·00	5·25
MS780	90×80 mm. £1.50 Earth as seen from Moon (*circular, 40 mm diam*). Wmk sideways. P 14	3·75	5·00

187 King George VI, Queen Elizabeth and Prime Minister Winston Churchill, 1940

188 Babies with Toys

(Des D. Miller. Litho Cartor)

1999 (20 Aug). "Queen Elizabeth the Queen Mother's Century". T **187** and similar horiz designs. Multicoloured (except £1.50). W w **16** (sideways). P 13½.

781	15p. Type **187**	1·50	1·50
782	35p. With Prince Charles at Coronation, 1953	2·00	2·00
783	40p. On her 88th Birthday, 1988	2·00	2·00
784	50p. With Guards' drummers, 1988	2·00	2·00
781/4	*Set of 4*	6·75	6·75
MS785	145×70 mm. £1.50 Lady Elizabeth Bowes-Lyon, and *Titanic* (liner) (black)	3·75	5·00

(Des A. Robinson. Litho Questa)

1999 (6 Oct). Christmas. T **188** and similar square designs. Multicoloured. W w **16**. P 14.

786	15p. Type **188**	1·75	1·75
787	35p. Children dressed as clowns	2·25	2·25
788	40p. Getting ready for bed	2·25	2·25
789	50p. Children dressed as pirates	2·25	2·25
786/9	*Set of 4*	7·75	7·75

189 *Anglia* (cable ship), 1900

(Litho Cartor)

1999 (13 Dec). Centenary of Cable & Wireless Communications plc on Ascension. T **189** and similar horiz designs. W w **14** (sideways). P 13½.

790	15p. black, reddish brown and bistre-brown	2·25	2·25
791	35p. black, reddish brown and bistre-brown	2·75	2·75
792	40p. multicoloured	2·75	2·75
793	50p. black, reddish brown and bistre-brown	2·75	2·75
790/3	*Set of 4*	9·50	9·50
MS794	105×90 mm. £1.50, multicoloured	3·75	4·00

Designs: 35p. *Cambria* (cable ship), 1910; 40p. Cable network map; 50p. *Colonia* (cable ship), 1910; £1.50 *Seine* (cable ship), 1899.

190 Baby Turtles

191 Prince William as Toddler

(Litho Questa)

2000 (8 Mar). Turtle Project on Ascension. T **190** and similar horiz designs. Multicoloured. W w **14** (sideways). P 13½×14.

795	15p. Type **190**	1·25	1·50
796	35p. Turtle on beach	1·75	2·00
797	40p. Turtle with tracking device	1·75	2·00
798	50p. Turtle heading for sea	1·75	2·00
795/8	*Set of 4*	5·75	6·75
MS799	197×132 mm. 25p. Head of turtle; 25p. Type **190**; 25p. Turtle on beach 25p. Turtle entering sea (*each* 40×26 *mm*). P 14	5·00	6·00

(Litho Questa)

2000 (8 May). "The Stamp Show 2000" International Stamp Exhibition, London. As No. **MS** 799 but with "The Stamp Show 2000" added to the bottom right corner of the margin. W w **14** (sideways). P 14.

MS800	197×132 mm. 25p. Head of turtle 25p. Type **190**; 25p. Turtle on beach; 25p. Turtle entering sea (*each* 40×26 *mm*)	2·75	3·25

(Des A. Robinson. Litho Questa)

2000 (21 June). 18th Birthday of Prince William. T **191** and similar multicoloured designs. W w **14** (sideways on 15p. and 35p.). P 14×14½ (vert) or 14½×14 (horiz).

801	15p. Type **191**	1·00	1·00
802	35p. Prince William in 1994	1·50	1·50
803	40p. Skiing at Klosters, Switzerland (*horiz*)	1·50	1·50
804	50p. Prince William in 1997 (*horiz*)	1·50	1·50
801/4	*Set of 4*	6·00	6·00
MS805	175×95 mm. 10p. As baby with toy mouse (*horiz*) and Nos. 801/4. Wmk sideways. P 14½	7·50	7·00

192 Royal Marine and Early Fort, 1815

193 Ships and Dockside Crane ("I saw Three Ships")

(Des E. Nisbet. Litho Questa)

2000 (14 Aug). Forts. T **192** and similar horiz designs. Multicoloured. W w **14** (sideways). P 14.

806	15p. Type **192**	2·25	2·25
807	35p. Army officer and Fort Thornton, 1817	3·00	3·00
808	40p. Soldier and Fort Hayes, 1860	3·00	3·00
809	50p. Naval lieutenant and Fort Bedford, 1940	3·00	3·00
806/9	*Set of 4*	10·00	10·00

(Des R. Watton. Litho Walsall)

2000 (16 Oct). Christmas. Carols. T **193** and similar horiz designs. Multicoloured. W w **16** (sideways). P 14.

810	15p. Type **193**	1·75	1·50
811	25p. Choir and musicians on beach ("Silent Night")	2·00	1·50
812	40p. Donkeys and church ("Away in a Manger")	2·75	2·25
813	90p. Carol singers outside church ("Hark the Herald Angels Sing")	5·00	8·00
810/13	*Set of 4*	10·50	12·00

194 Green Turtle

195 Captain William Dampier

(Des A. Robinson. Litho Questa)

2001 (1 Feb). "Hong Kong 2001" Stamp Exhibition. Sheet, 150×90 mm, containing T **194** and similar horiz design showing turtle. Multicoloured. W w **14** (sideways). P 14½×14.

MS814 25p. Type **194**; 40p. Loggerhead Turtle .... 4·25 5·00

(Des A. Robinson. Litho Questa)

2001 (25 Feb). Centenary of Wreck of the Roebuck. T **195** and similar multicoloured designs. W w **14** (sideways on 35, 40p.). P 14.

815 15p. Type **195** .... 2·50 2·50
816 35p. Construction drawing (*horiz*) .... 3·25 3·25
817 40p. Cave dwelling at Dampier's Drip (*horiz*) 3·25 3·25
818 50p. Map of Ascension .... 4·50 4·50
815/18 *Set of 4* .... 12·00 12·00

196 Alfonso de Albuquerque

197 Great Britain 1d. Stamp used on Ascension, 1855

(Des G. Vasarhelyi. Litho B.D.T.)

2001 (25 May). 500th Anniv of the Discovery of Ascension Island. T **196** and similar vert designs. Multicoloured. W w **16**. P 14½×14.

819 15p. Type **196** .... 2·75 2·75
820 35p. Portuguese caravel .... 3·75 3·75
821 40p. Cantino map .... 3·75 3·75
822 50p. Rear Admiral Sir George Cockburn .... 3·75 3·75
819/22 *Set of 4* .... 12·50 12·50

(Des N. Shewring. Litho Questa)

2001 (24 May). Death Centenary of Queen Victoria. T **197** and similar multicoloured designs. W w **14** (sideways on horiz designs). P 14.

823 15p. Type **197** .... 1·25 1·25
824 25p. Navy church parade, 1901 (*horiz*) .... 1·50 1·50
825 35p. H.M.S. *Phoebe* (cruiser) (*horiz*) .... 2·00 2·00
826 40p. The Red Lion, 1863 (*horiz*) .... 2·00 2·00
827 50p. "Queen Victoria" .... 2·00 2·00
828 65p. Sir Joseph Hooker (botanist) .... 2·00 2·75
823/8 *Set of 6* .... 9·75 10·50
MS829 105×80 mm. £1.50 Queen Victoria's coffin on the steps of St. George's Chapel, Windsor (*horiz*) .... 5·50 6·50

198 Islander Hostel

199 Female Ascension Frigate Bird

(Des A. Robinson. Litho Questa)

2001 (9 June). "BELGICA 2001" International Stamp Exhibition, Brussels. Tourism. T **198** and similar horiz designs. Multicoloured. W w **14**. P 14×14½.

830 35p. Type **198** .... 3·00 3·50
a. Sheetlet. Nos. 830/3 .... 11·00 12·50
831 35p. The Residency .... 3·00 3·50
832 40p. The Red Lion .... 3·00 3·50
833 40p. Turtle Ponds .... 3·00 3·50
830/3 *Set of 4* .... 11·00 12·50

Nos. 830/3 were printed together, *se-tenant*, as a sheetlet containing the stamps as a horizontal strip of 4 above a map of the island.

(Des A. Robinson. Litho Questa)

2001 (1 Oct). BirdLife World Bird Festival (1st Series). Ascension Frigate Birds. T **199** and similar multicoloured designs. W w **14** (sideways on 15p. and 35p.). P 14×14½ (vert) or 14½×14 (horiz).

834 15p. Type **199** .... 1·25 1·25
835 35p. Fledgeling .... 1·75 1·75
836 40p. Male bird in flight (*horiz*) .... 1·75 1·75
837 50p. Male bird with pouch inflated (*horiz*) .... 1·75 1·75
834/7 *Set of 4* .... 5·75 5·75
MS838 175×80 mm. 10p. Male and female birds on rock (*horiz*) and Nos. 834/7. Wmk sideways. P 14½.. 8·00 9·00

See also Nos. 889/**MS**894 and 921/**MS**926.

200 Princess Elizabeth and Dog

201 Royal Marines landing at English Bay

(Des A. Robinson. Litho Questa)

2002 (6 Feb). Golden Jubilee. T **200** and similar designs. W w **14** (sideways). P 14½.

839 15p. agate, mauve and gold .... 1·50 1·50
840 35p. multicoloured .... 2·00 2·00
841 40p. multicoloured .... 2·00 2·00
842 50p. multicoloured .... 2·00 2·00
839/42 *Set of 4* .... 6·75 6·75
MS843 162×95 mm. Nos. 839/42 and 60p. multicoloured. P 13½ (60p.) or 14½ (others) .... 7·50 8·50

Designs: *Horiz* (*as Type* **200**)—35p. Queen Elizabeth wearing tiara, 1978; 40p Princess Elizabeth, 1946; 50p. Queen Elizabeth visiting Henley-on-Thames, 1998. *Vert* (38×51 *mm*)—50p. Queen Elizabeth after Annigoni.

Designs as Nos. 839/42 in No. **MS**843 omit the gold frame around each stamp and the "Golden Jubilee 1952–2002" inscription.

(Des A. Robinson. Litho B.D.T.)

2002 (14 June). 20th Anniv of Liberation of the Falkland Islands. T **201** and similar horiz designs. Multicoloured. W w **14** (sideways). P 14.

844 15p. Type **201** .... 1·75 1·75
845 35p. Weapons testing .... 2·25 2·25
846 40p. H.M.S. *Hermes* (aircraft carrier) .... 2·50 2·50
847 50p. R.A.F. Vulcan at Wideawake Airfield .... 2·50 2·50
844/7 *Set of 4* .... 8·00 8·00

202 Duchess of York at Harrow Hospital, 1931

203 Travellers Palm and Vinca

(Des A. Robinson. Litho Questa)

2002 (5 Aug). Queen Elizabeth the Queen Mother Commemoration. T **202** and similar vert designs. W w **14**. P 14½×14.

848 35p. brownish black, gold and purple .... 1·40 1·40
849 40p. multicoloured .... 1·40 1·40
MS850 145×70 mm. 50p. blackish brown and gold; £1 multicoloured. Wmk sideways .... 6·50 7·50

Designs:— 40p. Queen Mother on her birthday, 1997; 50p. Duchess of York, 1925; £1 Queen Mother, Scrabster, 1992.

Designs in No. **MS**850 omit the "1900–2002" inscription and the coloured frame.

(Litho B.D.T.)

2002 (28 Aug). Island Views. T **203** and similar horiz designs. Multicoloured. W w **14** (sideways). P 14.

851 10p. Type **203** .... 85 1·25

852	15p. Broken Tooth (volcanic crater) and Mexican Poppy	1·25	85
853	20p. St. Mary's Church and Ascension Lily	1·25	85
854	25p. Boatswain Bird Island and Goatweed	1·75	1·50
855	30p. Cannon and Mauritius Hemp	1·75	1·75
856	35p. The Guest House and Frangipani	1·75	1·50
857	40p. Wideawake Tern and Ascension Spurge	2·50	2·00
858	50p. The Pier Head and Lovechaste	2·50	2·50
859	65p. Sisters' Peak and Yellowboy	2·75	3·25
860	90p. Two Boats School and Persian Lilac	3·50	3·75
861	£2 Green Turtle and Wild Currant	8·00	9·00
862	£5 Wideawake Airfield and Coral Tree	14·00	15·00
851/62	*Set of* 12	38·00	38·00

204 "Ecce Ancilla Dominii" (Dante Rossetti)

205 Ariane 4 Rocket on Gantry

(Litho B.D.T.)

2002 (9 Oct). Christmas. Religious Paintings. T **204** and similar multicoloured designs. W w **14** (sideways on 25p.). P 14.

863	15p. Type **204**	70	70
864	25p. "The Holy Family and Shepherd" (Titian) (*horiz*)	95	95
865	35p. "Christ carrying the Cross" (A. Bergognone)	1·25	1·25
866	75p. Sketch for "The Ascension" (Benjamin West)	2·50	3·50
863/6	*Set of* 4	4·75	5·75

(Des A. Robinson. Litho Walsall)

2003 (13 Jan). Ariane Downrange Station. T **205** and similar multicoloured designs. W w **14** (inverted on vert or sideways on horiz). P 14½.

867	35p. Type **205**	1·40	1·40
868	40p. Map of Ariane Downrange stations (*horiz*)	1·50	1·50
869	65p. Automated Transfer Vehicle (ATV) in Space (*horiz*)	2·50	2·50
870	90p. Launch of Ariane 5	3·75	4·25
867/70	*Set of* 4	8·25	8·25
MS871	170×88 mm. Nos. 867/70. Wmk sideways	8·25	8·25

206 Coronation Coach in Procession

207 Queen Elizabeth II

(Des A. Robinson. Litho DLR)

2003 (2 June). 50th Anniv of Coronation. T **206** and similar horiz design. Multicoloured. W w **14** (sideways). P 14×14½.

872	40p. Type **206**	1·50	1·00
873	£1 Newly crowned Queen with bishops and peers	3·25	3·75
MS874	95×115 mm. As Nos. 872/3	4·75	4·75

Nos. 872/3 have scarlet frame; stamps from **MS**874 have no frame and country name in mauve panel.

(Des CASB Studio. Litho BDT)

2003 (2 June). W w **14** . P 13½.

875	**207**	£3 grey-black, yellowish green and myrtle-green	6·50	7·00

208 Prince William at Tidworth Polo Club and on Skiing Holiday, 2002

209 Bleriot XI

(Des A. Robinson. Litho DLR)

2003 (21 June). 21st Birthday of Prince William of Wales. T **208** and similar square design. Multicoloured. W w **14** (sideways). P 14½.

876	75p. Type **208**	2·75	2·75
	a Horiz pair. Nos. 876/7	5·50	5·50
877	75p. On Raleigh International Expedition, 2000 and at Queen Mother's 101st Birthday, 2001	2·75	2·75

Nos. 876/7 were printed together, *se-tenant*, as horizontal pairs in sheets of ten (2×5) with enlarged illustrated left-hand margins.

(Des J. Batchelor. Litho DLR)

2003 (12 Aug). Centenary of Powered Flight. T **209** and similar horiz designs. Multicoloured. W w **14**. P 14.

878	15p. Type **209**	85	85
879	20p. Vickers VC–10	90	90
880	35p. BAe Harrier FRS Mk1	1·60	1·60
881	40p. Westland Sea King HAS Mk. 4 helicopter	1·75	1·75
882	50p. Rockwell Space Shuttle	1·75	1·75
883	90p. General Dynamics F–16 Fighting Falcon	3·25	3·50
878/83	*Set of* 6	9·00	9·25
MS884	115×65 mm. £1.50, Fairy Swordfish MK II. Wmk sideways	7·50	8·50

Nos. 878/83 were each printed in sheets of 20 containing vertical rows of stamps alternated with rows of illustrated half stamp-size labels.

210 Casting Vote into Ballot Box

211 Adult with Fledgling

(Des J. Vasarhelyi. Litho BDT)

2003 (1 Nov). Christmas. First Anniv of Democracy on Ascension. T **210** and similar horiz designs. Multicoloured. W w **14** (sideways). P 14.

885	15p. Type **210**	75	55
886	25p. Island Council session	90	65
887	40p. Students ("HIGHER EDUCATION")	1·40	1·10
888	£1 Government Headquarters	2·75	4·00
885/8	*Set of* 4	5·25	5·75

(Des R. Gorringe. Litho DLR)

2004 (6 Feb). BirdLife International (2nd series). Masked Booby. T **211** and similar multicoloured designs. W w **14** (sideways on 35p., 40p.). P 14½×13½ (horiz) or 13½×14½ (vert).

889	15p. Type **211**	85	75
890	35p. 890 35p. Pair (*vert*)	1·40	1·00
891	40p. In flight (*vert*)	1·40	1·25
892	50p. Adult calling	1·50	1·50
893	90p. Masked Booby	3·00	3·50
889/93	*Set of* 5	7·25	7·25
MS894	175×80 mm. Nos. 889/93. Wmk sideways. P 14½	7·00	7·50

212 *Bougainvillea glabra* (orange)

213 Blue Marlin

(Des R. Watton. Litho BDT)

2004 (25 May). Bicentenary of the Royal Horticultural Society. T **212** and similar horiz designs. Multicoloured. W w **14** (sideways). P 14.

895	15p. Type **212**	75	75
896	35p. *Bougainvillea glabra* (pink)	1·40	1·00
897	40p. *Bougainvillea glabra* (white)	1·50	1·10
898	90p. *Bougainvillea spectabilis* (red)	2·75	3·50
895/8 *Set of 4*		5·75	5·75
MS899 105×80 mm. £1.50 *Pteris adscensionis*		6·00	6·50

(Des N. Shewring. Litho BDT)

2004 (26 July). Sport Fishing (1st series). T **213** and similar horiz designs. Multicoloured. W w **14** (sideways). P 13½.

900	15p. Type **213**	75	75
901	35p. Swordfish	1·40	1·00
902	40p. Sailfish	1·50	1·10
903	90p. White Marlin	2·75	3·50
900/3 *Set of 4*		5·75	5·75
MS904 61×51 mm. £1.50 Blue Marlin. Wmk inverted		5·00	6·00

See also Nos. 927/**MS**931 and 940/**MS**944.

214 Moon over Hummock Point

215 MV *Ascension*

(Des D. Miller. Litho BDT)

2004 (28 Oct). Lunar Eclipse. T **214** and similar vert designs. Multicoloured. W w **14**. P 13½.

905	15p. Type **214**	75	75
906	25p. Yellow moon over Sisters Peak (North side)	1·25	1·00
907	35p. Orange moon over Daly's Craggs	1·50	1·00
908	£1.25 Red moon and birds over Mars Bay	3·75	5·00
905/8 *Set of 4*		6·50	7·00
MS909 130×55 mm. £1.25 As No. 908		4·00	5·00

(Des A. Theobald. Litho Enschedé)

2004 (26 Oct). Merchant Ships. T **215** and similar horiz designs. Multicoloured. W w **14** (sideways). P 13×13½.

910	15p. Type **215**	1·50	1·25
911	35p. *St. Helena* (mail ship)	2·50	1·75
912	40p. *Caronia* (mail ship)	2·50	1·75
913	£1.25 MV *Maersk Gannet*	6·50	8·50
910/13 *Set of 4*		11·50	12·00

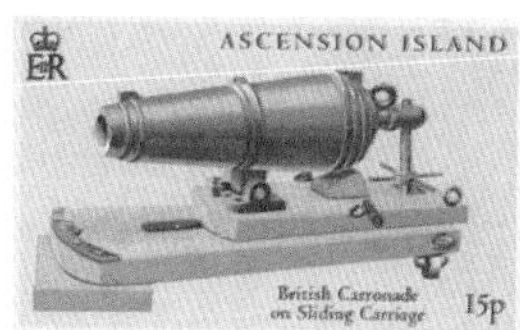

216 British Carronade on Sliding Carriage

(Des J. Batchelor. Litho Cartor)

2005 (29 Apr). Bicentenary of Battle of Trafalgar (1st. issue). T **216** and similar multicoloured designs. W w **14** (sideways on 15, 40, 50p., inverted on 25p, 35p) or no wmk (90p.). P 13½.

914	15p. Type **216**	85	75
915	25p. Royal Marine drummer boy, 1805 (*vert*)	1·40	1·00
916	35p. HMS *Britannia* (*vert*)	1·75	1·50
917	40p. Admiral Nelson	1·75	1·50
918	50p. HMS *Neptune* and *Santissima Trinidad*	2·25	2·00
919	90p. HMS *Victory*	3·50	5·00
914/19 *Set of 6*		10·00	10·50
MS920 120×80 mm. £1 *Lord Nelson* (*vert*); £1 Neptune (*vert*)		6·50	7·50

See also Nos. 937/9.

No. 919 contains traces of powdered wood from HMS *Victory*.

217 White Tern ("Fairy Tern")

218 Yellowfin Tuna

(Des R. Allen. Litho BDT)

2005 (27 May). BirdLife International (3rd series). "The Sea Birds Return". T **217** and similar horiz designs. Multicoloured. P 14.

921	15p. Type **217**	55	55
922	35p. White-tailed Tropic Bird	1·10	1·10
923	40p. Brown Booby	1·25	1·40
924	50p. Common Noddy ("Brown Noddy")	1·40	1·40
925	£1.25 Red-billed Tropic Bird	3·25	4·25
921/5 *Set of 5*		6·75	8·00
MS926 170×80 mm. Nos. 921/5		8·00	8·50

(Des N. Shewring. Litho BDT)

2005 (22 July). Sport Fishing (2nd series). Tuna. T **218** and similar horiz designs. Multicoloured. P 14.

927	35p. Type **218**	1·25	1·25
928	40p. Skipjack Tuna	1·40	1·40
929	50p. Albacore Tuna	1·50	1·50
930	£1.25 Bigeye Tuna	3·50	4·00
927/30 *Set of 4*		7·00	7·25
MS931 61×51 mm. £1.50 Yellowfin Tuna hunting herrings		4·50	5·50

219 Pope John Paul II

220 *The Little Fir Tree*

(Des A. Robinson. Litho BDT)

2005 (18 Aug). Pope John Paul II Commemoration. W w **14** (inverted). P 14.

932	**219** 40p. multicoloured	1·75	1·75

No. 932 was printed in sheetlets of eight stamps with an enlarged, illustrated right margin.

(Des V. Ambrus. Litho Enschedé)

2005 (3 Oct). Christmas. Birth Bicentenary of Hans Christian Andersen (writer). T **220** and similar vert designs. Multicoloured. W w **14** (inverted). P 14.

933	15p. Type **220**	1·00	1·00
934	25p. *The Mail-Coach Passengers*	1·25	1·25
935	35p. *The Little Match Girl*	1·50	1·50
936	£1.25 *The Snow Man*	4·00	5·00
933/6 *Set of 4*		7·00	8·00

Nos. 933/6 were each printed in sheetlets of ten with enlarged illustrated right margins.

221 HMS *Victory*

222 Black Jack

(Des J. Batchelor (40p) or Pauline Gyles (90p). Litho Cartor)

2005 (21 Oct). Bicentenary of the Battle of Trafalgar (2nd issue). T **221** and similar multicoloured designs. P 13½.

937	40p. Type **221**	1·50	1·40
938	65p. Ships engaged in battle (*horiz*)	2·50	3·00
939	90p. Admiral Lord Nelson	3·50	4·00
937/9 *Set of 3*		6·75	6·75

(Des N. Shewring. Litho BDT)

2006 (24 Jan). Sport Fishing (3rd series). Jacks. T **222** and similar horiz designs. Multicoloured. W w **14** (sideways). P 14.

940	20p. Type **222**	1·00	1·00
941	35p. Almaco jack	1·60	1·40
942	50p. Horse-eye jack	2·00	2·00
943	£1 Rainbow runner	3·50	4·25
940/3	*Set of* 4	7·25	7·25
MS944	61×50 mm. £1.50 Longfin crevalle jack	4·50	5·50

223 Princess Elizabeth

224 HMS *Beagle* (175th anniv of Darwin's voyage)

(Litho BDT)

2006 (21 Apr). 80th Birthday of Queen Elizabeth II. T **223** and similar horiz designs. Multicoloured. W w **14** (sideways). P 14.

945	20p. Type **223**	80	80
946	40p. Queen Elizabeth II, c. 1952	1·00	1·25
947	50p. Queen Elizabeth II	1·75	1·90
948	£1.30 Wearing Garter robes	4·25	8·00
945/8	*Set of* 4	7·00	8·00
MS949	144×75 mm. £1 Queen, c. 1952; £1 Queen in 1960s	6·00	7·00

(Des D. Miller. Litho Cartor)

2006 (24 July). Exploration and Innovation. Anniversaries. T **224** and similar vert designs. Multicoloured. W w **14**. P 13×13½.

950	20p. Type **224**	2·00	2·00
	a. Horiz pair. Nos. 950/1	4·00	4·00
951	20p. Charles Darwin (originator of theory of evolution)	2·00	2·00
952	35p. *Great Britain* (steam/sail)	2·75	2·75
	a. Horiz pair. Nos. 952/3	5·50	5·50
953	35p. Isambard Kingdom Brunel (engineer, birth bicentenary)	2·75	2·75
954	40p. *Nina* (Columbus)	2·75	2·75
	a. Horiz pair. Nos. 954/5	5·50	5·50
955	40p. Christopher Columbus (discoverer of New World, 500th death anniv)	2·75	2·75
956	50p. World map with lines of magnetic variation	2·75	2·75
	a. Horiz pair. Nos. 956/7	5·50	5·50
957	50p. Edmund Halley (astronomer, 350th birth anniv) and Halley's comet	2·75	2·75
590/7	*Set of* 8	18·00	18·00

Nos. 950/1, 952/3, 954/5 and 956/7 were each printed together, *se-tenant*, in horizontal pairs in sheetlets of eight stamps, each pair forming a composite background design.

225 Long Beach ("Greetings from Ascension")

226 Resplendent Angelfish

(Des A. Robinson. Litho BDT)

2006 (30 Oct). Christmas. Views of Ascension Island. T **225** and similar horiz designs. Multicoloured. W w **14** (sideways). P 14.

958	15p. Type **225**	85	85
959	25p. Coastal rocks at sunset ("Merry Christmas")	1·25	1·25
960	35p. Dewpond ("Seasons Greetings")	1·60	1·25
961	£1.25 Coast and Boatswain Bird Island ("Happy New Year")	4·25	5·50
958/61	*Set of* 4	7·25	8·00

(Des O. Bell. Litho BDT)

2007 (23 Mar). Endangered Species. Resplendent Angelfish (*Centropyge resplendens*). T **226** and similar horiz designs. Multicoloured. P 14.

962	35p. Type **226**	1·60	1·25
	a. Strip of 4. Nos. 962/5	8·50	8·75
963	40p. Shoal of resplendent angelfish	1·75	1·75
964	50p. Three angelfish near red coral and rocks	1·75	1·75
965	£1.25 Large male angelfish and three smaller females	4·25	5·00
962/5	*Set of* 4	8·50	8·75

Nos. 962/5 were printed together, *se-tenant*, as horizontal and vertical strips of four in sheetlets of 16, and also in separate sheets of 50.

227 Handley Page Victor K Mk2 Tanker

228 Ascension Scouts forming Fleur-de-Lis Emblem

(Des John Batchelor. Litho Cartor)

2007 (25 May). 25th Anniv of the Liberation of the Falkland Islands. T **227** and similar horiz designs. Multicoloured. P 13.

966	35p. Type **227**	1·50	1·25
967	40p. HMS *Dumbarton Castle* (offshore patrol vessel) and Chinook helicopter	1·90	1·90
968	50p. HMS *Fearless* with helicopter and landing craft	1·90	1·90
969	£1.25 Vulcan XM607 taking off	4·50	5·50
966/9	*Set of* 4	9·00	9·50
MS970	Two sheets, each 183×89 mm. (a) As Type **227**; 40p. Vickers VC10 Transport; 50p. Nimrod MR2 Maritime Reconnaissance; As No. 969. (b) 35p. RFA *Tidespring* refuelling HMS *Antrim*; As No. 967; As No. 968; £1.25 *Atlantic Conveyor* and Harrier fighter	9·00	11·00

Stamps from the two miniature sheets **MS**970a/b do not have white borders. The 50p. stamp from **MS**970(a) has an incorrect spelling "Reconaissance".

(Des Andrew Robinson. Litho BDT)

2007 (9 July). Centenary of Scouting. T **228** and similar horiz designs. Multicoloured. P 14.

971	35p. Type **228**	1·40	1·25
972	40p. Scouts rescuing stranded turtle	1·60	1·60
973	50p. Ascension Scout Troop sitting on gun from HMS *Hood*	1·60	1·60
974	£1.25 Scouts on top of their Land Rover near Butt Crater	4·00	5·50
971/4	*Set of* 4	7·75	9·00

229 Mother Teresa and Princess Diana, Rome, 1992

230 Engagement Photograph, July 1947

(Des Jason Witchard. Litho BDT)

2007 (31 Aug). Tenth Death Anniv of Diana, Princess of Wales. P 14.

975	**229**	50p. multicoloured	1·60	1·60

No. 975 was printed in sheetlets of eight stamps with enlarged illustrated left margins.

(Des Andrew Robinson. Litho BDT)

2007 (20 Nov). Diamond Wedding of Queen Elizabeth II and Duke of Edinburgh. T **230** and similar vert designs. Multicoloured. P 14.

976	35p. Type **230**	3·00	4·00
	a. Horiz strip of 3. Nos. 976/8	11·00	12·50
977	90p. Wedding programme	4·50	5·00
978	£1.25 Queen and Duke of Edinburgh at St. Paul?s Cathedral for 80th birthday Thanksgiving Service	4·50	5·00
976/8	*Set of* 3	11·00	12·50

Nos. 976/8 were printed together, *se-tenant*, as horizontal strips of three in sheetlets of 12 stamps.

231 BOU Base Camp near Mars Bay

(Des Nick Shewring. Litho BDT)

2007 (10 Dec). 50th Anniv of the British Ornithologists Union Centenary Expedition (1957–9). T **231** and similar horiz designs. Multicoloured. P 14.

No.	Description	Unused	Used
979	15p. Type **231**	2·00	2·00
	a. Horiz pair. Nos. 979/80	4·00	4·00
980	15p. Peter Mundy's drawing of extinct flightless rail, 1656	2·00	2·00
981	25p. Team member recording sooty tern ('Wideawake')	2·25	2·25
	a. Horiz pair. Nos. 981/2	4·50	4·50
982	25p. Sooty terns ('Wideawake')	2·25	2·25
983	40p. BOU outpost, Boatswainbird Island	3·00	3·00
	a. Horiz pair. Nos. 983/4	6·00	6·00
984	40p. Masked booby	3·00	3·00
985	50p. Team members with expedition dinghy *Overdraft*	3·00	3·00
	a. Horiz pair. Nos. 985/6	6·00	6·00
986	50p. Red-footed booby	3·00	3·00
979/86	*Set of* 8	18·00	18·00

Nos. 979/80, 981/2, 983/4 and 985/6 were each printed together, *se-tenant*, as horizontal pairs in sheetlets of eight stamps.

232 *Lampides boeticus* (long-tailed blue butterfly)

(Litho BDT)

2008 (5 Feb). Fauna and their Eggs. T **232** and similar horiz designs. Multicoloured. P 14.

No.	Description	Unused	Used
987	15p. Type **232**	1·40	1·40
988	20p. *Cheilomenes lunata* (ladybird)	1·50	1·50
989	25p. *Panulirus echinatus* (spiny lobster)	1·60	1·25
990	30p. *Schistocerca gregaria* (desert locust)	1·75	1·50
991	35p. *Chelonia mydas* (green turtle)	1·90	1·50
992	40p. *Gecarcinus lagostoma* (landcrab)	2·00	1·75
993	50p. *Sula sula* (red-footed booby)	2·75	2·50
994	65p. *Hemdactylus mercatorius* (coconut-palm gecko)	2·75	3·00
995	90p. *Estrilda astrild* (common waxbill)	4·50	4·50
996	£1 *Stegastes lubbocki* (yellowtail damselfish)	4·00	4·50
997	£2.50 *Oceanodroma castro* (Madeiran storm-petrel)	11·00	12·00
998	£5 *Francolinus afer* (red-necked francolin)	17·00	18·00
987/98	*Set of* 12	48·00	48·00

233 Bluntnose Sixgill Shark

(Des Nick Shewring. Litho BDT)

2008 (14 Mar). Sharks. T **233** and similar horiz designs. Multicoloured. P 14.

No.	Description	Unused	Used
999	35p. Type **233**	1·75	2·25
	a. Strip of 4. Nos. 999/1002	8·00	10·00
1000	40p. Scalloped hammerhead	1·75	2·25
1001	50p. Shortfin mako	1·75	2·25
1002	£1.25 Whale shark	3·75	4·25
999/1002	*Set of* 4	8·00	10·00
MS1003	70×45 mm. £1	5·00	6·00

Bigeye thresher 5.00 5.50 Nos. 999/1002 were printed together, *se-tenant*, as horizontal and vertical strips of four in sheetlets of 16, and also in separate sheets.

234 Bell X-1E NACA X-Plane, 1958

(Des Andrew Robinson. Litho BDT)

2008 (23 May). 50th Anniv of NASA. T **234** and similar horiz designs. Multicoloured. P 14.

No.	Description	Unused	Used
1004	35p. Type **234**	1·10	1·25
1005	35p. Apollo 11 Moon Walk, 1969	1·10	1·25
1006	40p. Apollo 17 Lunar Roving Vehicle, 1972	1·10	1·25
1007	50p. STS1 Space Shuttle *Columbia*, 1981	1·50	1·60
1008	65p. The Hubble Space Telescope, 1990	1·90	1·90
1009	90p. International Space Station, 2006	2·75	3·00
1004/9	*Set of* 6	8·50	9·00

Nos. 1004/9 were each printed in sheetlets of eight stamps with enlarged illustrated margins.

235 Sopwith 7F.1 Snipe

236 Valerius Cordus (1515–44) and *Cordia sebestena*

(Des Ross Watton. Litho BDT)

2008 (20 June). 90th Anniv of the Royal Air Force. T **235** and similar horiz designs. Multicoloured. P 14.

No.	Description	Unused	Used
1010	15p. Type **235**	1·50	1·10
1011	35p. Vickers Wellington Mk 1C	2·25	1·75
1012	40p. Supermarine Spitfire Mk IX	2·25	2·00
1013	50p. Gloster Meteor F.IV	2·25	2·25
1014	65p. BAe Hawk	3·00	3·25
1015	90p. Typhoon F2 (Eurofighter)	4·25	5·00
1010/15	*Set of* 5	14·00	14·00

(Des Andrew Robinson. Litho BDT)

2008 (28 Aug). Botanists and Plants named after them. T **236** and similar vert designs. Multicoloured. P 14.

No.	Description	Unused	Used
1016	35p. Type **236**	2·00	1·25
1017	40p. Nehemiah Grew (1641–1712) and *Grewia occidentalis*	2·25	1·75
1018	50p. Charles Plumier (1646–1704) and *Plumeria rubra*	2·25	2·00
1019	£2 Carl Peter Thunberg (1743–1828) and *Thunbergia grandiflora*	7·50	9·00
1016/19	*Set of* 4	12·50	12·50

237 Father Christmas

(Des Andrew Robinson. Litho BDT)

2008 (22 Oct). Christmas. T **237** and similar horiz designs showing illustrations of Father Christmas from *FatherChristmas* and *Father Christmas Goes on Holiday* by Raymond Briggs superimposed over Ascension Island scenes. Multicoloured. P 14.

No.	Description	Unused	Used
1020	15p. Type **237**	70	80
1021	25p. Father Christmas in reindeer-drawn sleigh above surf of western coast	1·00	1·00
1022	50p. Father Christmas lying on inflatable	1·75	1·75
1023	£2 Father Christmas and his laden sleigh above Green Mountain and Two Boats Village	6·50	8·00
1020/3	*Set of* 4	9·00	10·50

238 King Henry III (1216–72) and the Tower of London

(Des Andrew Robinson. Litho BDT)

2008 (15 Dec). Britain's Longest Reigning Monarchs. T **238** and similar horiz designs. Multicoloured. P 14.

1024	35p. Type **238**	2·50	1·75
1025	40p. King James VI (1567–1625) and Stirling Castle	2·50	2·25
1026	50p. King George III (1760–1820) and Windsor Castle	2·75	2·50
1027	65p. Queen Victoria (1837–1901) and Osborne House	3·25	3·50
1028	£1.25 Queen Elizabeth II (from 1952) and Buckingham Palace	5·50	6·50
1024/8	*Set of* 5	15·00	15·00

Nos. 1024/8 were each printed in separate sheetlets of eight stamps with enlarged illustrated.

239 Bottlenose Dolphin (*Tursiops truncatus*)

(Des Nick Shewring. Litho BDT)

2009 (23 Mar). Whales and Dolphins. T **239** and similar horiz designs. Multicoloured. P 14×15.

1029	35p. Type **239**	1·10	1·25
	a. Strip of 4. Nos. 1029/32	6·75	7·25
1030	40p. Pantropical spotted dolphin (*Stenella attenuata*)	1·25	1·40
1031	50p. Sperm whale (*Physeter macrocephalus*) and squid (prey)	1·50	1·60
1032	£1.25 Gervais' beaked whale (*Mesoplodon europeus*)	3·75	4·00
1029/32	*Set of* 4	6·75	7·25
MS1033	111×65 mm. £2 Humpback whale (*Megaptera novaeangliae*)	6·00	7·00

Nos. 1029/32 were printed together, *se-tenant*, as horizontal and vertical strips of four in sheets of 16, and also in separate sheets of 20 (2 panes 2×5).

240 Flt. SLt. Rex Warneford

(Des Ross Watton. Litho BDT)

2009 (7 May). Centenary of Naval Aviation. Victoria Crosses of the Fleet Air Arm. T **240** and similar horiz designs. Multicoloured. P 14.

1034	35p. Type **240**	2·50	2·50
	a. Horiz pair. Nos. 1034/5	5·00	5·00
1035	35p. Moraine-Saulnier L destroys Zeppelin LZ37, Belgium, 6/7 June 1915	2·50	2·50
1036	35p. Sqn. Cdr. Richard Bell Davies	2·50	2·50
	a. Horiz pair. Nos. 1036/7	5·00	5·00
1037	35p. Nieuport 10 takes off pursued by enemy soldiers, Bulgaria, 19 November 1915	2·50	2·50
1038	40p. Lt. Cdr. (A) Eugene Esmonde	2·50	2·50
	a. Horiz pair. Nos. 1038/9	5·00	5·00
1039	40p. Fairey Swordfish aircraft attacking German heavy cruisers, 12 February 1942	2·50	2·50
	a. Horiz pair. Nos. 1039/40	5·00	5·00
1040	50p. Lt. Robert Hampton Gray	2·50	2·50
	a. Horiz pair. Nos. 1040/1	5·00	5·00
1041	50p. Corsair bombing Japanese warship	2·50	2·50
1034/41	*Set of* 8	18·00	18·00

Nos. 1034/5, 1036/7, 1038/9 and 1040/1 were each printed together, *se-tenant*, as horizontal pairs in sheetlets of eight stamps, each pair forming a composite background design.

241 Blue Water Lily (*Nymphaea capensis*)

242 Dr. Archie Carr with Early Turtle Tracking Equipment

(Des Andrew Robinson. Litho BDT)

2009 (7 Sept). Introduced Plant Species. T **241** and similar horiz designs. Multicoloured. P 14.

1042	35p. Type **241**	1·10	1·25
1043	35p. Raspberry (*Rubus rosifolius*)	1·10	1·25
1044	40p. Prickly pear (*Optunia vulgaris*)	1·25	1·40
1045	50p. Ascension lily (*Hippeastrum reginae*)	1·50	1·60
1046	65p. Yellowboy (*Tecoma stans*)	1·90	2·25
1047	90p. Portraits of young and old Joseph Dalton Hooker (botanist)	2·75	3·25
1042/7	*Set of* 6	8·75	10·00

(Des Derek Miller. Litho BDT)

2009 (1 Oct). Turtle Research and Conservation and Birth Centenary of Dr. Archie Carr (sea turtle biologist). T **242** and similar horiz designs, each showing either head of turtle at left (Nos. 1048, 1050, 1052, 1054) or outline map of Ascension Island at right (others). Multicoloured. P 13½.

1048	15p. Type **242**	1·25	1·50
	a. Horiz pair. Nos. 1048/9	2·50	3·00
1049	15p. Dr. Archie Carr attaching tracking floats to turtle	1·25	1·50
1050	35p. Female laying eggs	1·75	2·00
	a. Horiz pair. Nos. 1050/1	3·50	4·00
1051	35p. Turtle hatchlings	1·75	2·00
1052	40p. Beach raking to remove turtle tracks after counting	1·75	2·00
	a. Horiz pair. Nos. 1052/3	3·50	4·00
1053	40p. Population monitoring	1·75	2·00
1054	65p. Rescuer with turtle	2·00	2·50
	a. Horiz pair. Nos. 1054/5	4·00	5·00
1055	65p. Two rescuers with turtle	2·00	2·50
1048/55	*Set of* 8	12·00	14·00

Nos. 1048/9, 1050/1, 1052/3 and 1054/5 were each printed together, *se-tenant*, as horizontal.

243 Charles Darwin and Marine Iguanas

(Des Julian Vasarhelyi. Litho BDT)

2009 (9 Nov). Birth Bicentenary of Charles Darwin (naturalist and evolutionary theorist). T **243** and similar horiz designs, each showing a different portrait. Multicoloured. P 14.

1056	35p. Charles Darwin and Woodpecker Finch	2·00	1·75
1057	40p. Type **243**	2·00	2·00
1058	50p. Charles Darwin and Galapagos tortoise	2·00	2·00
1059	£2 Charles Darwin as old man, Galapagos penguins and *Beagle*	7·50	9·00
1056/9	*Set of* 4	12·00	13·00

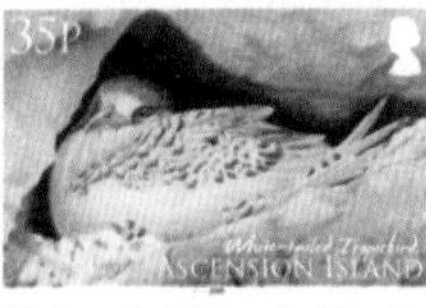

244 Juvenile White-tailed Tropic Bird

245 Hardback Soldier Fish (*Holocentrus adscensionis*)

(Des Andrew Robinson. Litho BDT)

2009 (4 Dec). White-tailed Tropic Bird (*Phaethon lepturus*). T **244** and similar horiz designs. Multicoloured. P 14.

1060	35p. Type **244**	1·75	2·00
	a. Strip of 4. Nos. 1060/3	8·00	9·00
1061	40p. Adult feeding juvenile	1·75	2·00
1062	50p. Juvenile in flight	1·75	2·00
1063	£1.25 Adult in flight	3·50	4·00

1060/3 *Set of* 4 ..... 8·00 9·00

Nos. 1060/3 were printed together, *se-tenant*, as horizontal and vertical strips of four in sheetlets of 16, and also in separate sheetlets of 20 (2 panes 5×2).

(Des Nick Shewring. Litho BDT)

2010 (19 Mar). Reef Fish. T **245** and similar horiz designs. Multicoloured. P 13½.

1064 35p. Type **245** ..... 2·00 2·25
a. Strip of 4. Nos. 1064/7 ..... 9·50 11·00
1065 40p. Grouper (*Epinephelus adscensionis*) ..... 2·00 2·25
1066 50p. Five fingers (*Abudefduf saxatilis*) ..... 2·00 2·50
1067 £1.25 Rock bullseye (*Heteropriacanthus cruentatus*) ..... 4·50 5·00
1064/7 *Set of* 4 ..... 9·50 11·00
MS1068 84×59 mm. £2 Softback soldier fish (*Myripristis jacobus*) ..... 7·50 8·00

Nos. 1064/7 were printed together, *se-tenant*, as horizontal and vertical strips of four in sheetlets of 16, and also in separate sheets of 20.

246 Guides

(Des Andrew Robinson. Litho BDT)

2010 (10 Apr). Centenary of Girl Guiding. T **246** and similar multicoloured designs. P 14.

1069 40p. Type **246** ..... 1·60 1·60
1070 50p. Guides and large fish catch ..... 1·75 1·75
1071 90p. Guide leaders and 'Celebrating 100 Years of Guiding' celebration cake ..... 3·00 3·50
1072 £1.25 Guide abseiling ..... 3·75 4·50
1069/72 *Set of* 4 ..... 9·00 10·00
MS1073 160×80 mm. £1×3 Olave, Lady Baden-Powell (Chief Guide 1918–77); Agnes Baden-Powell (founder); Lord Baden-Powell (founder of Scout Movement) (all vert) ..... 9·00 10·00

247 Supermarine Spitfire R6803, 65 Squadron

248 Juvenile Yellow Canary

(Des Robin Carter. Litho BDT)

2010 (7 May). London 2010 Festival of Stamps. 70th Anniv of the Battle of Britain. T **247** and similar horiz designs. Multicoloured. P 14.

1074 50p. Type **247** ..... 2·00 2·50
a. Sheetlet. Nos. 1074/81 ..... 14·50 18·00
1075 50p. Hawker Hurricane V7383, 615 Squadron ..... 2·00 2·50
1076 50p. Supermarine Spitfire X4036, 234 Squadron ..... 2·00 2·50
1077 50p. Hawker Hurricane R4175, 303 Squadron ..... 2·00 2·50
1078 50p. Supermarine Spitfire R6885, 41 Squadron ..... 2·00 2·50
1079 50p. Hawker Hurricane V6684, 303 Squadron ..... 2·00 2·50
1080 50p. Supermarine Spitfire K9998, 603 Squadron ..... 2·00 2·50
1081 50p. Hawker Hurricane R4118, 605 Squadron ..... 2·00 2·50
1074/81 *Set of* 8 ..... 14·50 18·00

Nos. 1074/81 were printed together, *se-tenant*, in sheetlets of eight, with Nos. 1080/1 forming a composite background design.

(Des Dag Peterson and Bee Design & Art. Litho BDT)

2010 (11 Oct). Yellow Canary (*Serinus flaviventris*). T **248** and similar vert designs. Multicoloured. P 13½.

1082 15p. Type **248** ..... 1·00 1·00
a. Strip of 4. Nos. 1082/5 ..... 6·75 6·75
1083 35p. Adult male (perched) ..... 1·50 1·50
1084 60p. Adult female ..... 2·25 2·25
1085 90p. Adult male (on ground) ..... 2·75 2·75
1082/5 *Set of* 4 ..... 6·75 6·75

Nos. 1082/5 were printed together, *se-tenant*, as horizontal and vertical strips of four stamps in sheetlets of 16, and also in separate sheets of 20.

249 Christmas Lunch

250 HMS *Erebus* and *Terror* approaching Ascension

(Des Julian Vasarhelyi. Litho BDT)

2010 (17 Nov). Christmas on Ascension Island. T **249** and similar horiz designs. Multicoloured. P 14.

1086 15p. Type **249** 60 60
1087 40p. Santa riding in decorated pick-up truck in Christmas parade ..... 1·40 1·25
1088 50p. Three children at Christingle service ..... 1·60 1·60
1089 £1.25 Children's nativity play ..... 3·75 5·00
1086/9 *Set of* 4 ..... 6·50 7·50

(Des Robin Carter. Litho BDT)

2011 (16 Feb). Parsley Fern (*Anogramma ascensionis*). T **250** and similar vert designs. Multicoloured. P 13½.

1090 15p. Type **250** 65 65
1091 25p. Parsley fern 90 90
1092 35p. Parsley fern in situ ..... 1·25 1·25
1093 40p. Parsley fern seedlings ..... 1·40 1·40
1094 £1 Parsley fern cultivation, Kew Gardens ..... 3·25 4·00
1090/4 *Set of* 5 ..... 6·75 7·25

251 Queen Elizabeth II, Westminster Abbey, 12 April 2001

(Litho BDT)

2011 (23 Mar). Queen Elizabeth II and Prince Philip 'A Lifetime of Service'. T **251** and similar diamond-shaped designs. Multicoloured. P 13½.

1095 15p. Type **251** 45 50
1096 25p. Queen Elizabeth and Prince Philip, 1953 ..... 80 90
1097 35p. Queen Elizabeth and Prince Philip, Buckingham Palace, 1999 ..... 1·10 1·25
1098 40p. Queen Elizabeth and Prince Philip, The Mall, London, 24 February 2009 ..... 1·25 1·40
1099 60p. Queen Elizabeth and Prince Philip in Balmoral Castle grounds, September 1960 ..... 1·75 2·00
1100 £1.25 Duke of Edinburgh, Westminster Abbey, 12 April 2001 ..... 3·75 4·25
1095/100 *Set of* 6 ..... 8·00 9·25
MS1101 174×163 mm. Nos. 1095/100 and three stamp-size labels ..... 9·00 10·00
MS1102 110×70 mm. £2 Queen Elizabeth II and Prince Philip, Westminster Abbey, 1977 ..... 6·00 7·00

Nos. 1095/100 were printed in separate sheetlets of eight stamps.

No. **MS**1101 forms a diamond shape but with the left, right and top corners removed.

252 Unloading Sea King Helicopter from Hold of Short Belfast Aircraft, 8 May 1982

253 Red and Yellow Peonies

(Des Robin Carter. Litho Cartor)

2011 (19 May). 70th Anniv of RAF Search and Rescue. T **252** and similar horiz designs. Multicoloured. P 13½.

1103	35p. Type **252**	1·50	1·25
1104	40p. Westland Sea King HAR3 helicopter XZ593 over Ascension Island	1·75	1·40
1105	90p. Sea King helicopter XZ593 delivering stores to HMS *Dumbarton Castle* (Castle Class patrol ship), 1982	4·00	4·25
1106	£1 Sea King helicopter XZ593 airlifting casualty from nuclear submarine HMS *Spartan*, 1982	4·50	4·75
1103/6	*Set of* 4	10·50	10·50
MS1107	64×94 mm. £2.50 Sea King helicopter XZ593	10·50	10·50

(Litho BDT)

2011 (22 June). The Peony. Sheet 105×140 mm containing T **253** and similar vert designs. Multicoloured. P 12½.

MS1108	50p.×4 Type **253**; White peony; Apricot peony; Pale yellow peony	5·25	5·75

254 Prince William and Miss Catherine Middleton at Friend's Wedding, 23 October 2010

(Des Andrew Robinson. Litho BDT)

2011 (20 July). Royal Wedding. T **254** and similar multicoloured designs. P 15×14 (**MS**1112) or 14 (others).

1109	35p. Type **254**	1·10	1·10
1110	90p. Prince William and Miss Catherine Middleton at St. James's Palace, November 2010	2·75	2·75
1111	£1.25 Duke and Duchess of Cambridge in carriage on their wedding day	3·75	3·75
1109/11	*Set of* 3	6·75	6·75
MS1112	94×64 mm. £2 Duke and Duchess of Cambridge leaving Westminster Abbey after wedding (*vert*)	5·25	5·25

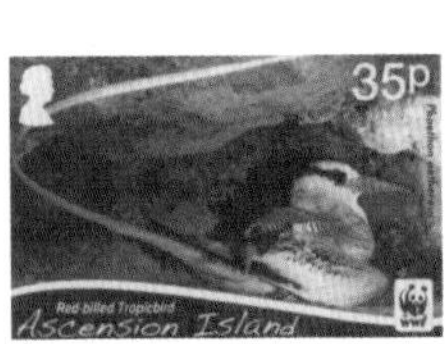

255 Red-billed Tropic Bird on Nest

256 Mother Goose

(Des Andrew Robinson. Litho BDT)

2011 (31 Aug). Endangered Species. Red-billed Tropicbird (*Phaethon aethereus*). T **255** and similar horiz designs. Multicoloured. P 14.

1113	35p. Type **255**	1·10	1·10
	a. Without white margin	1·10	1·10
	ab. Strip of 4. Nos. 1113a/16a	6·75	6·75
1114	40p. Pair in flight	1·25	1·25
	a. Without white margin	1·25	1·25
1115	50p. Adult and juvenile on nest	1·60	1·60
	a. Without white margin	1·60	1·60
1116	£1.25 Red-billed tropic bird in flight over sea	3·50	3·50
	a. Without white margin	3·50	3·50
1113/16	*Set of* 4	6·75	6·75

Nos. 1113a/16a (the stamps without white margins) were printed together, *se-tenant*, as horizontal and vertical strips of four stamps in sheetlets of 16.

Nos. 1113/16 have white margins and were printed in separate sheets of 20 (2×10).

(Des Julian Vasarhelyi. Litho BDT)

2011 (16 Nov). Christmas. Pantomimes. T **256** and similar vert designs. Multicoloured. P 14.

1117	15p. Type **256**	60	60
1118	40p. Jack and the Beanstalk	1·50	1·50
1119	50p. Aladdin	1·60	1·60
1120	£1.25 Cinderella	3·75	3·75
1117/20	*Set of* 4	6·75	6·75

257 Queen Elizabeth II, Windsor, 2011

(Litho BDT)

2012 (6 Feb). Diamond Jubilee. T **257** and similar diamond-shaped designs. Multicoloured. P 13½.

1121	15p. Type **257**	45	45
1122	25p. At reception on eve of Prince Charles' 50th birthday, Buckingham Palace, 13 November 1998	75	75
1123	35p. Attending Maundy Service, Lichfield, 1988	1·10	1·10
1124	40p. Official portrait by Peter Grugeon, Windsor Castle, October 1975	1·25	1·25
1125	60p. Formal photograph, Buckingham Palace, 1961	1·75	1·75
1126	£1.25 Wearing Coronation gown, 4 June 1953	3·75	3·75
1121/6	*Set of* 6	8·00	8·00
MS1127	174×164 mm. Nos. 1121/6 and three stamp-size labels	9·00	9·00
MS1128	111×70 mm. £2 In Westminster Abbey, 1977	6·00	6·00

Nos. 1121/6 were printed in separate sheetlets of eight stamps.

No. **MS**1127 forms a diamond-shape but with the left, right and top corners removed.

(Des Nick Shewring. Litho BDT)

2012 (15 Apr). Reef Fish (2nd series). Horiz designs as T **245**. Multicoloured. P 13½.

1129	35p. Trumpetfish (*Aulostomus strigosus*)	1·50	1·50
	a. Strip of 4. Nos. 1129/32	8·00	8·00
1130	40p. Peacock flounder (*Bothus lunatus*)	1·75	1·75
1131	90p. Queen triggerfish (*Balistes vetula*)	2·75	2·75
1132	£1 Scrawled filefish (*Aluterus scriptus*)	2·75	2·75
1129/32	*Set of* 4	8·00	8·00
MS1133	85×61 mm. £2 Yellow goatfish (*Mulloidichthys martinicus*)	6·50	6·50

Nos. 1129/32 were printed together, *se-tenant*, as horizontal and vertical strips of four in sheets of 16 stamps. They were also issued in separate sheets of 20.

258 The Departure of *Titanic*

(Des John Batchelor. Litho BDT)

2012 (1 Aug). Centenary of Sinking of the *Titanic*. T **258** and similar horiz designs. Multicoloured. P 14.

1134	20p. Type **258**	90	90
1135	45p. The Boat Deck	1·75	1·75
1136	50p. The Iceberg	1·90	1·90
1137	£1 The Sinking	3·00	3·00
1134/7	*Set of* 4	6·75	6·75
MS1138	94×64 mm. £2 Abandoning Ship	6·50	6·50

259 Sir Ernest Shackleton

260 Scrooge

(Des Andrew Robinson. Litho Cartor)

2012 (17 Sept). Shackleton-Rowett Expedition, 1921–2. T **259** and similar multicoloured designs. P 13½.

No.	Description		
1139	45p. Type **259**	1·75	1·75
	a. Horiz strip of 3. Nos. 1139/41	4·75	4·75
1140	45p. John Quiller Rowett (expedition sponsor) (18×36 *mm*)	1·75	1·75
1141	45p. Frank Wild	1·75	1·75
1142	50p. *Quest* leaving London	1·75	1·75
	a. Horiz strip of 3. Nos. 1142/4	4·75	4·75
1143	50p. *Quest* at Ascension Island (18×36 *mm*)	1·75	1·75
1144	50p. *Quest* in ice	1·75	1·75
1139/44	*Set of 6*	9·50	9·50

Nos. 1139/41 and 1142/4 were each printed together, *se-tenant*, as horizontal strips of three in sheetlets of 12 stamps.

(Des Gyula Vasarhelyi. Litho Cartor)

2012 (15 Nov). Christmas. A Christmas Carol by Charles Dickens. T **260** and similar multicoloured designs. P 13×13½ (horiz) or 13½×13 (vert).

No.	Description		
1145	25p. Type **260**	75	75
1146	40p. Ghost of Jacob Marley appearing to Scrooge	1·25	1·25
1147	50p. Scrooge carrying Tiny Tim (*vert*)	1·50	1·50
1148	£1.25 Scrooge giving Christmas turkey to Bob Cratchit (*vert*)	3·75	3·75
1145/8	*Set of 4*	6·50	6·50

261 Sooty Tern ('Wideawake Tern')

262 Fairey Swordfish

(Des Robin Carter. Litho Cartor)

2012 (5 Dec). 70th Anniv of Wideawake Airfield. Sheet 113×95 mm containing T **261** and similar horiz designs. Multicoloured. P 13.

MS1149 45p. Type **261**; 50p. Douglas DC-3 Dakota; £1 Eurofighter Typhoon; £1.45 Masked booby ... 12·00 12·00

(Des Robin Carter. Litho BDT)

2013 (15 Jan). Aircraft. T **262** and similar horiz designs. Multicoloured. P 13½.

No.	Description		
1150	15p. Type **262**	45	45
1151	20p. North American B-25 Mitchell	60	60
1152	25p. Lockheed C-130K Hercules	75	75
1153	30p. Hawker Siddeley Nimrod MR2	90	90
1154	40p. BAE Sea Harrier FRS1	1·25	1·25
1155	45p. Lockheed C-5 Galaxy	1·40	1·40
1156	50p. Douglas DC-3 Dakota	1·50	1·50
1157	65p. Avro Vulcan	1·90	1·90
1158	90p. McDonnell Douglas Phantom F-4	2·75	2·75
1159	£1 Eurofighter Typhoon	3·00	3·00
1160	£2.50 Lockheed C-121	7·00	7·00
1161	£5 Short's Belfast	10·00	10·00
1150/61	*Set of 12*	28·00	28·00

263 Queen Victoria, Soldiers and Cavalry ("Battles of Her Majestys Reign")

264 Empress Josephine of France, c. 1801 (Francis Pascal Simon Gerard)

(Litho BDT)

2013 (6 Feb). 60th Anniv of Coronation. T **263** and similar multicoloured designs. P 14 (1162/6) or 15×14 (**MS**1167).

No.	Description		
1162	45p. Type **263**	1·40	1·40
1163	50p. King Edward VII and Queen Alexandra	1·50	1·50
1164	70p. King George V and Queen Mary	2·10	2·10
1165	£1.10 King George VI, Queen Elizabeth, Princess Elizabeth and Princess Margaret	3·00	3·00
1166	£1.25 Queen Elizabeth II in Coronation Coach	3·75	3·75
1162/6	*Set of 5*	10·50	10·50

MS1167 110×70 mm. £2 Coronation photograph of Queen Elizabeth II with Orb and Sceptre (32×48 *mm*) ... 11·00 11·00

Nos. 1162/6 were printed in separate sheets of eight stamps and a central stamp-size label, all with enlarged illustrated margins.

(Des Andrew Robinson. Litho BDT)

2013 (21 May). Bicentenary of British Settlement (2015) (1st issue). The Napoleonic Years. T **264** and similar vert designs. Multicoloured. P 13½.

No.	Description		
1168	45p. Type **264**	1·75	1·75
1169	50p. Bonaparte at the Bridge of Arcole (Antoine-Jean Gros) (Italian Campaign, 1796)	1·75	1·75
1170	60p. Napolean and his General Staff (oil on panel) (Egyptian Campaign, 1798)	2·00	2·00
1171	£1.45 Napolean as First Consul (after Jean-Baptiste Isabey, 1799)	4·50	4·50
1168/71	*Set of 4*	9·00	9·00

Nos. 1168/71 were printed in separate sheetlets of eight stamps with enlarged illustrated margins.

265 Conservative Party Leader Margaret Thatcher outside her Chelsea Home, November 1976

266 Pair of Ascension Frigatebirds

(Des Andrew Robinson. Litho BDT)

2013 (14 June). Margaret Thatcher (1925–2013, Prime Minister 1979–90) Commemoration. T **265** and similar vert designs. Multicoloured. P 13½.

No.	Description		
1172	45p. Type **265**	2·00	1·75
1173	50p. Prime Minister Margaret Thatcher inspecting Sea Harrier at British Aerospace factory, Dunsfold, Surrey, 18 December 1982	2·00	1·75
1174	60p. The Residency, Ascension Island, June 1992	2·25	2·25
1175	£1.45 Baroness Thatcher, appointed Lady of the Garter, 1995	4·75	5·25
1172/5	*Set of 4*	10·00	10·00

(Des Bee Design. Litho Cartor)

2013 (16 Aug). Ascension Frigatebird (*Fregata aquila*). T **266** and similar horiz designs. Multicoloured. P 13×13½.

No.	Description		
1176	20p. Type **266**	1·25	1·25
1177	45p. Male Frigatebird on egg and hatching egg	1·75	1·75
1178	50p. Chick	1·75	1·75
1179	60p. Female Frigatebird and chick	1·90	1·90
1180	£1.10 Juvenile Frigatebird	3·25	3·25
1181	£1.45 Male Frigatebird in flight	4·50	4·50
1176/81	*Set of 6*	13·00	13·00

267 Fire Worm (*Hermodice carunculata*)

268 Catholic Grotto of Our Lady

(Des Bee Design. Litho Cartor)

2013 (29 Aug). Shallow Marine Surveys Group. T **267** and similar multicoloured designs. P 13½×13 (**MS**1186) or 13×13½ (others).

1182 45p. Type **267** ..... 1·75 1·75
a. Without white frame ..... 1·75 1·75
b. Strip of 4. Nos. 1182a/5a ..... 9·00 9·00
1183 50p. Black Bar Soldier Fish (*Myripristis jacobus*) ..... 1·75 1·75
a. Without white frame ..... 1·75 1·75
1184 60p. Endemic White Hawk Fish (*Amblycirrhitus earnshawi*) ..... 1·90 1·90
a. Without white frame ..... 1·90 1·90
1185 £1.45 Atlantic Blue Tang (*Acanthurus coeruleus*) ..... 4·50 4·50
a. Without white frame ..... 4·50 4·50
1182/5 *Set of 4* ..... 9·00 9·00
MS1186 113×74 mm. £1 Anemone (*Isarachnanthus maderensis*); Falkland Islands £1 Painted Shrimp (*Campylonotus vagans*); South Georgia & South Sandwich Islands £1 Starfish (*Henricia pagenstecheri*) (*all vert*) ..... 9·00 9·50

Nos. 1182/5 have white frames around the stamps and were printed in ordinary sheets of 20.

Nos. 1182a/5a, with no white frames and designs which extend to the perforations, were printed together, *se-tenant*, as horizontal and vertical strips of four stamps in sheetlets of 16. The miniature sheet **MS**1186 contains three stamps one each from Ascension Island, Falkland Islands and South Georgia and the South Sandwich Islands. Identical miniature sheets were issued by all three territories on the same date.

(Des Bee Design. Litho BDT)

2013 (18 Nov). Christmas. T **268** and similar multicoloured designs. P 13.

1187 45p. Type **268** ..... 1·50 1·50
a. Horiz strip of 4. Nos. 1187/90 ..... 7·00 7·00
1188 50p. Falklands memorial window showing Madonna and Child, St. Mary's Church (20×36 *mm*) ..... 1·60 1·60
1189 60p. St. Mary's Anglican Church ..... 1·75 1·75
1190 £1 Falklands memorial window showing St. Michael, St. Mary's Church (20×36 *mm*) ..... 3·00 3·00
1187/90 *Set of 4* ..... 7·00 7·00

Nos. 1187/90 were printed together, *se-tenant*, as horizontal strips of four stamps in sheets of 20 (4×5). They were also issued in separate sheets of ten stamps.

STAMP BOOKLETS

1963 (23 May). Buff cover. Stitched.

SB1 10s.6d. booklet containing 1d., 1½d., 2d., 3d., 6d. and 1s.6d. (Nos. 70/3, 75, 79), each in block of 4 ..... 70·00

1971 (15 Feb). White cover. Stitched.

SB2 44p. booklet containing ½p., 1p., 1½p., 2p., 2½p. and 3½p. (Nos. 135/40), each in block of 4 ..... 24·00
a. "5/71" imprint on back cover ..... 40·00

1981 (9 Nov)–**84**. Printed cover, 104×58 mm, showing Ascension landscape.

SB3 £1.20 booklet containing 2p., 3p., 10p. and 15p. (Nos. 283A/4A, 288A, 290A), each in block of 4 (black and pink cover stapled at left) ..... 14·00
a. Black and lemon cover stapled at right (4.84) ..... 13·00

1982 (15 June). Blue, red and brown cover, 101×60 mm, showing World War II aircraft. *A*. Cover stapled at left and inscriptions printed in brown. *B*. Cover stapled at right and inscriptions printed in blue.

SB4 60p. booklet containing 5p. and 10p. (Nos. 318/19), each in block of 4 (inscr in brown. Stapled at left) ..... 6·00
a. Inscr in blue. Stapled at right ..... 6·00

1989 (17 Nov). Blackish olive and deep brown cover, 54×41 mm, showing turtle and outline map of Ascension. Panes attached by selvedge.

SB5 £1 booklet containing pane of 6 (No. 510a) ..... 6·00
SB6 £1 booklet containing pane of 4 (No. 511a) ..... 4·50

1989 (17 Nov). As Nos. SB5/6, but with "Expo 89" logo printed on cover in black.

SB7 £1 booklet containing pane of 6 (No. 510a) ..... 8·00
SB8 £1 booklet containing pane of 4 (No. 511a) ..... 8·00

1997 (1 Sept). Cover as Nos. SB5/6. Pane attached by selvedge.

SB9 £1 booklet containing pane of 4 (No. 726a) ..... 8·50

POSTAGE DUE STAMPS

D **1** Outline Map of Ascension

(Des L. Curtis. Litho Questa)

1986 (9 June). W w **16**. P 14½×14.

D1 D **1** 1p. deep brown and cinnamon 15 30
D2 2p. deep brown and bright orange 15 30
D3 5p. deep brown and orange-vermilion 15 30
D4 7p. black and bright reddish violet 20 40
D5 10p. black and violet-blue 25 45
D6 25p. black and pale emerald ..... 65 1·10
D1/6 *Set of 6* ..... 1·40 2·50

St. Helena

CROWN COLONY

PRICES FOR STAMPS ON COVER TO 1945	
Nos. 1/5	*from* × 12
Nos. 6/30	*from* × 10
Nos. 34/45	*from* × 15
Nos. 46/52	*from* × 6
Nos. 53/67	*from* × 5
No. 71	—
Nos. 72/86	*from* × 5
Nos. 87/8	*from* × 12
Nos. 89/95	*from* × 5
No. 96	—
Nos. 97/110	*from* × 5
Nos. 111/13	—
Nos. 114/40	*from* × 4

PERKINS BACON "CANCELLED". For notes on these handstamps, showing "CANCELLED" between horizontal bars forming an oval, see Catalogue Introduction.

1

ONE PENNY (2) FOUR PENCE (3)

(Recess P.B.)

1856 (1 Jan). Wmk Large Star, W w **1**. Imperf.

1	**1**	6d. blue (H/S "CANCELLED" in oval £10000)	£500	£180

1861 (April (?). Wmk Large Star, W w **1**.

		(a) Clean-cut perf 14 to 16		
2	**1**	6d. blue	£1700	£275
		(b) Rough perf 14 to 16		
2*a*	**1**	6d. blue	£425	£130

NOTE: The issues which follow consist of 6d. stamps, T **1**, printed in various colours and (except in the case of the 6d. values) surcharged with a new value, as T **2** to **10**, *e.g.* stamps described as "1d." are, in fact, 1d. on 6d stamps, and so on.

The numbers in the Type column below refer to the *types of the lettering* of the surcharged value.

(Printed by D.L.R. from P.B. plate)

Two Types of Bar on 1d. value:
A. Bar 16–17 mm long.
B. Bar 18½–19 mm long.

1863 (July). Surch as T **2/3** with thin bar approximately the same length as the words. Wmk Crown CC. Imperf.

3	**2**	1d. lake (Type A)	£150	£250
		a. Surch double	£6500	£4250
		b. Surch omitted	£21000	
		w. Wmk inverted	£650	
4		1d. lake (Type B)	£150	£275
		a. Vert pair. Nos. 3/4	£11000	
5	**3**	4d. carmine (*bar* 15½–16½ mm)	£500	£250
		a. Surch double	£15000	£7500

ONE PENNY (**4** (A)) ONE PENNY (**4** (B)) ONE PENNY (**4** (C))

TWO PENCE (**5**) THREE PENCE (**6**) FOUR PENCE (**7**)

ONE SHILLING (**8**) FIVE SHILLINGS (**9**)

Three Types of Bar:
A. Thin bar (16½ to 17 mm) nearly the same length as the words.
B. Thick bar (14 to 14½ mm) much shorter than the words, except on the 2d. (Nos. 9, 22, 28) where it is nearly the same length.
C. Long bar (17 to 18 mm) same length as the words.

1864–80. 6d. as T **1**, without surcharge. Wmk Crown CC.

		(a) P 12½ (1864–73)		
6	**4**	1d. lake (Type A) (1864)	70·00	29·00
		a. Surch double	£12000	
7		1d. lake (Type B) (1868)	£225	60·00
		a. Surch double		
		b. Imperf	£3000	
		x. Wmk reversed	—	£160
		w. Wmk inverted	—	£225
8	**4**	1d. lake (Type C) (1871)	£140	17·00
		a. Surch in blue-black	£1000	£550
		x. Wmk reversed	£275	55·00
		y. Wmk inverted and reversed	£375	
9	**5**	2d. yellow (Type B) (1868)	£180	60·00
		a. Imperf	£10000	
		x. Wmk reversed	£475	
10		2d. yellow (Type C) (1873)	£160	45·00
		a. Surch in blue-black	£4000	£2250
		b. Surch double, one albino	£2000	
		x. Wmk reversed	£225	80·00
11	**6**	3d. deep dull purple (Type B) (1868)	£120	50·00
		a. Surch double	—	£7500
		b. Imperf	£850	
		c. Light purple	£3000	£750
		x. Wmk reversed	£275	
12		3d. deep dull purple (Type A) (1873)	£150	65·00
13	**7**	4d. carmine (Type A) (*words* 17 *mm long*) (1864)	£170	50·00
		a. Surch double	†	£6000
14		4d. carmine (Type B) (*words* 18 *mm long*) (1868)	£150	60·00
		a. Surch double	†	£6000
		b. Surch double (18+19 *mm widths*)	£26000	£12000
		c. Imperf	£12000	
		x. Wmk reversed	£325	£140
15		4d. carmine-rose (Type B) (*words* 19 *mm long*) (1868)	£325	£120
		a. Surch omitted	†	£6000
		x. Wmk reversed	—	£225
16	–	6d. dull blue (1871)	£850	£110
		a. Ultramarine (1873)	£550	85·00
		x. Wmk reversed	£1600	£250
17	**8**	1s. deep yellow-green (Type A) (1864)	£450	28·00
		a. Surch double	†	£24000
		w. Wmk inverted	—	85·00
18		1s. deep yellow-green (Type B) (1868)	£750	£130
		a. Surch double	£20000	
		b. Imperf	£18000	
		c. Surch omitted*	£20000	
19		1s. deep green (Type C) (1871)	£750	16·00
		a. Surch in blue-black		
		x. Wmk reversed	£900	75·00
20	**9**	5s. orange (Type B) (1868)	60·00	70·00
		a. Yellow	£450	£450
		w. Wmk inverted	£550	
		x. Wmk reversed	£170	£190
		(b) P 14×12½ (1876)		
21	**4**	1d. lake (Type B)	85·00	15·00
		w. Wmk inverted	£250	
22	**5**	2d. yellow (Type B)	£140	50·00
23		3d. purple (Type B)	£350	70·00
24		4d. carmine (Type B) (*words* 16½ *mm long*)	£170	60·00
		y. Wmk inverted and reversed	£170	75·00
25	–	6d. milky blue	£500	50·00
26	**8**	1s. deep green (Type C)	£900	24·00
		(c) P 14 (1880)		
27	**4**	1d. lake (Type B)	£120	20·00
		w. Wmk inverted	£400	
28	**5**	2d. yellow (Type B)	£150	35·00
29	–	6d. milky blue	£550	50·00
		x. Wmk reversed	†	£170
30	**8**	1s. yellow-green (Type B)	21·00	12·00
		y. Wmk inverted and reversed	—	£130

Two used examples of No. 15a are known, one being in the Royal Collection and the other damaged at bottom right. The price is for the latter.

*No. 18c is from a sheet of the 1s. with surcharge misplaced, the fifth row of 12 stamps being thus doubly surcharged and the tenth row without surcharge.

2½d (**10**)

11

12

1884–94. T **1** surch. Bars similar to Type B above (except 2½d., T **10**, and the 1s., in which the bar is nearly the same length as the words). The 6d. as before without surcharge. Wmk Crown CA. P 14.

34	–	½d. emerald (*words* 17 *mm*) (1884)	17·00	23·00

No.	Type	Description	Unused	Used
		a. "N" and "Y" spaced	£1100	£1200
		b. Surch double	£1300	£1400
		ba. Ditto. "N" and "Y" spaced	£11000	
		w. Wmk inverted	—	60·00
		y. Wmk inverted and reversed	—	60·00
35	–	½d. green (*words 17 mm*) (1885)	12·00	20·00
		a. "N" and "Y" spaced	£475	£700
		x. Wmk reversed	12·00	22·00
36	–	½d. green (*words 14½ mm*) (1893)	2·50	2·75
		a. "N" and "Y" spaced	£1600	
37	**4**	1d. red (1887)	4·75	3·75
		x. Wmk reversed	5·50	4·50
38		1d. pale red (1890)	7·00	3·25
		x. Wmk reversed	12·00	6·00
39	**5**	2d. yellow (1894)	3·00	8·00
40	**10**	2½d. ultramarine (1893)	3·00	5·50
		a. Surch double	£24000	
		b. Stamp doubly printed	£10000	
		w. Wmk inverted	28·00	
		x. Wmk reversed	38·00	
41	**6**	3d. deep mauve (1887)	7·50	11·00
		a. Surch double	—	£10000
42		3d. deep reddish lilac (1887)	7·50	5·00
		a. Surch double	£10000	£6000
		w. Wmk reversed	8·50	5·00
43	**7**	4d. pale brown (*words 16½ mm*) (1890)	42·00	38·00
		by. Wmk inverted and reversed	55·00	
43*c*		4d. sepia (*words 17 mm*) (1894)	27·00	17·00
		ca. Additional thin bar in surch (R. 7/2)	£850	£850
		cx. Wmk reversed	38·00	28·00
44	–	6d. grey (1887)	38·00	5·00
		x. Wmk reversed	50·00	4·75
		y. Wmk inverted and reversed	—	£100
45	**8**	1s. yellow-green (1894)	65·00	30·00
		a. Surch double	£4750	
36/45 *Set of 8*			£130	70·00
40s/1s, 43bys, 44s Optd "SPECIMEN" *Set of 4*			£200	

Examples of the above are sometimes found showing no watermark; these are from the bottom row of the sheet, which had escaped the watermark, the paper being intended for stamps of a different size to Type **1**.

Some are found without bar and others with bar at top of stamp, due to careless overprinting.

Nos. 34a and 35a occur on R. 18/12 and show a minimum space between the letters of 0.8 mm. Normal examples are spaced 0.5 mm, but some stamps show intermediate measurements due to loose type. On No. 34ba only one impression of the surcharge shows "N" and "Y" spaced. On the reset surcharge, No. 36, a similar variety occurs on R. 5/9.

Of the 2½d. with double surcharge only six copies exist, and of the 2½d. doubly printed, one row of 12 stamps existed on one sheet only.

CANCELLATIONS. Nos. 40/5 and No. 20 were sold as remainders in 1904 defaced with a violet diamond-shaped grill with four interior bars extending over two stamps. These cannot be considered as *used* stamps, and they are consequently not priced in the list.

This violet obliteration is easily removed and many of these remainders have been cleaned and offered as unused; some are repostmarked with a date and name in thin type rather larger than the original, a usual date being "Ap.4.01."

Die I

Die II

In Die I there are lines of shading in the middle compartment of the diadem which are absent from Die II.

(Typo D.L.R.)

1890–97. Die I for the 1½d. Die II for the other values. Wmk Crown CA. P 14.

No.	Type	Description	Unused	Used
46	**11**	½d. green (1897)	2·75	6·50
47		1d. carmine (1896)	19·00	2·00
48		1½d. red-brown and green (1890)	4·50	11·00
49		2d. orange-yellow (1896)	5·00	12·00
50		2½d. ultramarine (1896)	18·00	12·00
51		5d. mauve (1896)	11·00	30·00
52		10d. brown (1896)	25·00	65·00
46/52 *Set of 7*			75·00	£120
46s/52s Optd "SPECIMEN" *Set of 7*			£350	

The note below No. 45a *re* violet diamond-shaped grill cancellation also applies to Nos. 48/52.

1902. Wmk Crown CA. P 14.

No.	Type	Description	Unused	Used
53	**12**	½d. green (Mar)	1·50	2·75
54		1d. carmine (24 Feb)	13·00	70
53s/4s Optd "SPECIMEN" *Set of 2*			95·00	

13 Government House

14 The Wharf

(Typo D.L.R.)

1903 (May). Wmk Crown CC. P 14.

No.	Type	Description	Unused	Used
55	**13**	½d. brown and grey-green	2·00	3·25
		w. Wmk inverted	£200	£275
56	**14**	1d. black and carmine	1·50	35
		w. Wmk inverted	—	£650
57	**13**	2d. black and sage-green	9·00	1·25
58	**14**	8d. black and brown	23·00	32·00
59	**13**	1s. brown and brown-orange	26·00	40·00
60	**14**	2s. black and violet	65·00	95·00
55/60 *Set of 6*			£110	£150
55s/60s Optd "SPECIMEN" *Set of 6*			£275	

15

(Typo D.L.R.)

1908 (May)–**11**. Ordinary paper (2½d.) or chalk-surfaced paper (4d., 6d.). P 14.

No.	Type	Description	Unused	Used
		(a) Wmk Mult Crown CA		
64	**15**	2½d. blue	2·00	1·50
66		4d. black and red/*yellow*	13·00	30·00
		a. Ordinary paper (1911)	6·00	18·00
67		6d. dull and deep purple	38·00	48·00
		a. Ordinary paper (1911)	9·50	14·00
		(b) Wmk Crown CA. Chalk-surfaced paper		
70	**15**	10s. green and red/*green*	£275	£325
64/70 *Set of 4*			£275	£325
64s/70s Optd "SPECIMEN" *Set of 4*			£300	

Examples of Nos. 58/60 and 66/70 are known showing a forged St. Helena postmark dated "JY 28 1".

1911. Wmk Mult Crown CA. P 14. Prepared for use but not issued.

No.	Type	Description	Unused	Used
71s	**14**	1d. red (optd "SPECIMEN")	£400	

This stamp was printed in error, as a result of a misunderstanding between the Postmaster and De La Rue. The supply was sent to St. Helena, but withdrawn and destroyed. Specimen examples were sent to UPU member countries.

16

17

(Typo D.L.R.)

1912–16. Wmk Mult Crown CA. P 14.

No.	Type	Description	Unused	Used
72	**16**	½d. black and green	2·25	10·00
73	**17**	1d. black and carmine-red	4·75	1·75
		a. Black and scarlet (1916)	10·00	20·00
74		1½d. black and dull orange (1913)	3·50	9·00
75	**16**	2d. black and greyish slate	5·50	1·75
76	**17**	2½d. black and bright blue	3·50	7·00
77	**16**	3d. black and purple/*yellow* (1913)	3·50	5·00
78	**17**	8d. black and dull purple	8·00	55·00
79	**16**	1s. black/*green*	9·00	35·00
80	**17**	2s. black and blue/*blue*	50·00	95·00
81		3s. black and violet (1913)	75·00	£160
72/81 *Set of 10*			£150	£350
72s/81s Optd "SPECIMEN" *Set of 10*			£375	

No. 73*a* is on thicker paper than 73.

18

19

Split "A" (R. 8/3 of left pane)

(Typo D.L.R.)

1912. Chalk-surfaced paper. Wmk Mult Crown CA. P 14.

No.	Type	Description	Unused	Used
83	**18**	4d. black and red/*yellow*	15·00	25·00
84		6d. dull and deep purple	4·00	5·00
83s/4s Optd "SPECIMEN" *Set of 2*			£130	

1913. Wmk Mult Crown CA. P 14.

No.	Type	Description	Unused	Used
85	**19**	4d. black and red/*yellow*	8·00	2·75
		a. Split "A"	£400	£300
86		6d. dull and deep purple	14·00	28·00
		a. Split "A"	£650	£950
85s/6s Optd "SPECIMEN" *Set of 2*			£130	

WAR TAX

ONE PENNY
(**20**)

WAR TAX

(**21**)

1916 (Sept). As No. 73*a*, on thin paper, surch with T **20**.

No.	Type	Description	Unused	Used
87	**17**	1d.+1d. black and scarlet	3·50	3·25
		a. Surch double	†	£18000
		s. Optd "SPECIMEN"	65·00	

1919. No. 73 on thicker paper, surch with T **21**.

No.	Type	Description	Unused	Used
88	**17**	1d.+1d. black and carmine-red (*shades*)	2·00	4·50
		s. Optd "SPECIMEN"	65·00	

1922 (Jan). Printed in one colour. Wmk Mult Script CA. P 14.

No.	Type	Description	Unused	Used
89	**17**	1d. green	2·75	50·00
		w. Wmk inverted	£550	
		y. Wmk inverted and reversed	£325	
90		1½d. rose-scarlet	11·00	45·00
91	**16**	3d. bright blue	25·00	90·00
		y. Wmk inverted and reversed	£325	£650
89/91 *Set of 3*			35·00	£170
89s/91s Optd "SPECIMEN" *Set of 3*			£180	

22 Badge of St. Helena

PLATE FLAWS ON THE 1922–37 ISSUE. Many constant plate varieties exist on both the vignette and duty plates of this issue. The three major varieties are illustrated and listed below.

a. Broken mainmast. Occurs on R. 2/1 of all sheets from the second printing onwards. It does not appear on Nos. 93/6 and 111/13 as these stamps only exist from the initial printing invoiced in May 1922.

1936 and subsequent printings show additional minor varieties to the vignette of this stamp; a dent in the lower left frame and breaks in the bottom frame.

b. Torn flag. Occurs on R. 4/6 of all sheets from printings up to and including that invoiced in December 1922. The flaw was retouched for the printing invoiced in December 1926 and so does not occur on Nos. 97*g*, 99*e*, 103/*d*, 107/10 and 111*d*.

c. Cleft rock. Occurs on R. 5/1 of all sheets from the second printing onwards. It does not appear on Nos. 93/6 and 111/13 as these stamps only exist from the initial printing invoiced in May 1922.

Damaged value tablet (R. 1/4 of first printing and part of second (1932) printing)

(Des T. Bruce. Typo D.L.R.)

1922 (June)–**37**. P 14

(a) Wmk Mult Crown CA. Chalk-surfaced paper

No.	Type	Description	Unused	Used
92	**22**	4d. grey and black/*yellow* (2.23)	14·00	6·00
		a. Broken mainmast	£275	£300
		b. Torn flag	£275	£300
		c. Cleft rock	£250	£275
93		1s.6d. grey and green/*blue-green*	22·00	70·00
		b. Torn flag	£550	£1100
94		2s.6d. grey and red/*yellow*	25·00	75·00
		b. Torn flag	£650	£1200
95		5s. grey and green/*yellow*	50·00	£120
		b. Torn flag	£950	£1500
96		£1 grey and purple/*red*	£450	£650
		b. Torn flag	£3750	
92/6 *Set of 5*			£500	£850
92s/6s Optd "SPECIMEN" *Set of 5*			£650	

The paper of No. 93 is bluish on the surface with a full green back.

(b) Wmk Mult Script CA. Ordinary paper (1s.6d., 2s.6d., 5s.) or chalk-surfaced paper (others)

No.	Type	Description	Unused	Used
97	**22**	½d. grey and black (2.23)	4·25	4·00
		a. Broken mainmast	85·00	£120
		b. Torn flag	£275	£325
		c. Cleft rock	75·00	£120
		d. "A" of "CA" missing from wmk	†	£1500
		e. Damaged value tablet	£250	
		fw. Wmk inverted	£500	£550
		g. Grey-black and black (6.36)	12·00	4·00
		ga. Broken mainmast	£250	£200
		gc. Cleft rock	£250	£190
98		1d. grey and green	3·50	1·60
		a. Broken mainmast	85·00	95·00
		b. Torn flag	£250	£300
		c. Cleft rock	75·00	95·00
99		1½d. rose-red (*shades*) (2.23)	2·75	13·00
		a. Broken mainmast	£100	£200
		b. Torn flag	£100	£200

	c. Cleft rock	90·00	£200
	dw. Wmk inverted	£1300	
	dx. Wmk reversed	£1600	£1500
	e. Deep carmine-red (1937)	85·00	85·00
	ea. Broken mainmast	£1300	£1200
	ec. Cleft rock	£1300	£1200
100	2d. grey and slate (2.23)	3·75	2·00
	a. Broken mainmast	£140	£170
	b. Torn flag	£325	£375
	c. Cleft rock	£130	£170
101	3d. bright blue (2.23)	2·00	4·00
	a. Broken mainmast	£130	£200
	b. Torn flag	£130	£200
	c. Cleft rock	£110	£190
	x. Wmk reversed	£700	
103	5d. green and deep carmine/*green* (1927)	4·50	5·50
	a. Broken mainmast	£250	£325
	c. Cleft rock	£250	£325
	d. Green and carmine-red/green (1936)	7·00	5·50
	da. Broken mainmast	£325	£350
	dc. Cleft rock	£300	£350
104	6d. grey and bright purple	5·00	8·00
	a. Broken mainmast	£275	£425
	b. Torn flag	£275	£425
	c. Cleft rock	£250	£400
105	8d. grey and bright violet (2.23)	4·00	8·00
	a. Broken mainmast	£200	£375
	b. Torn flag	£200	£375
	c. Cleft rock	£180	£375
	w. Wmk inverted	†	£1800
106	1s. grey and brown	6·50	9·00
	a. Broken mainmast	£375	£475
	b. Torn flag	£475	£600
	c. Cleft rock	£350	£450
107	1s.6d. grey and green/*green* (1927)	15·00	60·00
	a. Broken mainmast	£425	£850
	c. Cleft rock	£425	£850
108	2s. purple and blue/*blue* (1927)	21·00	55·00
	a. Broken mainmast	£425	£800
	c. Cleft rock	£425	
109	2s.6d. grey and red/*yellow* (1927)	16·00	75·00
	a. Broken mainmast	£425	£1200
	c. Cleft rock	£400	£1200
110	5s. grey and green/*yellow* (1927)	42·00	85·00
	a. Broken mainmast	£750	£1300
	c. Cleft rock	£700	£1300
111	7s.6d. grey-brown and yellow-orange	£130	£190
	b. Torn flag	£1000	£2250
	d. Brownish grey and orange (1937)	£1000	£1700
	da. Broken mainmast	£13000	
	dc. Cleft rock	£13000	
112	10s. grey and olive-green	£170	£250
	b. Torn flag	£1700	£2750
113	15s. grey and purple/*blue*	£1000	£2750
	b. Torn flag	£6500	£11000
97/112 *Set of* 15		£375	£700
97s/113s Optd "SPECIMEN" *Set of* 16		£1600	

Examples of all values are known showing a forged St. Helena postmark dated "DE 18 27".

23 Lot and Lot's Wife

24 The "Plantation"

25 Map of St. Helena

26 Quay at Jamestown

27 James Valley

28 Jamestown

29 Munden's Promontory

30 St. Helena

31 High Knoll

32 Badge of St. Helena

(Recess B.W.)

1934 (23 April). Centenary of British Colonisation. T **23/32**. Wmk Mult Script CA. P 12.

114	**23**	½d. black and purple	1·00	80
115	**24**	1d. black and green	65	85
116	**25**	1½d. black and scarlet	2·50	3·25
117	**26**	2d. black and orange	3·75	1·25
118	**27**	3d. black and blue	1·40	4·50
119	**28**	6d. black and light blue	3·25	3·00
120	**29**	1s. black and chocolate	6·50	18·00
121	**30**	2s.6d. black and lake	50·00	60·00
122	**31**	5s. black and chocolate	£100	£100
123	**32**	10s. black and purple	£300	£350
114/23 *Set of* 10			£425	£475
114s/23s Perf "SPECIMEN" *Set of* 10			£450	

Examples of all values are known showing a forged St. Helena postmark dated "MY 12 34".

Diagonal line by turret (Plate 2A R. 10/1 and 10/2)

Dot to left of Chapel (Plate 2B R. 8/3)

Dot by flagstaff (Plate 4 R. 8/4)

Dash by turret (Plate 4 R. 3/6)

1935 (6 May). Silver Jubilee. As Nos. 31/4 of Ascension but printed by D.L.R. P 13½×14.

124	1½d. deep blue and carmine	1·00	5·50
	f. Diagonal line by turret	£100	£200
125	2d. ultramarine and grey	3·50	90
	f. Diagonal line by turret	£160	£200
	g. Dot to left of chapel	£325	
126	6d. green and indigo	9·50	3·25
	a. Frame printed double, one albino	£2750	
	f. Diagonal line by turret	£400	
	g. Dot to left of chapel	£650	
	h. Dot by flagstaff	£600	
127	1s. slate and purple	25·00	24·00
	h. Dot by flagstaff	£750	£800
	i. Dash by turret	£900	
124/7 *Set of* 4		35·00	30·00
124s/7s Perf "SPECIMEN" *Set of* 4		£180	

1937 (19 May). Coronation. As Nos. 35/7 of Ascension. P 14.

128	1d. green	40	75
129	2d. orange	55	45
130	3d. bright blue	80	50
128/30 *Set of 3*		1·60	1·50
128s/30s Perf "SPECIMEN" *Set of 3*		£130	

33 Badge of St. Helena

(Recess Waterlow)

1938 (12 May)–**44**. Wmk Mult Script CA. P 12½.

131	**33**	½d. violet	15	65
132		1d. green	10·00	2·50
132*a*		1d. yellow-orange (8.7.40)	30	30
133		1½d. scarlet	30	40
134		2d. red-orange	30	15
135		3d. ultramarine	80·00	18·00
135*a*		3d. grey (8.7.40)	30	30
135*b*		4d. ultramarine (8.7.40)	2·50	2·50
136		6d. light blue	2·00	2·75
136*a*		8d. sage-green (8.7.40)	3·75	1·00
		b. Olive-green (24.5.44)	5·50	4·00
137		1s. sepia	1·25	1·50
138		2s.6d. maroon	20·00	7·00
139		5s. chocolate	20·00	16·00
140		10s. purple	20·00	19·00
131/40 *Set of 14*			£140	60·00
131s/40s Perf "SPECIMEN" *Set of 14*			£550	

See also Nos. 149/51.

1946 (21 Oct). Victory. As Nos. 48/9 of Ascension.

141	2d. red-orange	40	50
142	4d. blue	60	30
141s/2s Perf "SPECIMEN" *Set of 2*		£140	

1948 (20 Oct). Royal Silver Wedding. As Nos. 50/1 of Ascension.

143	3d. black	30	30
144	10s. violet-blue	27·00	42·00

1949 (10 Oct). 75th Anniv of U.P.U. As Nos. 52/5 of Ascension.

145	3d. carmine	25	1·00
146	4d. deep blue	3·00	1·75
147	6d. olive	1·25	3·50
148	1s. blue-black	35	1·10
145/8 *Set of 4*		4·25	6·50

1949 (1 Nov). Wmk Mult Script CA. P 12½.

149	**33**	1d. black and green	1·50	1·50
150		1½d. black and carmine	1·50	1·50
151		2d. black and scarlet	1·50	1·50
149/51 *Set of 3*			4·00	4·00

1953 (2 June). Coronation. As No. 56 of Ascension.

152	3d. black and deep reddish violet	1·75	1·50

34 Badge of St. Helena

34a Flax plantation

35 Heart-shaped Waterfall

35a Lace-making

36 Drying flax

37 St. Helena Sand Plover

38 Flagstaff and The Barn

39 Donkeys carrying flax

40 Island map

41 The Castle

42 Cutting flax

43 Jamestown

44 Longwood House

(Recess D.L.R.)

1953 (4 Aug)–**59**. T **34/44**. Wmk Mult Script CA. P 14.

153	**34**	½d. black and bright green	30	30
154	**34a**	1d. black and deep green	15	20
155	**35**	1½d. black and reddish purple	4·75	1·50
		a. Black & deep reddish purple (14.1.59)	12·00	4·25
156	**35a**	2d. black and claret	50	30
157	**36**	2½d. black and red	40	30
158	**37**	3d. black and brown	3·25	30
159	**38**	4d. black and deep blue	40	1·00
160	**39**	6d. black and deep lilac	40	30
161	**40**	7d. black and grey-black	1·25	1·75
162	**41**	1s. black and carmine	40	70
163	**42**	2s.6d. black and violet	20·00	8·00
164	**43**	5s. black and deep brown	25·00	10·00
165	**44**	10s. black and yellow-orange	38·00	13·00
153/65 *Set of 13*			85·00	35·00

45 Stamp of 1856

46 Arms of East India Company

(Recess D.L.R.)

1956 (3 Jan). St. Helena Stamp Centenary. Wmk Mult Script CA. P 11½.

166	**45**	3d. Prussian blue and carmine	15	10
167		4d. Prussian blue and reddish brown	15	20
168		6d. Prussian blue & deep reddish purple	15	25
166/8 *Set of 3*			40	50

(Recess Waterlow)

1959 (5 May). Tercentenary of Settlement. T **46** and similar horiz designs. W w **12**. P 12½×13.

169	3d. black and scarlet	20	15
170	6d. light emerald and slate-blue	75	75
171	1s. black and orange	50	75
169/71 *Set of 3*		1·25	1·50

Designs:—6d. East Indiaman *London* off James Bay; 1s. Commemoration Stone.

ST. HELENA
Tristan Relief
9d +
(**49**)

1961 (12 Oct). Tristan Relief Fund. Nos. 46 and 49/51 of Tristan da Cunha surch as T **49** by Govt Printer, Jamestown.

172	2½c. +3d.black and brown-red	£1500	£650
173	5c. +6d.black and blue	£1800	£700
174	7½c. +9d.black and rose-carmine	£2750	£1100
175	10c. +1s.black and light brown	£2250	£1200
172/5	*Set of* 4	£7500	£3250

The above stamps were withdrawn from sale on 19 October, 434 complete sets having been sold.

50 St. Helena Butterflyfish

51 Yellow Canary

53 Queen Elizabeth II

63 Queen Elizabeth II with Prince Andrew (after Cecil Beaton)

(Des V. Whiteley. Photo Harrison)

1961 (12 Dec)–**65**. T **50/1**, **53**, **63** and similar designs. W w **12**. P 11½×12 (horiz), 12×11½ (vert) or 14½×14 (£1).

176	1d. bright blue, dull violet, yellow and carmine	40	20
	a. Chalk-surfaced paper (4.5.65)	1·75	30
177	1½d. yellow, green, black and light drab	50	20
178	2d. scarlet and grey	15	20
179	3d. light blue, black, pink and deep blue	1·00	20
	a. Chalk-surfaced paper (30.11.65)	4·50	75
180	4½d. yellow-green, green, brown and grey	60	60
181	6d. red, sepia and light yellow-olive	5·50	70
	a. Chalk-surfaced paper (30.11.65)	8·50	70
182	7d. red-brown, black and violet	35	70
183	10d. brown-purple and light blue	35	70
184	1s. greenish yellow, bluish green and brown	55	1·25
185	1s.6d. grey, black and slate-blue	11·00	4·75
186	2s.6d. red, pale yellow and turquoise (*chalk-surfaced paper*)	2·50	2·50
187	5s. yellow, brown and green	14·00	4·75
188	10s. orange-red, black and blue	13·00	10·00
189	£1 chocolate and light blue	20·00	21·00
	a. Chalk-surfaced paper (30.11.65)	55·00	48·00
176/89	*Set of* 14	60·00	42·00

Designs: *Horiz* (*as T* **50**)—2d. Brittle Starfish; 7d. Trumpetfish; 10d. Feather Starfish; 2s.6d. Orange Starfish; 10s. Deep-water Bullseye. *Vert* (*as T* **51**)—4½d. Red-wood Flower; 6d. Madagascar Red Fody; 1s. Gumwood Flower; 1s.6d. White Tern; 5s. Night-blooming Cereus.

1963 (4 June). Freedom from Hunger. As No. 84 of Ascension.

190	1s.6d. ultramarine	75	40

1963 (2 Sept). Red Cross Centenary. As Nos. 85/6 of Ascension.

191	3d. red and black	30	25
192	1s.6d. red and blue	70	1·75

FIRST LOCAL POST
4th JANUARY 1965
(**64**)

1965 (4 Jan). First Local Post. Nos. 176, 179, 181 and 185 optd with T **64**.

193	1d. bright blue, dull violet, yellow and carmine	10	25
194	3d. light blue, black, pink and deep blue	10	25
195	6d. red, sepia and light yellow-olive	40	30
196	1s.6d. grey, black and slate-blue	60	35
193/6	*Set of* 4	1·10	1·00

1965 (17 May). I.T.U. Centenary. As Nos. 87/8 of Ascension.

197	3d. blue and grey-brown	25	25
198	6d. bright purple and bluish green	35	25

1965 (15 Oct). International Co-operation. Year. As Nos. 89/90 of Ascension.

199	1d. reddish purple and turquoise-green	30	15
200	6d. deep bluish green and lavender	30	15
	w. Wmk inverted		

1966 (24 Jan). Churchill Commemoration. As Nos. 91/4 of Ascension.

201	1d. new blue	15	25
202	3d. deep green	25	25
203	6d. brown	40	30
204	1s.6d. bluish violet	45	85
201/4	*Set of* 4	1·10	1·50

1966 (1 July). World Cup Football Championship. As Nos. 95/6 of Ascension.

205	3d. violet, yellow-green, lake and yellow-brown	50	35
206	6d. chocolate, blue-green, lake and yellow-brown	75	35

1966 (20 Sept). Inauguration of W.H.O. Headquarters, Geneva. As Nos. 97/8 of Ascension.

207	3d. black, yellow-green and light blue	75	20
208	1s.6d. black, light purple and yellow-brown	2·25	1·00

1966 (1 Dec). 20th Anniversary of U.N.E.S.C.O. As Nos. 107/9 of Ascension.

209	3d. slate-violet, red, yellow and orange	75	20
210	6d. orange-yellow, violet and deep olive	1·25	60
211	1s.6d. black, bright purple and orange	2·25	2·00
209/11	*Set of* 3	3·75	2·50

65 Badge of St. Helena

66 Fire of London

(Des W. H. Brown. Photo Harrison)

1967 (5 May). New Constitution. W w **12** (sideways). P 14½×14.

212	**65**	1s. multicoloured	10	10
213		2s.6d. multicoloured	20	20
		a. Red (ribbon, etc.) omitted	£1300	

(Des M. Goaman. Recess D.L.R.)

1967 (4 Sept). 300th Anniv of Arrival of Settlers after Great Fire of London. T **66** and similar horiz designs. W w **12**. P 13.

214	1d. carmine-red and black	15	10
	a. Carmine and black	2·25	1·75
215	3d. ultramarine and black	20	10
216	6d. slate-violet and black	20	15
217	1s.6d. olive-green and black	20	20
214/17	*Set of* 4	65	50

Designs:—3d. East Indiaman *Charles*; 6d. Settlers landing at Jamestown; 1s.6d. Settlers clearing scrub.

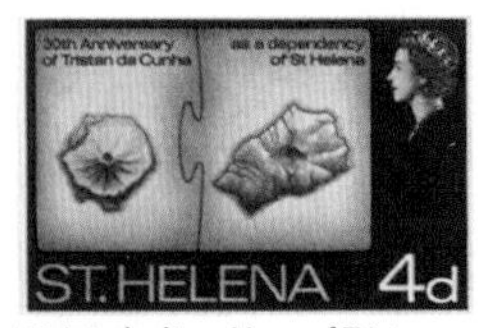

70 Interlocking Maps of Tristan and St. Helena

(Des Jennifer Toombs. Photo Harrison)

1968 (4 June). 30th Anniv of Tristan da Cunha as a Dependency of St. Helena. T **70** and similar horiz design. W w **12**. P 14×14½.

218	**70**	4d. purple and chocolate	10	10
219	–	8d. olive and brown	10	30
220	**70**	1s.9d. ultramarine and chocolate	10	40
221	–	2s.3d. greenish blue and brown	15	40
218/21		*Set of* 4	40	1·10

Design:—8d., 2s.3d. Interlocking maps of St. Helena and Tristan.

72 Queen Elizabeth and Sir Hudson Lowe

(Des M. Farrar Bell. Litho D.L.R.)

1968 (4 Sept). 150th Anniv of the Abolition of Slavery in St. Helena. T **72** and similar horiz design. Multicoloured. W w **12** (sideways). P 13×12½.

222	3d. Type **72**	10	15
223	9d. Type **72**	10	20
224	1s.6d. Queen Elizabeth and Sir George Bingham	15	30
225	2s.6d. As 1s. 6d	25	45
222/5	*Set of 4*	55	1·00

74 Blue Gum Eucalyptus and Road Construction

(Des Sylvia Goaman. Litho P.B.)

1968 (4 Nov). Horiz designs as T **74**. Multicoloured. W w **12** (sideways*). P 13½.

226	½d. Type **74**	10	10
227	1d. Cabbage-tree and electricity development	10	10
	w. Wmk Crown to right of CA	7·00	
228	1½d. St. Helena Redwood and dental unit	15	10
229	2d. Scrubweed and pest control	15	10
230	3d. Tree-fern and flats in Jamestown	30	10
231	4d. Blue gum Eucalyptus, pasture and livestock improvement	20	10
232	6d. Cabbage-tree and schools broadcasting	50	10
233	8d. St. Helena Redwood and country cottages	30	10
234	10d. Scrubweed and new school buildings	30	10
235	1s. Tree-fern and reafforestation	30	10
236	1s.6d. Blue gum Eucalyptus and heavy lift crane	70	3·00
237	2s.6d. Cabbage-tree and Lady Field Children's Home	70	3·50
238	5s. St. Helena Redwood and agricultural training	70	3·50
239	10s. Scrubweed and New General Hospital	2·00	4·50
240	£1 Tree-fern and lifeboat *John Dutton*	9·00	15·00
226/40	*Set of 15*	14·00	27·00

*The normal sideways watermark shows Crown to left of CA, *as seen from the back of the stamp.*

A distinct shade of the £1 value was issued in 1971, with the decimal currency definitives.

89 Brig *Perseverance*

93 W.O. and Drummer of the 53rd Foot, 1815

(Des J.W. Litho P.B.)

1969 (19 Apr). Mail Communications. T **89** and similar horiz designs. Multicoloured. W w **12** (sideways). P 13½.

241	4d. Type **89**	20	20
242	8d. *Phoebe* (screw steamer)	25	40
243	1s.9d. *Llandovery Castle* (liner)	25	60
244	2s.3d. *Good Hope Castle* (cargo liner)	25	75
241/4	*Set of 4*	85	1·75

No. 242 is inscribed "DANE" in error.

(Des R. North. Litho Format)

1969 (3 Sept). Military Uniforms. T **93** and similar vert designs. Multicoloured. W w **12**. P 14.

245	6d. Type **93**	15	25
	w. Wmk inverted	£160	
246	8d. Officer and Surgeon, 20th Foot, 1816	15	25
247	1s.8d. Drum Major, 66th Foot, 1816, and Royal Artillery Officer, 1820	20	45
248	2s.6d. Private, 91st Foot, and 2nd Corporal, Royal Sappers and Miners, 1832	20	55
245/8	*Set of 4*	65	1·40

97 Dickens, Mr. Pickwick and Job Trotter (*Pickwick Papers*)

(Des Jennifer Toombs. Litho P.B.)

1970 (9 June). Death Centenary of Charles Dickens. T **97** and similar horiz designs each incorporating a portrait of Dickens. Multicoloured. Chalk-surfaced paper. W w **12** (sideways*). P 13½×13.

249	4d. Type **97**	80	15
	a. Shiny unsurfaced paper	50	1·40
	b. Yellow omitted	£600	
	w. Wmk Crown to right of CA	50·00	
250	8d. Mr. Bumble and Oliver (*Oliver Twist*)	90	15
	a. Shiny unsurfaced paper	50	1·60
251	1s.6d. Sairey Gamp and Mark Tapley (*Martin Chuzzlewit*)	1·00	20
	a. Shiny unsurfaced paper	60	2·25
252	2s.6d. Jo and Mr. Turveydrop (*Bleak House*)	1·00	25
	a. Shiny unsurfaced paper	70	2·50
249/52	*Set of 4*	3·25	65
249a/52a	*Set of 4*	2·10	7·00

*The normal sideways watermark shows Crown to left of CA, *as seen from the back of the stamp.*

Supplies sent to St. Helena were on paper with a dull surface which reacts to the chalky test and with PVA gum. Crown Agents supplies were from a later printing on shiny paper which does not respond to the chalky test and with gum arabic.

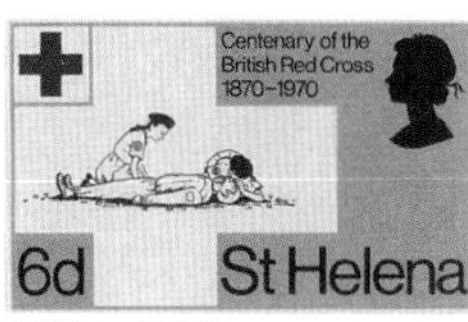

98 "Kiss of Life"

99 Officer's Shako Plate (20th Foot)

(Des Jennifer Toombs. Litho J.W.)

1970 (15 Sept). Centenary of British Red Cross. T **98** and similar horiz designs. W w **12** (sideways). P 14.

253	6d. bistre, vermilion and black	15	15
254	9d. turquoise-green, vermilion and black	15	20
255	1s.9d. pale grey, vermilion and black	20	30
256	2s.3d. pale lavender, vermilion and black	20	45
253/6	*Set of 4*	65	1·00

Designs:—9d. Nurse with girl in wheelchair; 1s.9d. Nurse bandaging child's knee; 2s.3d. Red Cross emblem.

(Des J.W. Litho Questa)

1970 (2 Nov). Military Equipment (1st issue). T **99** and similar vert designs. Multicoloured. W w **12**. P 12.

257	4d. Type **99**	20	20
258	9d. Officer's Breast-plate (66th Foot)	25	30
259	1s.3d. Officer's Full Dress Shako (91st Foot)	25	40
260	2s.11d. Ensign's Shako (53rd Foot)	40	60
257/60	*Set of 4*	1·00	1·40

100 Electricity Development

101 St. Helena holding the "True Cross"

(Litho P.B.)

1971 (15 Feb). Decimal Currency. Designs as Nos. 227/40, but with values inscr in decimal currency as in T **100**. W w **12** (sideways*). P 13½.

No.	Description		
261	½p. multicoloured	10	10
262	1p. multicoloured (as 1½d.)	10	10
	w. Wmk Crown to right of CA	50	1·25
263	1½p. multicoloured (as 2d.)	10	10
264	2p. multicoloured (as 3d.)	1·75	1·00
265	2½p. multicoloured (as 4d.)	10	10
266	3½p. multicoloured (as 6d.)	30	10
267	4½p. multicoloured (as 8d.)	10	10
268	5p. multicoloured (as 10d.)	10	10
269	7½p. multicoloured (as 1s.)	40	35
270	10p. multicoloured (as 1s. 6d.)	30	35
271	12½p. multicoloured (as 2s. 6d.)	30	50
272	25p. multicoloured (as 5s.)	60	1·25
273	50p. multicoloured (as 10s.)	1·00	2·00
274	£1 multicoloured †	20·00	15·00
261/74	*Set of* 14	22·00	18·00

*The normal sideways watermark shows Crown to left of CA, *as seen from the back of the stamp.*

†Although the design of No. 274 in no way differs from that of No. 240, it was reprinted specially for decimalisation, and differs considerably in shade from No. 240, as do others from their counterparts in the 1968 set.

The main differences in No. 274 are in the mountain which is blue rather than pinkish blue and in the sea which is light blue instead of greenish blue.

See also No. 309.

(Des R. Granger Barrett. Litho Questa)

1971 (5 Apr). Easter. W w **12**. P 14×14½.

No.	Type	Description		
275	**101**	2p. multicoloured	10	10
276		5p. multicoloured	10	15
277		7½p. multicoloured	15	20
278		12½p. multicoloured	20	25
275/8		*Set of* 4	50	60

102 Napoleon (after painting by J. L. David) and Tomb on St. Helena

(Des J.W. Litho Questa)

1971 (5 May). 150th Death Anniv of Napoleon, T **102** and similar vert design. Multicoloured. W w **12**. P 13½.

No.	Description		
279	2p. Type **102**	20	50
280	34p. "Napoleon at St. Helena" (H. Delaroche)	45	1·00

(Des J.W. Litho Questa)

1971 (10 Nov). Military Equipment (2nd issue). Multicoloured designs as T **99**. W w **12**. P 14.

No.	Description		
281	1½p. Artillery Private's hanger	20	30
282	4p. Baker rifle and socket bayonet	25	60
283	6p. Infantry Officer's sword	25	80
284	22½p. Baker rifle and sword bayonet	40	1·25
281/4	*Set of* 4	1·00	2·75

(Des and litho J.W.)

1972 (19 June). Military Equipment (3rd issue). Multicoloured designs as T **99**. W w **12**. P 14.

No.	Description		
285	2p. multicoloured	15	20
286	5p. reddish lilac, new blue and black	15	40
287	7½p. multicoloured	20	50
288	12½p. pale olive-sepia, brown and black	30	60
285/8	*Set of* 4	70	1·50

Designs:—2p. Royal Sappers and Miners breast-plate, post 1823; 5p. Infantry sergeant's spontoon *circa* 1830; 7½p. Royal Artillery officer's breast-plate, *circa* 1830; 12½p. English military pistol, *circa* 1800.

103 St. Helena Sand Plover and White Tern

(Des (from photograph by D. Groves) and photo Harrison)

1972 (20 Nov). Royal Silver Wedding. Multicoloured; background colour given. W w **12**. P 14×14½.

No.	Type	Description		
289	**103**	2p. slate-green	20	40
		w. Wmk inverted	32·00	
290		16p. lake-brown	30	85
		w. Wmk inverted	95·00	

(Des J.W. Litho Questa)

1973 (20 Sept). Military Equipment (4th issue). Multicoloured designs as T **99**. W w **12** (sideways). P 14.

No.	Description		
291	2p. Other Rank's shako, 53rd Foot, 1815	25	55
292	5p. Band and Drums sword, 1830	30	1·00
293	7½p. Royal Sappers and Miners Officer's hat, 1830	40	1·25
294	12½p. General's sword, 1831	45	1·50
291/4	*Set of* 4	1·30	4·00

1973 (14 Nov). Royal Wedding. Vert designs as T **54a**.

No.	Description		
295	2p. violet-blue	15	10
296	18p. light emerald	25	20

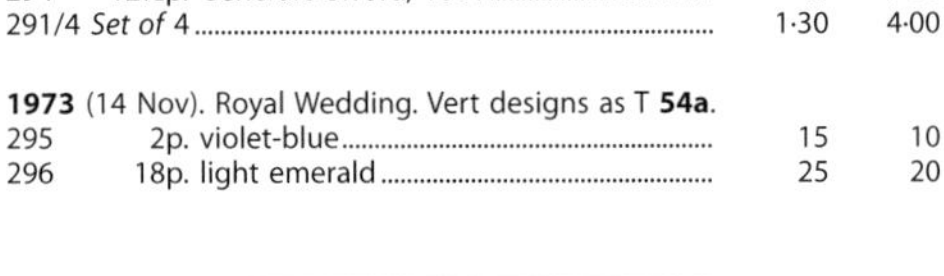

104 *Westminster* and *Claudine* beached, 1849

(Des J.W. Litho Questa)

1973 (17 Dec). Tercentenary of East India Company Charter. T **104** and similar horiz designs. Multicoloured. W w **12**. P 14.

No.	Description		
297	1½p. Type **104**	25	45
298	4p. *True Briton*, 1790	35	65
299	6p. *General Goddard* in action, 1795	35	65
300	22½p. *Kent* burning in the Bay of Biscay, 1825	70	1·75
297/300	*Set of* 4	1·50	3·25

105 U.P.U Emblem and Ships

(Des J.W. Litho Questa)

1974 (15 Oct). Centenary of Universal Postal Union. T **105** and similar horiz design. Multicoloured. W w **12** (sideways on **MS**303). P 14.

No.	Description		
301	5p. Type **105**	20	25
302	25p. U.P.U. emblem and letters	40	55
MS303	89×84 mm. Nos. 301/2	75	1·50

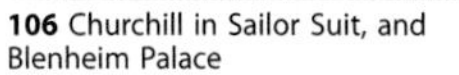

106 Churchill in Sailor Suit, and Blenheim Palace

107 Capt. Cook and H.M.S. *Resolution*

(Des Jennifer Toombs. Litho Questa)

1974 (30 Nov). Birth Centenary of Sir Winston Churchill. T **106** and similar horiz design. W w **14** (sideways). P 14.

304	5p. multicoloured	20	20
305	25p. black, flesh and reddish purple	30	60
MS306	108×93 mm. Nos. 304/5. W w **12** (sideways*)	75	2·00
	w. Wmk Crown to right of CA	£425	

Design:—25p. Churchill and River Thames.

*The normal sideways watermark shows Crown to left of CA, *as seen from the back of the stamp.*

(Des J. Cooter. Litho Questa)

1975 (14 July). Bicentenary of Capt. Cook's Return to St. Helena. T **107** and similar horiz design. Multicoloured. W w **14** (sideways on 25p.). P 13½.

307	5p. Type **107**	30	20
308	25p. Capt. Cook and Jamestown	40	40

(Litho Questa)

1975 (13 Aug). As No. 264 but whiter paper. P 14.

309	2p. multicoloured	65	5·00

108 *Mellissia begonifolia* (tree)

109 £1 Note

(Des Jennifer Toombs. Litho J.W.)

1975 (20 Oct). Centenary of Publication of "St. Helena" by J. C. Melliss. T **108** and similar multicoloured designs. W w **14** (sideways on 12 and 25p.). P 13.

310	2p. Type **108**	15	30
311	5p. *Melissius adumbratus* (beetle)	15	35
312	12p. St. Helena Sand Plover (*horiz*)	50	80
313	25p. Melliss's Scorpionfish (*horiz*)	50	1·00
310/13	*Set of* 4	1·10	2·25

(Des V. Whiteley Studio. Litho J.W.)

1976 (15 Mar). First Issue of Currency Notes. T **109** and similar horiz design. Multicoloured. W w **12** (sideways*). P 13½.

314	8p. Type **109**	30	30
	w. Wmk Crown to left of CA	85	
315	33p. £5 Note	60	80

*The normal sideways watermark shows Crown to right of CA, *as seen from the back of the stamp.*

110 1d. Stamp of 1863

(Des C. Abbott. Litho J.W.)

1976 (4 May). Festival of Stamps, London. T **110** and similar designs. W w **14** (sideways on 5 and 25p.). P 13½.

316	5p. light red-brown, black and light flesh	15	15
317	8p. black, green and pale dull green	20	30
318	25p. multicoloured	35	45
316/18	*Set of* 3	65	80

Designs: *Vert*—8p. 1d. stamp of 1922. *Horiz*—25p. Mail carrier *Good Hope Castle*.

For miniature sheet containing No. 318 see Ascension No. **MS**218.

111 "High Knoll, 1806" (Capt. Barnett)

(Des C. Abbott. Litho Questa)

1976 (14 Sept)–**82**. Aquatints and Lithographs of St. Helena. T **111** and similar horiz designs. Multicoloured. W w **14** (sideways*). P 13½ (£1, £2) or 14 (others).

A. On white paper. Without imprint date

319A	1p. Type **111**	1·50	1·50
	a. Cream paper (13.6.80)	1·50	1·75
	aw. Wmk Crown to right of CA	£130	
320A	3p. "The Friar Rock, 1815" (G. Bellasis)	1·50	1·50
	a. Cream paper (13.6.80)	1·50	1·75
321A	5p. "The Column Lot, 1815" (G. Bellasis)	30	1·25
322A	6p. "Sandy Bay Valley, 1809" (H. Salt) (23.11.76)	30	1·25
323A	8p. "Scene from Castle Terrace, 1815" (G. Bellasis)	40	1·25
324A	9p. "The Briars, 1815" (23.11.76)	40	1·25
	w. Wmk Crown to right of CA	3·75	4·75
325A	10p. "Plantation House, 1821" (J. Wathen)	50	60
326A	15p. "Longwood House, 1821" (J. Wathen) (23.11.76)	45	55
327A	18p. "St. Paul's Church" (V. Brooks)	45	1·50
328A	26p. "St. James's Valley, 1815" (Capt. Hastings)	45	1·50
329A	40p. "St. Matthew's Church, 1860" (V. Brooks)	70	1·75
330A	£1 "St. Helena, 1815" (G. Bellasis) (47×34 *mm*)	1·50	3·75
	a. Gold omitted	£1800	
331A	£2 "Sugar Loaf Hill, 1821" (J. Wathen) (47×34 *mm*) (23.11.76)	2·00	6·00
319A/31A	*Set of* 13	7·25	20·00

B. On cream paper with imprint date ("1982") (10.5.82)

319B	1p. Type **111**	30	75
325B	10p. "Plantation House, 1821" (J. Wathen)	50	1·50
331B	£2 "Sugar Loaf Hill, 1821" (J. Wathen) (47×34 *mm*)	2·00	5·00
319B/31B	*Set of* 3	2·50	6·50

*The normal sideways watermark shows Crown to left of CA, *as seen from the back of the stamp.* No. 319Aaw occurs in stamp booklets.

112 Duke of Edinburgh paying Homage

(Des M. Shamir. Litho J.W.)

1977 (7 Feb). Silver Jubilee. T **112** and similar horiz designs. Multicoloured. W w **14** (sideways). P 13.

332	8p. Royal visit, 1947	10	20
333	15p. Queen's sceptre with dove	20	25
334	26p. Type **112**	30	35
332/4	*Set of* 3	55	70

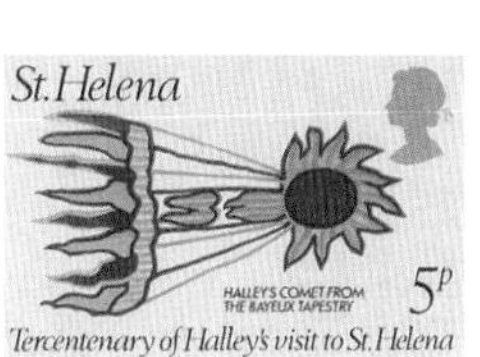

113 Halley's Comet (from Bayeux Tapestry)

114 Sea Lion

(Des C. Abbott. Litho Questa)

1977 (23 Aug). Tercentenary of Halley's Visit. T **113** and similar horiz designs. Multicoloured. W w **14** (sideways). P 14.

335	5p. Type **113**	35	30
336	8p. Late 17th-century sextant	50	30
337	27p. Halley and Halley's Mount, St. Helena	1·00	75
335/7	*Set of* 3	1·75	1·25

(Des Jennifer Toombs. Litho Questa)

1978 (2 June). 25th Anniv of Coronation. T **114** and similar vert designs. P 15.

338	25p. agate, cerise and silver	30	50
	a. Sheetlet. Nos. 338/40×2	1·50	
339	25p. multicoloured	30	50
340	25p. agate, cerise and silver	30	50
338/40	*Set of* 3	80	1·40

Designs:—No. 338, Black Dragon of Ulster; No. 339, Queen Elizabeth II; No. 340, Type **114**.

Nos. 338/40 were printed together in small sheets of 6, containing two *se-tenant* strips of 3, with horizontal gutter margin between.

115 Period Engraving of St. Helena

116 H.M.S. *Discovery*

(Des J.W. Litho Questa)

1978 (14 Aug). Wreck of the Witte Leeuw. T **115** and similar horiz designs. Multicoloured. W w **14** (sideways). P 14½.

341	3p. Type **115**	15	15
342	5p. Chinese porcelain	15	20
343	8p. Bronze cannon	15	30
344	9p. Chinese porcelain (*different*)	15	35
345	15p. Pewter mug and ceramic flasks	20	55
346	20p. Dutch East Indiaman	30	70
341/6	*Set of* 6	1·00	2·00

(Des and litho (25p. also embossed) Walsall)

1979 (19 Feb). Bicentenary of Captain Cook's Voyages, 1768–79. T **116** and similar vert designs. Multicoloured. P 11.

347	3p. Type **116**	15	15
348	8p. Cook's portable observatory	15	25
349	12p. *Pharnaceum acidum* (based on sketch by Joseph Banks)	20	35
350	25p. Flaxman/Wedgwood medallion of Captain Cook	30	90
347/50	*Set of* 4	70	1·50

117 Sir Rowland Hill

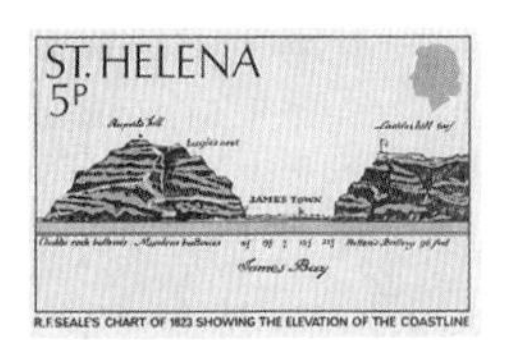

118 R. F. Seal's Chart of 1823 showing the Elevation of the Coastline

(Des J.W. Litho Questa)

1979 (10 Dec). Death Centenary of Sir Rowland Hill. T **117** and similar designs. W w **14** (sideways* on 8 to 32p). P 14.

351	5p. multicoloured	10	15
	w. Wmk inverted	£160	
352	8p. multicoloured	15	20
353	20p. multicoloured	30	40
	w. Wmk Crown to right of CA	16·00	
354	32p. black, magenta and deep mauve	40	55
	w. Wmk Crown to right of CA	19·00	
351/4	*Set of* 4	80	1·10

Designs: *Horiz*—8p, 1965 1d. 1st Local Post stamp; 20p. 1863 1d. on 6d. stamps; 32p. 1902 1d. stamp.

*The normal sideways watermark shows Crown to left of CA, *as seen from the back of the stamp.*

(Des G. Vasarhelyi. Litho Questa)

1979 (10 Dec). 150th Anniv of the Inclined Plane. T **118** and similar designs. W w **14** (sideways on 5 and 8p.). P 14.

355	5p. black, brownish grey and stone	15	15
356	8p. black, brownish grey and stone	15	20
357	50p. multicoloured	60	75
355/7	*Set of* 3	80	1·00

Designs: *Horiz*—8p. The Inclined Plane in 1829. *Vert*—50p. The Inclined Plane in 1979.

119 Napoleon's Tomb, 1848

120 East Indiaman

(Des J.W. Litho Questa)

1980 (23 Feb). Centenary of Empress Eugenie's Visit. T **119** and similar horiz designs. W w **14** (sideways). P 14.

358	5p. gold, reddish brown and pale red-brown	10	20
359	8p. gold, reddish brown and pale bistre	15	25
360	62p. gold, reddish brown & pale orange-brn	65	80
358/60	*Set of* 3	80	1·10
MS361	180×110 mm. Nos. 358/60	80	1·10

Designs:—8p. Landing at St. Helena; 62p. At the tomb of Napoleon.

(Des C. Abbott. Litho Format)

1980 (6 May). "London 1980" International Stamp Exhibition. T **120** and similar vert designs. Multicoloured. W w **14**. P 14½.

362	5p. Type **120**	10	15
363	8p. *Dolphin* postal stone	10	15
364	47p. Postal stone outside Castle entrance, Jamestown	50	60
362/4	*Set of* 3	60	80
MS365	111×120 mm. Nos. 362/4	75	80

121 Queen Elizabeth the Queen Mother in 1974

(Des and litho Harrison)

1980 (18 Aug*). 80th Birthday of Queen Elizabeth the Queen Mother. W w **14** (sideways). P 14.

366	**121** 24p. multicoloured	35	50

*This is the local date of issue; the Crown Agents released the stamp on 4 August.

122 The Briars, 1815

(Des C. Abbott. Litho Questa)

1980 (17 Nov). 175th Anniv of Wellington's Visit. T **122** and similar multicoloured design. W w **14** (sideways* on 9p). P 14.

367	9p. Type **122**	15	15
	w. Wmk Crown to right of CA	9·00	
368	30p. "Wellington" (Goya) (*vert*)	45	45

*The normal sideways watermark shows Crown to left of CA, *as seen from the back of the stamp.*

Nos. 367/8 were each printed in small sheets of 10 stamps.

123 Redwood

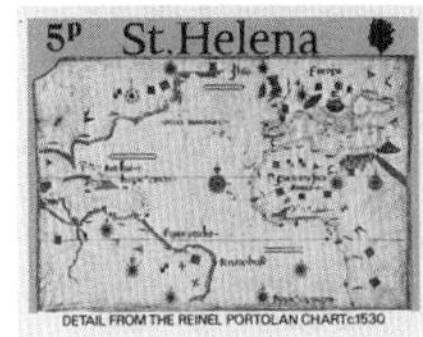

124 Detail from Reinel Portolan Chart, *circa* 1530

(Des Daphne Padden. Litho Enschedé)

1981 (5 Jan). Endemic Plants. T **123** and similar horiz designs. Multicoloured. W w **14** (sideways*). P 13½.

369	5p. Type **123**	15	20
	w. Wmk Crown to left of CA	6·00	
370	8p. Old Father Live Forever	15	20
371	15p. Gumwood	20	25
372	27p. Black Cabbage	35	45
369/72	*Set of 4*	75	1·00

*The normal sideways watermark shows Crown to right of CA on the 5p. and 8p., but Crown to left of CA on the 15p. and 27p, *all as seen from the back of the stamp.*

(Des Harrison. Litho Walsall)

1981 (22 May). Early Maps. T **124** and similar horiz designs. W w **14** (sideways). P 14×14½.

373	5p. multicoloured	15	15
374	8p. black, brown-lake and grey	15	20
375	20p. multicoloured	30	35
376	30p. multicoloured	35	50
373/6	*Set of 4*	85	1·10
MS377	114×83 mm. 24p. black and grey	40	65

Designs:—8p. John Thornton's Map of St. Helena, *circa* 1700; 20p. Map of St. Helena, 1815; 30p. Map of St. Helena, 1817; miniature sheet, Part of Gastaldi's map of Africa, 16th-century.

125 Prince Charles as Royal Navy Commander

126 Atlantic Trumpet Triton (*Charonia variegata*)

(Des J.W. Litho Questa)

1981 (22 July). Royal Wedding. T **125** and similar vert designs. Multicoloured. W w **14**. P 14.

378	14p. Wedding bouquet from St. Helena	15	20
379	29p. Type **125**	25	30
	w. Wmk inverted	1·25	
380	32p. Prince Charles and Lady Diana Spencer	30	35
378/80	*Set of 3*	60	75

(Des J.W. Litho Walsall)

1981 (10 Sept). Sea Shells. T **126** and similar vert designs. Multicoloured. W w **14**. P 14.

381	7p. Type **126**	15	20
382	10p. St. Helena Cowrie (*Cypraea spurca sanctaehelenae*)	15	20
383	25p. Common Purple Janthina (*Janthina janthina*)	30	40
384	53p. Rude Pen Shell (*Pinna rudis*)	50	1·00
381/4	*Set of 4*	1·00	1·60

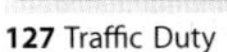

127 Traffic Duty

128 *Sympetrum dilatatum* (dragonfly)

(Des BG Studio. Litho Questa)

1981 (5 Nov). 25th Anniv of Duke of Edinburgh Award Scheme. T **127** and similar vert designs. Multicoloured. W w **14**. P 14.

385	7p. Type **127**	15	10
386	11p. Signposting	15	15
387	25p. Animal care	30	30
388	50p. Duke of Edinburgh, in Guards' uniform, on horse back	50	60
385/8	*Set of 4*	1·00	1·00

(Des C. Abbott. Litho Questa)

1981 (4 Jan). Insects (1st series). T **128** and similar horiz designs. Multicoloured. W w **14** (sideways on 7, 10 and 25p., inverted on 32p.). P 14½.

389	7p. Type **128**	20	20
390	10p. *Aplothorax burchelli* (beetle)	20	20
391	25p. *Ampulex compressa* (wasp)	35	35
392	32p. *Labidura herculeana* (earwig)	35	35
389/92	*Set of 4*	1·00	1·00

The 32p. is larger, 45×27 mm.

See also Nos. 411/14.

129 Charles Darwin

130 Prince and Princess of Wales at Balmoral, Autumn 1981

(Des L. Curtis. Litho Questa)

1982 (19 Apr). 150th Anniv of Charles Darwin's Voyage. T **129** and similar horiz designs. Multicoloured. W w **14** (sideways). P 14.

393	7p. Type **129**	20	20
394	14p. Flagstaff Hill and Darwin's hammer	25	35
395	25p. Ring-necked Pheasant and Chukar Partridge	50	70
396	29p. H.M.S. *Beagle* off St. Helena	60	80
393/6	*Set of 4*	1·40	1·90

(Des C. Abbott. Litho Format)

1982 (1 July). 21st Birthday of Princess of Wales. T **130** and similar vert designs. Multicoloured. W w **14**. P 13½×14 (7, 55p.) or 13½ (others).

397	7p. St. Helena coat of arms	10	15
398	11p. Type **130**	25	15
399	29p. Bride on Palace Balcony	30	35
	a. Perf 13½×14	15·00	22·00
	b. Imperf (pair)	£550	
400	55p. Formal portrait	70	60
397/400	*Set of 4*	1·10	1·10

1st PARTICIPATION
COMMONWEALTH GAMES 1982
(**131**)

132 Lord Baden-Powell

1982 (25 Oct). Commonwealth Games, Brisbane. Nos. 326A and 328A optd with T **131**.

401	15p. "Longwood House, 1821" (J. Wathen)	25	25
402	26p. "St. James's Valley, 1815" (Capt. Hastings)	45	45

(Des L. McCombie. Litho Walsall)

1982 (29 Nov). 75th Anniv of Boy Scout Movement. T **132** and similar designs. W w **14** (inverted on 3p., 29p.; sideways on 11p., 59p.). P 14.

403	3p. lake-brown, grey and orange-yellow	15	15
404	11p. lake-brown, grey & bright yellow-green	20	25
405	29p. lake-brown, grey and reddish orange	30	60

406	59p. lake-brown, grey & bright yellow-green	60	1·25
403/6	*Set of 4*	1·10	2·00

Designs: *Horiz*—11p. Boy Scout (drawing by Lord Baden Powell); 59p. Camping at Thompsons Wood. *Vert*—29p. Canon Walcott.

133 King and Queen Rocks

134 *Trametes versicolor* ("*Coriolus versicolor*")

(Des C. Abbott. Litho B.D.T.)

1983 (14 Jan). Views of St. Helena by Roland Svensson. T **133** and similar multicoloured designs. W w **14** (sideways on 29p., 59p.). P 14.

407	7p. Type **133**	15	20
408	11p. Turk's Cap	15	25
409	29p. Coastline from Jamestown (*horiz*)	35	65
410	59p. Mundens Point (*horiz*)	60	1·40
407/10	*Set of 4*	1·10	2·25

(Des C. Abbott. Litho Questa)

1983 (22 Apr). Insects (2nd series). Horiz designs as T **128**. Multicoloured. W w **14** (sideways). P 14½.

411	11p. *Acherontia atropos* (hawk moth)	15	30
412	15p. *Helenasaldula aberrans* (shore-bug)	15	35
413	29p. *Anchastus compositarum* (click beetle)	25	55
414	59p. *Lamprochrus cossonoides* (weevil)	55	1·25
411/14	*Set of 4*	1·00	2·25

(Des Garden Studio. Litho Format)

1983 (16 June). Fungi. T **134** and similar multicoloured designs. W w **14** (sideways on 29p.). P 14.

415	11p. Type **134**	20	25
416	15p. *Pluteus brunneisucus*	20	40
417	29p. *Polyporus induratus* (*horiz*)	30	60
418	59p. *Coprinus angulatus*	55	1·25
415/18	*Set of 4*	1·10	2·25

135 Java Sparrow

136 Birth of St. Helena

(Des J.W. Litho Questa)

1983 (12 Sept). Birds. T **135** and similar vert designs. Multicoloured. W w **14**. P 14.

419	7p. Type **135**	30	20
420	15p. Madagascar Red Fody	45	35
421	33p. Common Waxbill	80	70
422	59p. Yellow Canary	1·50	1·40
419/22	*Set of 4*	2·75	2·50

(Des Jennifer Toombs. Litho Questa)

1983 (17 Oct). Christmas. Life of St. Helena (1st series). T **136** and similar vert design. Multicoloured. W w **14**. P 14×13½.

423	10p. Type **136**	20	55
	a. Sheetlet. Nos. 423/4, each×5	2·00	
424	15p. St. Helena being taken to convent	20	55

Nos. 423/4 were printed together in small sheets of 10, containing horizontal strips of 5 for each value separated by a horizontal gutter margin.

See also Nos. 450/3 and 468/71.

137 1934 ½d. Stamp

138 Prince Andrew and H.M.S. *Invincible* (aircraft carrier)

(Des C. Abbott. Litho Questa)

1984 (3 Jan). 150th Anniv of St. Helena as a British Colony. T **137** and similar square designs showing values of the 1934 Centenary of British Colonisation issue or Colony Arms. Multicoloured. W w **14** (sideways). P 13½.

425	1p. Type **137**	10	20
426	3p. 1934 1d. stamp	10	20
427	6p. 1934 1½d. stamp	10	30
428	7p. 1934 2d. stamp	15	30
429	11p. 1934 3d. stamp	20	40
430	15p. 1934 6d. stamp	25	45
431	29p. 1934 1s. stamp	40	95
432	33p. 1934 5s. stamp	45	1·25
433	59p. 1934 10s. stamp	65	2·00
434	£1 1934 2s. 6d. stamp	1·00	3·25
435	£2 St. Helena Coat of Arms	1·75	5·00
425/35	*Set of 11*	4·50	13·00

(Des D. Bowen. Litho Format)

1984 (4 Apr). Visit of Prince Andrew. T **138** and similar horiz design. Multicoloured. W w **14** (sideways*). P 14.

436	11p. Type **138**	25	25
	w. Wmk Crown to right of CA	85·00	
437	60p. Prince Andrew and H.M.S. *Herald* (survey ship)	75	1·40

*The normal sideways watermark shows Crown to left of CA, *as seen from the back of the stamp.*

139 *St. Helena* (schooner)

140 Twopenny Coin and Donkey

(Des A. Theobald. Litho Questa)

1984 (14 May). 250th Anniv of "Lloyd's List" (newspaper). T **139** and similar vert designs. Multicoloured. W w **14**. P 14½×14.

438	10p. Type **139**	20	20
439	18p. Solomons Facade (local agent)	25	35
440	25p. Lloyd's Coffee House, London	30	55
441	50p. *Papanui* (freighter)	75	1·00
438/41	*Set of 4*	1·40	1·90

(Des G. Drummond. Litho Format)

1984 (23 July). New Coinage. T **140** and similar horiz designs. Multicoloured. W w **14** (sideways). P 14.

442	10p. Type **140**	20	35
443	15p. Five pence coin and St. Helena Sand Plover	20	45
444	29p. Penny coin and Yellow-finned Tuna	30	75
445	50p. Ten pence coin and Arum Lily	40	1·25
442/5	*Set of 4*	1·00	2·50

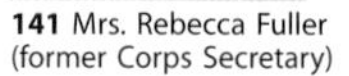

141 Mrs. Rebecca Fuller (former Corps Secretary)

142 Queen Elizabeth the Queen Mother aged Two

(Des L. Curtis. Litho Walsall)

1984 (12 Oct). Centenary of Salvation Army on St. Helena. T **141** and similar multicoloured designs. W w **14** (sideways on 11p., 25p.). P 14.

446	7p. Type **141**	15	35
447	11p. Meals-on-wheels service (*horiz*)	15	45
448	25p. Salvation Army Citadel, Jamestown (*horiz*)	25	80
449	60p. Salvation Army band at Jamestown Clock Tower	55	2·00
446/9 *Set of 4*		1·00	3·25

(Des Jennifer Toombs. Litho Questa)

1984 (9 Nov). Christmas. Life of St. Helena (2nd series). Vert designs as T **136**. Multicoloured. W w **14**. P 14.

450	6p. St. Helena visits prisoners	15	20
451	10p. Betrothal of St. Helena	20	30
452	15p. Marriage of St. Helena to Constantius	25	40
453	33p. Birth of Constantine	50	70
450/3 *Set of 4*		1·00	1·40

(Des A. Theobald (70p.), C. Abbott (others). Litho Questa)

1985 (7 June). Life and Times of Queen Elizabeth the Queen Mother. T **142** and similar vert designs. Multicoloured. W w **16**. P 14½×14.

454	11p. Type **142**	20	25
455	15p. At Ascot with the Queen	20	35
	w. Wmk inverted	60·00	
456	29p. Attending Gala Ballet at Covent Garden	40	65
457	55p. With Prince Henry at his christening	60	1·00
454/7 *Set of 4*		1·25	2·00
MS458 91×73 mm. 70p. The Queen Mother with Ford "V8 Pilot". Wmk sideways		1·75	1·60

143 Axillary Cardinalfish

144 John J. Audubon

(Des L. Curtis. Litho Walsall)

1985 (12 July). Marine Life. T **143** and similar horiz designs. Multicoloured. W w **14** (sideways*). P 13×13½.

459	7p. Type **143**	15	25
460	11p. Chub Mackerel	15	30
461	15p. Skipjack Tuna	20	40
462	33p. Yellow-finned Tuna	35	75
463	50p. Stump	50	1·25
	w. Wmk Crown to right of CA	50·00	
459/63 *Set of 5*		1·25	2·75

*The normal sideways watermark shows Crown to left of CA, *as seen from the back of the stamp.*

(Des Josephine Martin (11p.). Litho Format)

1985 (2 Sept). Birth Bicentenary of John J. Audubon (ornithologist). T **144** and similar designs. W w **14** (inverted on 11p., sideways on others). P 14.

464	11p. black and blackish brown	15	25
465	15p. multicoloured	30	35
466	25p. multicoloured	40	55
467	60p. multicoloured	65	1·40
	w. Wmk Crown to left of CA		
464/7 *Set of 4*		1·40	2·25

Designs: *Horiz* (from original Audubon paintings)—15p. Moorhen ("Common Gallinule"); 25p. White-tailed Tropic Bird; 60p. Common Noddy.

The normal sideways watermark on Nos. 465 and 467 shows Crown to the right of CA, on No. 466 it is to the left of CA, both *as seen from the back of the stamp.*

(Des Jennifer Toombs. Litho Questa)

1985 (14 Oct). Christmas. Life of St. Helena (3rd series). Vert designs as T **136**. Multicoloured. W w **14**. P 14×13½.

468	7p. St. Helena journeys to the Holy Land	20	25
469	10p. Zambres slays the bull	20	30
470	15p. The bull restored to life: conversion of St. Helena	25	40
471	60p. Resurrection of the corpse: the true Cross identified	75	1·50
468/71 *Set of 4*		1·25	2·25

145 Church Provident Society for Women Banner

146 Plaque at Site of Halley's Observatory on St. Helena

(Des A. Theobald. Litho J.W.)

1986 (7 Jan). Friendly Societies' Banners. T **145** and similar horiz designs. Multicoloured. W w **16** (sideways*). P 13×13½.

472	10p. Type **145**	15	25
473	11p. Working Men's Christian Association	15	25
474	25p. Church Benefit Society for Children	25	55
475	29p. Mechanics and Friendly Benefit Society	25	65
476	33p. Ancient Order of Foresters	30	70
	w. Wmk Crown to left of CA	10·00	
472/6 *Set of 5*		1·00	2·10

*The normal sideways watermark shows Crown to right of CA, *as seen from the back of the stamp.*

(Des A. Theobald. Litho Questa)

1986 (21 Apr). 60th Birthday of Queen Elizabeth II. Vert designs as T **110** of Ascension. Multicoloured. W w **16**. P 14½×14.

477	10p. Princess Elizabeth making 21st birthday broadcast, South Africa, 1947	15	20
478	15p. Silver Jubilee photograph, 1977	25	30
479	20p. Princess Elizabeth on board H.M.S. *Vanguard*, 1947	30	35
480	50p. In the U.S.A., 1976	45	1·00
481	65p. At Crown Agents Head Office, London, 1983	50	1·10
477/81 *Set of 5*		1·50	2·75

(Des L. Curtis. Litho Walsall)

1986 (15 May). Appearance of Halley's Comet. T **146** and similar vert designs. Multicoloured. W w **14**. P 14½×14.

482	9p. Type **146**	35	35
483	12p. Edmond Halley	35	35
484	20p. Halley's planisphere of the southern stars	65	70
485	65p. *Unity* on passage to St. Helena, 1676	2·25	3·25
482/5 *Set of 4*		3·25	4·25

(Des D. Miller. Litho Questa)

1986 (23 July). Royal Wedding. Square designs as T **112** of Ascension. Multicoloured. W w **16**. P 14.

486	10p. Prince Andrew and Miss Sarah Ferguson	20	25
	w. Wmk inverted	23·00	
487	40p. Prince Andrew with GovernorJ. Massingham on St. Helena	80	85
	w. Wmk inverted	23·00	

147 James Ross and H.M.S. *Erebus*

(Des C. Abbott. Litho Questa)

1986 (22 Sept). Explorers. T **147** and similar horiz designs. W w **16** (sideways). P 14½.

488	1p. deep brown and pink	30	1·50
489	3p. royal blue and grey-blue	30	1·50
490	5p. bronze-green and deep yellow-green	30	1·50
491	9p. purple-brown and claret	40	1·50
492	10p. deep brown and light brown	40	1·50
493	12p. myrtle-green and light green	40	1·50
494	15p. red-brown and brown-rose	50	1·50
495	20p. deep dull blue and light blue	55	1·50
496	25p. sepia and salmon-pink	55	1·50
497	40p. bottle-green and dull blue-green	60	1·75
498	60p. reddish brown and pale orange-brown	70	2·00
499	£1 deep turquoise-blue and turquoise-blue	1·00	3·00
500	£2 deep lilac and reddish lilac	1·50	5·00
488/500 *Set of 13*		7·00	23·00

Designs:—3p. Robert FitzRoy and H.M.S. *Beagle*; 5p. Adam Johann von Krusenstern and *Nadezhda*; 9p. William Bligh and H.M.S. *Resolution*; 10p. Otto von Kotzebue and *Rurik*; 12p. Philip Carteret and H.M.S. *Swallow*; 15p. Thomas Cavendish and *Desire*; 20p. Louis-Antoine de Bougainville and *La Boudeuse*; 25p. Fyedor Petrovich Litke and *Senyavin*; 40p. Louis Isidore Duperrey and *La Coquille*; 60p. John Byron and H.M.S. *Dolphin*; £1 James Cook and H.M.S. *Endeavour*; £2 Jules Dumont d'Urville and *L'Astrolabe*.

148 Prince Edward and H.M.S. *Repulse* (battle cruiser), 1925

149 St. Helena Tea Plant

(Des E. Nisbet. Litho Questa)

1987 (16 Feb). Royal Visits to St. Helena. T **148** and similar horiz designs. Multicoloured. W w **16** (sideways). P 14.

501	9p. Type **148**	1·75	1·25
502	13p. King George VI and H.M.S. *Vanguard* (battleship), 1947	2·25	1·50
503	38p. Prince Philip and Royal Yacht *Britannia*, 1957	4·00	3·50
504	45p. Prince Andrew and H.M.S. *Herald* (survey ship), 1984	4·00	3·50
501/4	*Set of 4*	11·00	8·75

(Des Annette Robinson. Litho Questa)

1987 (3 Aug). Rare Plants (1st series). T **149** and similar vert designs. Multicoloured. W w **16**. P 14½×14.

505	9p. Type **149**	65	60
506	13p. Baby's Toes	80	80
507	38p. Salad Plant	1·50	2·50
508	45p. Scrubwood	1·75	2·75
505/8	*Set of 4*	4·25	6·00

See also Nos. 531/4.

150 Lesser Rorqual

151 *Defence* and Dampier's Signature, 1691

(Des A. Riley. Litho Questa)

1987 (24 Oct). Marine Mammals. T **150** and similar horiz designs. Multicoloured. W w **16** (sideways). P 14.

509	9p. Type **150**	1·25	75
510	13p. Risso's Dolphin	1·25	1·00
511	45p. Sperm Whale	3·00	3·50
512	60p. Euphrosyne Dolphin	3·25	4·25
509/12	*Set of 4*	8·00	8·50
MS513	102×72 mm. 75p. Humpback Whale (48×31 mm). P 13½×14	6·50	7·00

1987 (9 Dec). Royal Ruby Wedding. Nos. 477/81 optd with T **119** of Ascension in silver.

514	10p. Princess Elizabeth making 21st birthday broadcast, South Africa, 1947	20	35
515	15p. Silver Jubilee photograph, 1977	20	40
	a. Opt omitted (vert pair with normal)	£140	
516	20p. Princess Elizabeth on board H.M.S. *Vanguard*, 1947	40	55
517	50p. In the U.S.A., 1976	50	1·10
518	65p. At Crown Agents Head Office, London, 1983	50	1·50
514/18	*Set of 5*	1·60	3·50

No. 515a occurred on the top row of several sheets.

(Des A. Theobald. Litho Walsall)

1988 (1 Mar). Bicentenary of Australian Settlement. T **151** and similar horiz designs showing ships and signatures. Multicoloured. W w **16** (sideways). P 14×14½.

519	9p. Type **151**	1·50	90
520	13p. H.M.S. *Resolution* (Cook), 1775	2·00	2·00
521	45p. H.M.S. *Providence* (Bligh), 1792	3·25	4·00
522	60p. H.M.S. *Beagle* (Darwin), 1836	4·25	5·50
519/22	*Set of 4*	10·00	11·00

152 "The Holy Virgin with the Child"

153 Ebony

(Des N. Harvey. Litho Questa)

1988 (11 Oct). Christmas. T **152** and similar vert designs showing religious paintings. Multicoloured. W w **14**. P 14.

523	5p. Type **152**	10	30
524	20p. "Madonna"	40	50
525	38p. "The Holy Family with St. John"	75	1·50
526	60p. "The Holy Virgin with the Child"	1·25	2·00
523/6	*Set of 4*	2·25	3·75

(Des D. Miller (8p.), E. Nisbet and D. Miller (others). Litho Questa)

1988 (1 Nov). 300th Anniv of Lloyd's of London. Designs as T **123** of Ascension. W w **16** (sideways on 20, 45p.). P 14.

527	9p. agate and brown	40	50
528	20p. multicoloured	2·00	1·00
529	45p. multicoloured	2·50	1·75
530	60p. multicoloured	2·75	2·25
527/30	*Set of 4*	7·00	5·00

Designs: *Vert*—9p. Lloyd's Underwriting Room, 1886; 60p. *Spangereid* (full-rigged ship) on fire, St. Helena, 1920. *Horiz*—20p. *Edinburgh Castle* (liner); 45p. *Bosun Bird* (freighter).

(Des L. Ninnes. Litho Questa)

1989 (6 Jan). Rare Plants (2nd series). T **153** and similar vert designs. Multicoloured. W w **16**. P 14.

531	9p. Type **153**	40	40
532	20p. St. Helena Lobelia	70	70
533	45p. Large Bellflower	1·40	2·00
534	60p. She Cabbage Tree	1·60	2·50
531/4	*Set of 4*	3·75	5·00

154 Private, 53rd Foot

PHILEXFRANCE 89

(**155**)

(Des C. Collins. Litho Format)

1989 (5 June). Military Uniforms of 1815. T **154** and similar vert designs. Multicoloured. W w **16**. P 14.

535	9p. Type **154**	65	90
	a. Horiz strip of 5. Nos. 535/9	4·75	6·50
536	13p. Officer, 53rd Foot	75	1·00
537	20p. Royal Marine	85	1·10
538	45p. Officer, 66th Foot	1·40	1·90
539	60p. Private, 66th Foot	1·60	2·25
535/9	*Set of 5*	4·75	6·50

Nos. 535/9 were printed together, *se-tenant*, in horizontal strips of five throughout the sheet.

1989 (7 July). "Philexfrance 89" International Stamp Exhibition, Paris. Nos. 535/9 optd with T **155**.

540	9p. Type **154**	80	1·10
	a. Horiz strip of 5. Nos. 540/4	5·25	7·25
541	13p. Officer, 53rd Foot	90	1·25
542	20p. Royal Marine	1·10	1·40
543	45p. Officer, 66th Foot	1·50	2·00
544	60p. Private, 66th Foot	1·60	2·25
540/4	*Set of 5*	5·25	7·25

156 Agricultural Studies

157 "The Madonna with the Pear" (Dürer)

(Des A. Edmonston. Litho Questa)

1989 (24 Aug). New Prince Andrew Central School. T **156** and similar horiz designs. Multicoloured. W w **16** (sideways). P 14×14½.

545	13p. Type **156**	85	85
546	20p. Geography lesson	1·40	1·40
547	25p. Walkway and classroom block	1·50	1·50
548	60p. Aerial view of School	3·00	5·25
545/8	*Set of* 4	6·00	8·00

(Des D. Miller. Litho Questa)

1989 (23 Oct). Christmas. Religious Paintings. T **157** and similar vert designs. Multicoloured. W w **14**. P 14.

549	10p. Type **157**	60	50
550	20p. "The Holy Family under the Appletree" (Rubens)	85	90
551	45p. "The Virgin in the Meadow" (Raphael)	2·00	2·50
552	60p. "The Holy Family with St. John" (Raphael)	2·50	3·50
549/52	*Set of* 4	5·50	6·75

158 Chevrolet "6" 30 cwt Lorry, 1930

159 Sheep

(Des E. Nesbit. Litho Questa)

1989 (1 Dec). Early Vehicles. T **158** and similar horiz designs. Multicoloured. W w **16** (sideways). P 14½.

553	9p. Type **158**	85	80
554	20p. Austin "Seven", 1929	1·50	1·50
555	45p. Morris "Cowley" 11.9h.p., 1929	2·25	2·75
556	60p. Sunbeam 25h.p., 1932	2·75	4·25
553/6	*Set of* 4	7·00	8·50
MS557	93×74 mm. £1 Ford "Model A Fordor"	8·00	9·50

(Des Doreen McGuiness. Litho Questa)

1990 (1 Feb). Farm Animals. T **159** and similar vert designs. Multicoloured. W w **16**. P 14.

558	9p. Type **159**	50	65
559	13p. Pigs	60	80
560	45p. Cow and calf	1·50	2·50
561	60p. Geese	2·00	3·50
558/61	*Set of* 4	4·25	6·75

160 1840 Twopence Blue

161 Satellite Dish

(Des D. Miller. Litho Walsall)

1990 (3 May). "Stamp World London 90" International Stamp Exhibition, London. T **160** and similar horiz designs. W w **14** (sideways). P 14.

562	13p. black and cobalt	50	50
563	20p. multicoloured	75	85
564	38p. multicoloured	1·25	2·00
565	45p. multicoloured	1·60	2·25
562/5	*Set of* 4	3·75	5·00

Designs:—20p. 1840 Penny Black and 19th-century St. Helena postmark; 38p. Delivering mail to sub-post office; 45p. Mail van and Post Office, Jamestown.

(Des N. Shewring. Litho B.D.T.)

1990 (28 July). Modern Telecommunications Links. T **161** and similar vert designs. Multicoloured. W w **14**. P 13½.

566	20p. Type **161**	75	1·10
	a. Block of 4. Nos. 566/9	2·75	4·00
567	20p. Digital telephone exchange	75	1·10
568	20p. Public card phone	75	1·10
569	20p. Facsimile machine	75	1·10
566/9	*Set of* 4	2·75	4·00

Nos. 566/9 were printed together, *se-tenant*, in blocks of 4 throughout the sheet of 16.

(Des D. Miller. Litho Questa)

1990 (4 Aug). 90th Birthday of Queen Elizabeth the Queen Mother. Vert designs as T **134** (25p.) or **135** (£1) of Ascension. W w **16**. P 14×15 (25p) or 14½ (£1).

570	25p. multicoloured	1·00	75
571	£1 black and purple-brown	2·25	3·50

Designs:—25p. Lady Elizabeth Bowes-Lyon, April 1923; £1 Queen Elizabeth visiting communal kitchen, 1940.

162 *Dane* (mail ship), 1857

163 Baptist Chapel, Sandy Bay

(Des L. Curtis. Litho Walsall)

1990 (13 Sept). Maiden Voyage of *St. Helena II*. T **162** and similar horiz designs. Multicoloured. W w **14** (sideways). P 14×14½.

572	13p. Type **162**	1·25	85
573	20p. *St. Helena I* offloading at St. Helena	1·60	1·40
574	38p. Launch of *St. Helena II*	2·25	2·75
575	45p. The Duke of York launching *St. Helena II*	2·75	3·50
572/5	*Set of* 4	7·00	7·75
MS576	100×100 mm. £1 *St. Helena II* and outline map of St. Helena	9·00	9·00

No. **MS**576 also contains two imperforate designs of similar stamps from Ascension and Tristan da Cunha without face values.

(Des G. Vasarhelyi. Litho Questa)

1990 (18 Oct). Christmas. Local Churches. T **163** and similar horiz designs. Multicoloured. W w **14** (sideways). P 14.

577	10p. Type **163**	40	40
578	13p. St. Martin in the Hills Church	50	50
579	20p. St. Helena and the Cross Church	75	75
580	38p. St. James Church	1·25	2·25
581	45p. St. Paul's Cathedral	1·50	2·25
577/81	*Set of* 5	4·00	5·50

164 "Funeral Cortege, Jamestown Wharf" (detail, V. Adam)

165 Officer, Leicestershire Regiment

(Des N. Harvey. Litho Questa)

1990 (15 Dec). 150th Anniv of Removal of Napoleon's Body. T **164** and similar horiz designs. W w **14** (sideways). P 13½×14.

582	13p. black, sepia and blue-green	1·75	1·25
583	20p. black, sepia and ultramarine	2·50	1·75
584	38p. black, sepia and deep magenta	4·00	3·75
585	45p. multicoloured	4·00	4·00
582/5	*Set of* 4	11·00	9·75

Designs:—20p. "Coffin being conveyed to the *Belle Poule*" (detail, V. Adam); 38p. "Transfer of the Coffin to the *Normandie*, Cherbourg" (detail, V. Adam); 45p. "Napoleon's Tomb, St. Helena" (T. Sutherland).

(Des C. Collins. Litho Questa)

1991 (2 May). Military Uniforms of 1897. T **165** and similar vert designs. Multicoloured. W w **14**. P 14.

586 13p. Type **165** ... 1·25 1·25
587 15p. Officer, York & Lancaster Regiment ... 1·25 1·25
588 20p. Colour-sergeant, Leicestershire Regt ... 1·50 1·50
589 38p. Bandsman, York & Lancaster Regt ... 2·50 3·00
590 45p. Lance-corporal, York & Lancaster Regt .. 3·00 3·50
586/90 *Set of 5* ... 8·50 9·50

(Des D. Miller. Litho Questa)

1991 (1 July). 65th Birthday of Queen Elizabeth II and 70th Birthday of Prince Philip. Vert designs as T **139** of Ascension. Multicoloured. W w **16** (sideways). P 14½×14.

591 25p. Queen Elizabeth II ... 1·00 1·40
a. Horiz pair. Nos. 591/2 separated by label ... 2·00 2·75
592 25p. Prince Philip in naval uniform ... 1·00 1·40

Nos. 591/2 were printed together, *se-tenant*, in sheetlets of 10 (2×5) with designs alternating and the vertical lines separated by inscribed labels.

166 "Madonna and Child" (T. Vecellio)

167 Matchless (346cc) Motorcycle, 1947

(Des G. Vasarhelyi. Litho Walsall)

1991 (2 Nov). Christmas. Religious Paintings. T **166** and similar vert designs. Multicoloured. W w **14**. P 14.

593 10p. Type **166** ... 70 55
594 13p. "The Holy Family" (A. Mengs) ... 80 65
595 20p. "Madonna and Child" (W. Dyce) ... 1·25 1·00
596 38p. "The Two Trinities" (B. Murillo) ... 2·00 2·50
597 45p. "The Virgin and Child" (G. Bellini) ... 2·25 3·00
593/7 *Set of 5* ... 6·25 7·00

(Des N. Shewring. Litho Questa)

1991 (16 Nov). "Phila Nippon '91" International Stamp Exhibition, Tokyo. Motorcycles. T **167** and similar horiz designs. W w **16** (sideways). P 14×14½.

598 13p. Type **167** ... 1·00 80
599 20p. Triumph "Tiger 100" (500cc), 1950 ... 1·50 1·10
600 38p. Honda "CD" (175cc), 1967 ... 2·25 2·75
601 45p. Yamaha "DTE 400", 1976 ... 2·50 3·00
598/601 *Set of 4* ... 6·50 7·00
MS602 72×49 mm. 65p. Suzuki "RM" (250cc), 1984 ... 7·50 9·00

168 *Eye of the Wind* (cadet brig) and Compass Rose

(Des. R. Watton. Litho Walsall)

1992 (24 Jan). 500th Anniv of Discovery of America by Columbus and Re-enactment Voyages. T **168** and similar horiz designs. Multicoloured. W w **14** (sideways). P 13½×14.

603 15p. Type **168** ... 2·00 1·25
604 25p. *Soren Larsen* (cadet brigantine) and map of Re-enactment Voyages ... 2·75 2·25
605 35p. *Santa Maria, Nina* and *Pinta* ... 3·50 3·50
606 50p. Columbus and *Santa Maria* ... 4·00 4·50
603/6 *Set of 4* ... 11·00 10·50

(Des D. Miller. Litho Questa (50p.), Walsall (others))

1992 (6 Feb). 40th Anniv of Queen Elizabeth II's Accession. Horiz designs as T **143** of Ascension. Multicoloured. W w **14** (sideways). P 14.

607 11p. Prince Andrew Central School ... 40 40
608 15p. Plantation House ... 55 55
609 25p. Jamestown ... 75 95
610 35p. Three portraits of Queen Elizabeth ... 90 1·25
611 50p. Queen Elizabeth II ... 1·10 1·90
607/11 *Set of 5* ... 3·25 4·50

169 H.M.S. *Ledbury* (minesweeper)

170 Shepherds and Angel Gabriel

(Des N. Shewring. Litho Questa)

1992 (12 June). 10th Anniv of Liberation of Falkland Islands. Ships. T **169** and similar square designs. Multicoloured. W w **14** (sideways). P 14.

612 13p. Type **169** ... 80 80
613 20p. H.M.S. *Brecon* (minesweeper) ... 1·10 1·10
614 38p. *St. Helena I* (mail ship) off South Georgia 1·75 2·25
615 45p. Launch collecting first mail drop, 1982 2·25 3·00
612/15 *Set of 4* ... 5·50 6·50
MS616 116×116 mm. 13p.+3p. Type **169**; 20p.+4p. As No. 613; 38p.+8p. As No. 614; 45p.+9p. As No. 615.. 5·50 5·50

The premiums on No. **MS**616 were for the S.S.A.F.A.

(Des G. Vasarhelyi. Litho Questa)

1992 (12 Oct). Christmas. Children's Nativity Plays. T **170** and similar horiz designs. W w **16** (sideways). P 13½×14.

617 13p. Type **170** ... 1·00 85
618 15p. Shepherds and Three Kings ... 1·10 95
619 20p. Mary and Joseph ... 1·25 1·00
620 45p. Nativity scene ... 2·50 4·00
617/20 *Set of 4* ... 5·25 6·50

171 Disc Jockey, Radio St. Helena (25th anniv)

172 Moses in the Bulrush

(Des D. Miller. Litho Questa)

1992 (4 Dec). Local Anniversaries. T **171** and similar horiz designs. Multicoloured. W w **14** (sideways). P 14×14½.

621 13p. Type **171** ... 75 75
622 20p. Scout parade (75th anniv of Scouting on St. Helena) ... 1·25 1·25
623 38p. H.M.S. *Providence* (sloop) and bread-fruit (bicent of Capt. Bligh's visit) ... 2·25 3·25
624 45p. Governor Brooke and Plantation House (bicent) ... 2·25 3·50
621/4 *Set of 4* ... 6·00 8·00

(Des M. Martineau. Litho Questa)

1993 (19 Mar). Flowers (1st series). T **172** and similar vert designs. Multicoloured. W w **16**. P 14½.

625 9p. Type **172** ... 1·00 75
626 13p. Periwinkle ... 1·25 90
627 20p. Everlasting Flower ... 1·60 1·25
628 38p. Cigar Plant ... 2·75 3·25
629 45p. *Lobelia erinus* ... 2·75 3·25
625/9 *Set of 5* ... 8·50 8·50

See also Nos. 676/80.

173 Adult St. Helena Sand Plover and Eggs

174 Yellow Canary ("Swainson's Canary")

(Des N. Arlott. Litho B.D.T.)

1993–16 Aug). Endangered Species. St. Helena Sand Plover ("Wirebird"). T **173** and similar horiz designs. Multicoloured. W w **14** (sideways). P 13½.

630	3p. Type **173**	90	90
631	5p. Male attending brooding female	90	90
632	12p. Adult with downy young	1·75	1·75
633	25p. Two birds in immature plumage	2·25	2·25
634	40p. Adult in flight	2·50	2·75
635	60p. Young bird on rocks	2·75	3·50
630/5	*Set of* 6	10·00	11·00

Nos. 634/5 are without the W.W.F. emblem.

(Des A. Robinson. Litho Questa)

1993 (26 Aug). Birds. T **174** and similar multicoloured designs. W w **14** (sideways on 25p., 35p., £1, £2). P 14½×14 (vert) or 14×14½ (horiz).

636	1p. Type **174**	50	1·25
637	3p. Rock Partridge	70	1·25
638	11p. Rock Dove	1·00	1·25
639	12p. Common Waxbill	1·00	1·00
640	15p. Common Mynah	1·10	1·00
641	18p. Java Sparrow	1·25	1·00
642	25p. Red-billed Tropic Bird (*horiz*)	1·50	1·00
643	35p. Madeiran Storm Petrel (*horiz*)	2·25	1·50
644	75p. Madagascar Red Fody	3·00	4·00
645	£1 White Tern ("Common Fairy Tern") (*horiz*)	3·25	4·00
646	£2 Giant Petrel (*horiz*)	5·50	8·50
647	£5 St. Helena Sand Plover ("Wirebird")	11·00	15·00
636/47	*Set of* 12	28·00	35·00

For miniature sheets containing the 75p or the design of the £5 reissued as a 75p. see Nos. **MS**740 and **MS**745.

175 Football and Teddy Bear

176 Arum Lily

(Des O. Ball and R. Moss. Litho Questa)

1993 (1 Oct). Christmas. Toys. T **175** and similar horiz designs. Multicoloured. W w **14** (sideways). P 14.

648	12p. Type **175**	85	85
649	15p. Yacht and doll	90	90
650	18p. Palette and rocking horse	95	95
651	25p. Model airplane and kite	1·40	1·60
652	60p. Guitar and roller skates	2·50	4·00
648/52	*Set of* 5	6·00	7·50

(Litho Questa)

1994 (6 Jan). Flowers and Children's Art. T **176** and similar vert designs. Multicoloured. W w **16**. P 14.

653	12p. Type **176**	40	65
	a. Horiz pair. Nos. 653/4	80	1·25
654	12p. "Arum Lily" (Delphia Mittens)	40	65
655	25p. Ebony	75	1·00
	a. Horiz pair. Nos. 655/6	1·50	2·00
656	25p. "Ebony" (Jason Rogers)	75	1·00
657	35p. Shell Ginger	95	1·10
	a. Horiz pair. Nos. 657/8	1·90	2·10
658	35p. "Shell Ginger" (Jeremy Moyce)	95	1·10
653/8	*Set of* 6	3·75	4·75

The two designs for each value, one showing an actual photograph (face value in yellow) and the other a child's painting (face value in black), were printed together, *se-tenant*, in horizontal pairs throughout the sheets.

177 Abyssinian Guinea Pig

178 Springer's Blenny

(Des Sharon Beeden. Litho Questa)

1994 (18 Feb). "Hong Kong '94" International Stamp Exhibition. Pets. T **177** and similar horiz designs. Multicoloured. W w **14** (sideways). P 14×14½.

659	12p. Type **177**	70	70
660	25p. Common tabby cat	1·40	1·40
661	53p. Plain white and black rabbits	2·25	3·00
662	60p. Golden Labrador	2·50	3·25
659/62	*Set of* 4	6·25	7·50

(Des R. Watton. Litho Walsall)

1994 (6 June). Fish. T **178** and similar horiz designs. Multicoloured. W w **16** (sideways). P 14×14½.

663	12p. Type **178**	75	75
664	25p. St. Helena Damselfish	1·50	1·50
665	53p. Melliss's Scorpionfish	2·25	3·25
666	60p. St. Helena Wrasse	2·75	3·50
663/6	*Set of* 4	6·50	8·00

179 *Lampides boeticus*

(Des I. Loe. Litho Walsall)

1994 (9 Aug). Butterflies. T **179** and similar horiz designs. Multicoloured. W w **14** (sideways). P 14.

667	12p. Type **179**	75	75
668	25p. *Cynthia cardui*	1·50	1·50
669	53p. *Hypolimnas bolina*	2·25	2·75
670	60p. *Danaus chrysippus*	2·75	3·25
667/70	*Set of* 4	6·50	7·50

180 "Silent Night!"

(Des Jennifer Toombs. Litho Questa)

1994 (6 Oct). Christmas. Carols. T **180** and similar horiz designs. Multicoloured. W w **16** (sideways). P 14½.

671	12p. Type **180**	55	45
672	15p. "While Shepherds watched their Flocks by Night"	60	50
673	25p. "Away in a Manger"	1·00	90
674	38p. "We Three Kings"	1·50	2·25
675	60p. "Angels from the Realms of Glory"	2·25	3·75
671/5	*Set of* 5	5·50	7·00

(Des M. Martineau, adapted D. Miller. Litho Walsall)

1994 (15 Dec). Flowers (2nd series). Vert designs as T **172**. Multicoloured. W w **16**. P 14½×14.

676	12p. Honeysuckle	35	35
677	15p. Gobblegheer	40	40
678	25p. African Lily	70	80
679	38p. Prince of Wales Feathers	1·00	1·60
680	60p. St. Johns Lily	1·75	3·25
676/80	*Set of* 5	3·75	5·75

181 Fire Engine

182 Site Clearance

(Des B. Dove. Litho Walsall)

1995 (2 Feb). Emergency Services. T **181** and similar horiz designs. Multicoloured. W w **16** (sideways). P 14.

681	12p. Type **181**	1·25	75
682	25p. Lifeboat	1·40	90
683	53p. Police car	2·75	3·00
684	60p. Ambulance	3·00	3·50
681/4	*Set of* 4	7·75	7·25

(Des N. Shewring. Litho Walsall)

1995 (6 Apr). Construction of Harpers Valley Earth Dam. T **182** and similar horiz designs. Multicoloured. W w **16** (sideways). P 14×14½.

685	25p. Type **182**	80	1·10
	a. Horiz strip of 5. Nos. 685/9	3·50	5·00
686	25p. Earthworks in progress	80	1·10
687	25p. Laying outlet pipes	80	1·10
688	25p. Revetment block protection	80	1·10
689	25p. Completed dam	80	1·10
685/9 *Set of 5*		3·50	5·00

Nos. 685/9 were printed together, *se-tenant*, in horizontal strips of 5 throughout the sheet, forming a composite design.

(Des R. Watton. Litho Questa)

1995 (8 May). 50th Anniv of End of Second World War. Multicoloured designs as T **161** of Ascension. W w **14**. P 14.

690	5p. *Lady Denison Pender* (cable ship)	1·00	1·40
	a. Horiz pair. Nos. 690/1	2·00	2·75
691	5p. H.M.S. *Dragon* (cruiser)	1·00	1·40
692	12p. R.F.A. *Darkdale* (tanker)	1·75	1·90
	a. Horiz pair. Nos. 692/3	3·50	3·75
693	12p. H.M.S. *Hermes* (aircraft carrier, launched 1919)	1·75	1·90
694	25p. Men of St. Helena Rifles	2·75	3·00
	a. Horiz pair. Nos. 694/5	5·50	6·00
695	25p. Governor Major W. J. Bain Gray taking salute	2·75	3·00
696	53p. 6-inch coastal gun, Ladder Hill	3·25	3·50
	a. Horiz pair. Nos. 696/7	6·00	7·00
697	53p. Flags signalling "VICTORY"	3·25	2·50
690/7 *Set of 8*		16·00	18·00
MS698 75×85 mm. £1 Reverse of 1939–45 War Medal (*vert*)		2·25	2·75

The two designs for each value were printed together, *se-tenant*, as horizontal pairs, forming composite designs, in sheets of 8 with decorated margins.

183 Blushing Snail

184 *Epidendrum ibaguense*

(Des I. Loe. Litho B.D.T.)

1995 (29 Aug). Endemic Invertebrates. T **183** and similar horiz designs. Multicoloured. W w **14** (sideways). P 14.

699	12p. Type **183**	1·10	1·10
700	25p. Golden Sail Spider	1·75	1·75
701	53p. Spiky Yellow Woodlouse	2·75	3·50
702	60p. St. Helena Shore Crab	3·00	3·75
699/702 *Set of 4*		7·75	9·00
MS703 85×83 mm. £1 Giant Earwig		6·00	7·00

(Des N. Shewring. Litho Questa)

1995 (1 Sept). "Singapore '95" International Stamp Exhibition. Orchids. Sheet, 122×74 mm, containing T **184** and similar vert design. Multicoloured. W w **16** (sideways). P 14½×14.

MS704 50p. Type **184**; 50p. "Vanda Miss Joaquim"	6·50	7·50

185 "Santa Claus outside Market" (Jason Alex Rogers)

186 *Walmer Castle*, 1915

(Des B. Dare. Litho Walsall)

1995 (17 Oct). Christmas. Children's Paintings. T **185** and similar horiz designs. Multicoloured. W w **14** (sideways). P 14½.

705	12p. Type **185**	35	35
706	15p. "Santa Claus and band" (Ché David Yon)	45	45
707	25p. "Santa Claus outside Community Centre" (Leon Williams)	70	75
708	38p. "Santa Claus in decorated street" (Stacey McDaniel)	1·00	1·40
709	60p. "Make a better World" (Kissha Karla Kacy Thomas)	1·75	3·50
705/9 *Set of 5*		3·75	5·75

(Des J. Batchelor. Litho Walsall)

1996 (8 Jan). Union Castle Mail Ships (1st series). T **186** and similar horiz designs. Multicoloured. W w **16** (sideways). P 14.

710	12p. Type **186**	2·25	1·25
711	25p. *Llangibby Castle*, 1934	3·00	1·75
712	53p. *Stirling Castle*, 1940	4·00	4·50
713	60p. *Pendennis Castle*, 1965	4·00	4·50
710/13 *Set of 4*		12·00	11·00

See also Nos. 757/60.

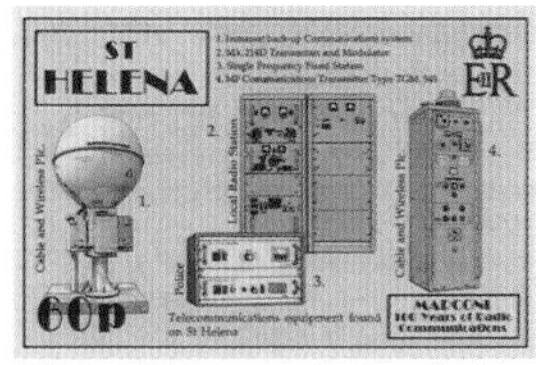

187 Early Telecommunications Equipment

(Des N. Shewring. Litho Walsall)

1996 (28 Mar). Centenary of Radio. T **187** and similar horiz design. Multicoloured. W w **14** (sideways). P 13½×14.

714	60p. Type **187**	1·50	2·00
715	£1 Guglielmo Marconi and *Elettra* (yacht)	2·50	3·50

(Des D. Miller. Litho Walsall)

1996 (22 Apr). 70th Birthday of Queen Elizabeth II. Vert designs as T **165** of Ascension, each incorporating a different photograph of the Queen. Mulicoloured. W w **16**. P 14½.

716	15p. Jamestown	50	40
717	25p. Prince Andrew School	75	65
718	53p. Castle entrance	1·50	2·25
719	60p. Plantation House	1·75	2·50
716/19 *Set of 4*		4·00	5·25
MS720 64×66 mm. £1.50 Queen Elizabeth II		3·25	4·50

188 Helicopter Mail to H.M.S. *Protector* (ice patrol ship), 1964

189 "Mr. Porteous's House"

(Des A. Theobald. Litho B.D.T.)

1996 (8 June). "CAPEX '96" International Stamp Exhibition, Toronto. Mail Transport. T **188** and similar horiz designs. Multicoloured. W w **16** (sideways). P 14.

721	12p. Type **188**	65	60
722	25p. Postman on motor scooter, 1965	90	80
723	53p. Loading mail plane, Wideawake Airfield, Ascension Island	1·50	2·25
724	60p. *St. Helena II* (mail ship) unloading at St. Helena	1·75	2·50
721/4 *Set of 4*		4·25	5·50
MS725 98×73 mm. £1 L.M.S. No. 5624 *St. Helena* locomotive (43×27 *mm*). P 13½		2·75	3·75

(Adapted (from contemporary paintings) D. Miller. Litho Walsall)

1996 (12 Aug). Napoleonic Sites. T **189** and similar horiz designs. Multicoloured. W w **14** (sideways). P 14×14½.

726	12p. Type **189**	1·75	1·25
727	25p. "The Briars' Pavilion"	2·50	1·75
728	53p. "Longwood House"	4·00	4·50
729	60p. "Napoleon's Tomb"	4·00	4·50
726/9 *Set of 4*		11·00	11·00

190 Frangipani and Sandy Bay from Diana's Peak

191 Black Cabbage Tree

(Des N. Shewring. Litho Questa)

1996 (1 Oct). Christmas. Flowers and Views. T **190** and similar vert designs. Multicoloured. W w **14**. P 14½×14.

730	12p. Type **190**	40	40
731	15p. Bougainvillaea and Upper Jamestown from Sampson's Battery	50	50
732	25p. Jacaranda and Jacob's Ladder	75	75
733	£1 Pink Periwinkle and Lot's Wife Ponds	2·75	5·00
730/3	*Set of* 4	4·00	6·00

(Des N. Shewring. Litho Questa)

1997 (17 Jan). Endemic Plants from Diana's Peak National Park. T **191** and similar vert designs. Multicoloured. W w **14** (sideways). P 14½×14.

734	25p. Type **191**	1·75	2·00
	a. Sheetlet. Nos. 734/9	9·50	11·00
735	25p. Whitewood	1·75	2·00
736	25p. Tree Fern	1·75	2·00
737	25p. Dwarf Jellico	1·75	2·00
738	25p. Lobelia	1·75	2·00
739	25p. Dogwood	1·75	2·00
734/9	*Set of* 6	9·50	11·00

Nos. 734/9 were printed together, *se-tenant*, in sheetlets of 6 with the backgrounds forming a composite design.

(Des D. Miller. Litho Questa)

1997 (3 Feb). "HONG KONG '97" International Stamp Exhibition. Sheet 130×90 mm, containing design as No. 644. W w **14** (sideways). P 14½×14.

MS740	75p. Madagascar Red Fody	2·50	2·75

192 João da Nova's Lookout sighting St. Helena, 1502

193 Flower Arrangement

(Des R. Watton. Litho Questa)

1997 (29 May). 500th Anniv of the Discovery of St. Helena (1st issue). T **192** and similar vert designs. Multicoloured. W w **14**. P 14×13½.

741	20p. Type **192**	1·75	1·40
742	25p. Don Fernando Lopez (first inhabitant) and cockerel, 1515	1·90	1·40
743	30p. Thomas Cavendish and *Desire*, 1588	2·00	1·60
744	80p. *Royal Merchant* (English galleon), 1591	4·00	5·25
741/4	*Set of* 4	8·75	8·75

See also Nos. 762/5, 786/9, 810/13, 828/31 and 857/60.

(Des D. Miller. Litho Walsall)

1997 (20 June). Return of Hong Kong to China. Sheet 130×90 mm, containing design as No. 647, but changed face value and imprint date. W w **14** (sideways). P 14½×14.

MS745	75p. St. Helena Sand Plover ("Wirebird")	1·75	2·25

(Des N. Shewring (No. **MS**752), D. Miller (others). Litho Questa (No. **MS**752), B.D.T. (others))

1997 (10 July). Golden Wedding of Queen Elizabeth and Prince Philip. Multicoloured designs as T **173** of Ascension. W w **16**. P 13½.

746	10p. Royal Family's Visit, 1947	85	90
	a. Horiz pair. Nos. 746/7	1·60	1·75
747	10p. Wedding photograph of Princess Elizabeth and Prince Philip	85	90
748	15p. Princess Elizabeth and Prince Philip, 1947	1·00	1·25
	a. Horiz pair. Nos. 748/9	2·00	2·50
749	15p. Presenting bouquets, Royal Visit, 1947	1·00	1·25
750	50p. Prince Philip on Royal Visit, 1957	1·90	2·50
	a. Horiz pair. Nos. 750/1	3·75	5·00
751	50p. Wedding party on balcony, 1947	1·90	2·50
746/51	*Set of* 6	6·75	8·25
MS752	111×70 mm. £1.50 Queen Elizabeth and Prince Philip in landau (*horiz*). W w **14** (sideways). P 14×14½	7·00	8·00

Nos. 746/7, 748/9 and 750/1 were each printed together, *se-tenant*, in horizontal pairs throughout the sheets.

(Des Jennifer Toombs. Litho Walsall)

1997 (29 Sept). Christmas. 25th Anniv of the Duke of Edinburgh's Award in St. Helena. T **193** and similar horiz designs. Multicoloured. W w **16** (sideways). P 13½×14.

753	15p. Type **193**	1·00	65
754	20p. Calligraphy	1·25	80
755	40p. Camping	2·50	2·50
756	75p. Table laid for Christmas dinner	3·75	6·00
753/6	*Set of* 4	7·75	9·00

(Des J. Batchelor. Litho Questa)

1998 (2 Jan). Union Castle Mail Ships (2nd series). Horiz designs as T **186**. Multicoloured. W w **16** (sideways). P 14.

757	20p. *Avondale Castle*, 1900	2·50	1·75
758	25p. *Dunnottar Castle*, 1936	2·50	1·75
759	30p. *Llandovery Castle*, 1943	2·75	2·00
760	80p. *Good Hope Castle*, 1977	5·00	6·50
757/60	*Set of* 4	11·50	11·50

(Des D. Miller. Litho Questa)

1998 (4 Apr). Diana, Princess of Wales Commemoration. Sheet 145×70 mm containing vert designs as T **177** of Ascension. W w **14** (sideways). P 14½×14.

MS761	30p. Wearing green and white hat, 1983; 30p. Wearing white jacket; 30p. Wearing green jacket, 1996; 30p. In evening dress, 1991 (*sold at* £1.20+20p. *charity premium*)	1·75	3·00

(Des R. Watton. Litho Walsall)

1998 (2 July). 500th Anniv of the Discovery of St. Helena (2nd issue). Multicoloured designs as T **192**, but horiz. W w **16** (sideways). P 14.

762	20p. Settlers planting crops, 1659	1·75	1·25
763	25p. Dutch invasion, 1672	2·00	1·40
764	30p. Recapture by the English, 1673	2·25	2·00
765	80p. Royal Charter of 1673	4·00	5·50
762/5	*Set of* 4	9·00	9·00

195 *Desire* (Cavendish), 1588

196 Metal Lanterns

(Des J. Batchelor. Litho Walsall)

1998 (25 Aug). Maritime Heritage. T **195** and similar horiz designs. Multicoloured. W w **14** (sideways). P 13½×14.

766	10p. Type **195**	2·00	2·00
767	15p. *Witte Leeuw* (Dutch East Indiaman), 1602	2·50	2·00
768	20p. H.M.S. *Swallow* and H.M.S. *Dolphin* (Carteret), 1751	2·75	1·50
769	25p. H.M.S. *Endeavour* (Cook), 1771	3·50	1·75
770	30p. H.M.S. *Providence* (sloop), 1792	2·75	1·50
771	35p. *St. Helena* (East India Company schooner), 1815	3·00	2·25
772	40p. H.M.S. *Northumberland* (ship of the line), 1815	3·00	2·25
773	50p. *Rurik* (Von Kotzebue), 1815	3·25	3·25
774	75p. H.M.S. *Erebus* (Ross), 1826	4·50	4·50
775	80p. *Keying* (junk), 1847	4·50	4·50
776	£2 *La Belle Poule* (French frigate), 1840	8·50	11·00
777	£5 H.M.S. *Rattlesnake* (screw corvette), 1861	15·00	19·00
766/77	*Set of* 12	50·00	50·00

No. 771 is inscribed "H.M.S." in error.

(Des Jennifer Toombs. Litho Questa)

1998 (28 Sept). Christmas. Island Crafts. T **196** and similar square designs. W w **16** (sideways). P 14.

778	15p. Type **196**	70	60
779	20p. Wood-turned bowls	80	65
780	30p. Inlaid woodwork on jewellery box	1·10	90
781	85p. Hessian and seedwork bag and hat	2·75	4·50
778/81	*Set of* 4	4·75	6·00

197 H.M.S. *Endeavour* (Cook), 1771

(Des J. Batchelor. Litho Questa)

1999 (5 Mar). "Australia '99" World Stamp Exhibition, Melbourne. Sheet 120×80 mm. W w **14** (sideways). P 13½×14.

MS782	**197** £1.50 multicoloured	8·00	9·00

(Des D. Miller. Litho Walsall)

1999 (19 June). Royal Wedding. Vert designs as T **185** of Ascension. Multicoloured. W w **16**. P 14.

783	30p. Photographs of Prince Edward and Miss Sophie Rhys-Jones	60	65
784	£1.30 Engagement photograph	2·50	3·25

198 1971 Napoleon 2p. Stamp

(Des D. Miller. Litho B.D.T.)

1999 (2 July). "PhilexFrance '99" International Stamp Exhibition, Paris. Sheet 100×70 mm. W w **16** (sideways). P 14.

MS785	**198** £1.50 multicoloured	3·50	4·50

(Des R. Watton. Litho Walsall)

1999 (12 July). 500th Anniv of the Discovery of St. Helena (3rd issue). Multicoloured designs as T **192**, but horiz. W w **14** (sideways). P 14.

786	20p. Jamestown fortifications	1·50	1·10
787	25p. Roadway up Ladder Hill, 1718	1·60	1·25
788	30p. Governor Skottowe with Captain Cook at St. James Church, 1775	3·50	1·75
789	80p. Presentation of sword of honour to Governor Brooke, 1799	3·75	5·00
786/9	*Set of 4*	9·25	8·25

199 King and Queen visiting Jamestown

(Des D. Miller. Litho Cartor)

1999 (3 Sept). "Queen Elizabeth the Queen Mother's Century". T **199** and similar horiz designs. Multicoloured. W w **16** (sideways). P 13½.

790	15p. Type **199**	80	65
791	25p. Viewing bomb damage, Buckingham Palace, 1940	95	75
792	30p. With Prince Andrew, 1997	1·10	90
793	80p. Presenting colour to R.A.F. Central Flying School, and with Red Arrows	2·50	3·75
790/3	*Set of 4*	4·75	5·50
MS794	145×70 mm. £1.50 Queen Elizabeth, 1937, and Royal Family on balcony after Coronation	4·00	4·50

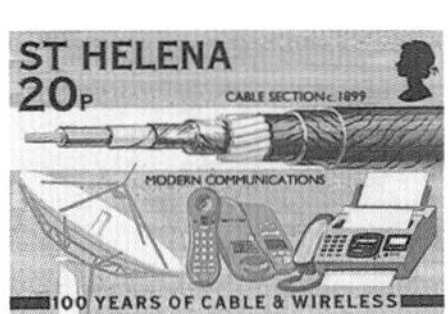

200 Modern Communications Equipment and Section of 1899 Cable

(Litho Questa)

1999 (26 Nov). Centenary of Cable & Wireless Communications plc on St. Helena. T **200** and similar horiz designs. W w **14** (sideways). P 14.

795	20p. multicoloured	1·50	1·25
796	25p. black, reddish brown and bistre-brown	2·00	1·50
797	30p. black, reddish brown and bistre-brown	2·00	1·75
798	80p. multicoloured	2·75	4·50
795/8	*Set of 4*	7·50	8·00

Designs—25p. *Seine* (cable ship); 30p. *Anglia* (cable ship); 80p. Cable & Wireless Headquarters, The Briars.

201 *Victoria* (cruise liner) at St. Helena

(Litho Questa)

1999 (23 Dec). Union Castle Line Centenary Voyage. Sheet 88×72 mm. W w **14** (sideways). P 13×13½.

MS799	**201** £2 multicoloured	16·00	16·00

202 King Edward VI

203 Distillation Plant at Ruperts

(Litho Walsall)

2000 (29 Feb). "Stamp Show 2000" International Stamp Exhibition, London. Kings and Queens of England. T **202** and similar vert designs. Multicoloured. W w **14**. P 14.

800	30p. Type **202**	1·90	1·90
	a. Sheetlet. Nos. 800/5	10·50	10·50
801	30p. King James I	1·90	1·90
802	30p. King William III and Queen Mary II	1·90	1·90
803	30p. King George II	1·90	1·90
804	30p. Queen Victoria	1·90	1·90
805	30p. King George VI	1·90	1·90
800/5	*Set of 6*	10·50	10·50

Nos. 800/5 were printed together, *se-tenant*, in sheetlets of 6 with an enlarged illustrated right-hand margin.

(Des A. Theobald. Litho Questa)

2000 (10 Apr). Centenary of Second Boer War (1st issue). T **203** and similar horiz designs. Multicoloured. W w **14** (sideways). P 14.

806	15p. Type **203**	1·40	1·25
807	25p. Camp at Broadbottom	2·00	1·60
808	30p. Committee of Boer prisoners	2·25	2·00
809	80p. General Cronje and family at Kent Cottage	5·00	5·75
806/9	*Set of 4*	9·50	9·50

(Des R. Watton. Litho Walsall)

2000 (23 May). 500th Anniv of the Discovery of St. Helena (4th issue). Designs as T **192**, but horiz. Multicoloured. W w **14** (sideways). P 14.

810	20p. East India Company flag with crest and Union Jack with colony badge	2·75	2·75
811	25p. Sir Hudson Lowe and Sir George Bingham with broken chains (abolition of slavery, 1832)	2·75	2·00
812	30p. Napoleon, British warship and funeral cortege	3·50	3·00
813	80p. Chief Dinizulu in exile, 1890	6·00	8·50
810/13	*Set of 4*	13·50	14·50

204 Princess Margaret

205 *Beauty and the Beast*

(Litho B.D.T.)

2000 (4 Aug). Royal Birthdays. Sheet, 145×75 mm, containing T **204** and similar multicoloured designs. W w **16** (sideways). P 14.

MS814	25p. Type **204**; 25p. Prince William; 25p. Duke of York; 25p. Princess Royal; 50p. Queen Mother (42×56 *mm*)	27·00	27·00

(Des G. Vasarhelyi. Litho Cartor)

2000 (10 Oct). Christmas. Pantomimes. T **205** and similar horiz designs. Multicoloured. W w **14** (sideways). P 13.

815	20p. Type **205**	1·40	1·75
	a. Horiz strip of 5. Nos. 815/19	6·25	8·00

816 20p. *Puss in Boots* ..... 1·40 1·75
817 20p. *Little Red Riding Hood* ..... 1·40 1·75
818 20p. *Jack and the Beanstalk* ..... 1·40 1·75
819 20p. *Snow White and the Seven Dwarfs* ..... 1·40 1·75
815/19 *Set of 5* ..... 6·25 8·00

Nos. 815/19 were printed together, *se-tenant*, in horizontal strips of 5 throughout the sheet.

206 Chinese White Dolphin

(Des A. Robinson. Litho Questa)

2001 (1 Feb). "HONG KONG 2001" Stamp Exhibition. Sheet, 150×90 mm, containing T **206** and similar horiz design showing dolphins. Multicoloured. W w **14** (sideways). P 14½.
MS820 30p. Type **206**; 40p. Striped Dolphin ..... 8·00 9·00

207 First St. Helena Postage Stamp

208 H.M.S. *Dunedin* (light cruiser)

(Des N. Shewring. Litho Questa)

2001 (24 May). Death Centenary of Queen Victoria. T **207** and similar multicoloured designs. W w **14** (sideways on 20p, 25p, 30p.). P 14.
821 10p. Type **207** ..... 1·10 1·10
822 15p. H.M.S. *Beagle* off St. Helena, 1836 ..... 1·75 1·50
823 20p. Jamestown Square (*horiz*) ..... 1·25 1·25
824 25p. Queen Victoria with Prince Albert and children (*horiz*) ..... 1·75 1·50
825 30p. Diamond Jubilee procession (*horiz*) ..... 2·75 4·00
826 50p. Lewis Carroll and characters from *Alice in Wonderland* ..... 4·50 5·00
821/6 *Set of 6* ..... 12·00 13·00
MS827 105×80 mm. £1.50 Sacks of St. Helena coffee at Great Exhibition. Wmk sideways ..... 4·00 5·00

(Des R. Watton. Litho B.D.T.)

2001 (19 July). 500th Anniv of the Discovery of St. Helena (5th series). Multicoloured designs as T **192**, but horiz. W w **14** (sideways). P 14×14½.
828 20p. Men of St. Helena Rifles ..... 2·75 2·25
829 25p. Prince Andrew School and Jamestown Community Centre ..... 2·50 2·25
830 30p. Flax industry ..... 2·50 2·50
831 80p. *St. Helena II* (mail ship) ..... 7·00 7·50
828/31 *Set of 4* ..... 13·00 13·00

(Des J. Batchelor. Litho Questa)

2001 (20 Sept). Royal Navy Ships of Second World War. T **208** and similar horiz designs. Multicoloured. W w **14** (sideways). P 14.
832 15p. Type **208** ..... 2·00 1·75
833 20p. H.M.S. *Repulse* (battle cruiser) ..... 2·25 2·50
834 25p. H.M.S. *Nelson* (battleship) ..... 2·50 1·75
835 30p. H.M.S. *Exmoor* (destroyer) ..... 2·50 2·00
836 40p. H.M.S. *Eagle* (aircraft carrier, launched 1918) ..... 3·25 3·25
837 50p. H.M.S. *Milford* (sloop) ..... 3·75 4·25
832/7 *Set of 6* ..... 14·50 14·00

209 Tammy Wynette and "It came upon the Midnight Clear"

(Litho Questa)

2001 (11 Oct). Christmas. Carols. T **209** and similar multicoloured designs, each showing carol title and Tammy Wynette ("First Lady of Country Music"). W w **14**. P 14.
838 10p. Type **209** 60 60
839 15p. "Joy to the World" 70 70
840 20p. "Away in a Manger" 80 80
841 30p. "Silent Night" 95 95
838/41 *Set of 4* ..... 2·75 2·75
MS842 65×99 mm. £1.50 Tammy Wynette (*vert*) ..... 3·00 4·50

210 Napoleon as a Young Man

(Des G. Vasarhelyi. Litho Questa)

2001 (1 Nov). 180th Death Anniv of Napoleon Bonaparte. T **210** and similar horiz designs. Multicoloured. W w **14** (sideways). P 14.
843 20p. Type **210** ..... 2·00 1·75
844 25p. Napoleon at military school ..... 2·25 1·75
845 30p. Napoleon dancing ..... 2·50 2·25
846 80p. Napoleon with children ..... 6·00 7·00
843/6 *Set of 4* ..... 11·50 11·50

211 Princess Elizabeth and Princess Margaret as Girl Guides

212 Young St. Helena Sand Plover

(Des A. Robinson. Litho Questa)

2002 (6 Feb). Golden Jubilee. T **211** and similar designs. W w **14** (sideways). P 14½.
847 20p. agate, Indian red and gold ..... 1·25 85
848 25p. multicoloured ..... 1·40 1·00
849 30p. blackish brown, Indian red, and gold ..... 1·50 1·25
850 80p. multicoloured ..... 3·50 3·75
847/50 *Set of 4* ..... 7·00 6·25
MS851 162×95 mm. Nos. 847/50 and 50p. multicoloured. P 13½ (50p.) or 14½ (others) ..... 8·50 8·00

Designs: *Horiz* (*as Type* **211**)— 25p. Queen Elizabeth in evening dress, 1967; 30p. Queen Elizabeth with Prince Charles and Princess Anne, 1952; 80p. Queen Elizabeth on Remembrance Sunday, Durban,1999. *Vert* (38×51 *mm*)—50p. Queen Elizabeth after Annigoni.

Designs as Nos. 847/50 in No. **MS**851 omit the gold frame around each stamp and the "Golden Jubilee 1952-2002" inscription.

(Des N. Arlott. Litho Questa)

2002 (15 Apr). BirdLife International (1st Series). St. Helena Sand Plover ("Wirebird"). T **212** and similar multicoloured designs. W w **14** (sideways on horiz designs.). P 14½×14 (horiz) or 14×14½ (vert).
852 10p. Type **212** 85 90
853 15p. Chick running (*vert*) ..... 1·25 1·10
854 30p. Adult bird in flight ..... 1·50 1·40
855 80p. Chick ..... 3·25 4·00
852/5 *Set of 4* ..... 6·00 6·75
MS856 175×80 mm. 25p. Adult bird (*vert*) and Nos. 852/5. Wmk sideways. P 14½ ..... 7·00 8·00

See also Nos. 1028/31.

213 Sir William Doveton (Council member) and Jamestown Harbour

(Des N. Shewring. Litho B.D.T.)

2002 (21 May). 500th Anniv of the Discovery of St. Helena (6th issue). Local Celebrities. Horiz designs as T **213** all showing Jamestown Harbour. Multicoloured. W w **14** (sideways). P 14.
857 20p. Type **213** ..... 1·25 1·25

No.	Description	Unused	Used
858	25p. Canon Lawrence Walcott	1·40	1·40
859	30p. Governor Hudson Janisch	1·50	1·50
860	80p. Dr. Wilberforce Arnold	3·00	4·50
857/60	*Set of 4*	6·50	7·75

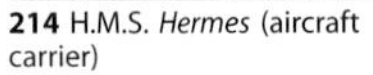

214 H.M.S. *Hermes* (aircraft carrier)

215 Queen Mother with Prince Andrew, 1960

(Des E. Nisbet. Litho Walsall)

2002 (14 June). Royal Navy Ships from the Falklands War. T **214** and similar horiz designs. Multicoloured. W w **14** (sideways). P 14.

No.	Description	Unused	Used
861	15p. Type **214**	1·25	1·25
862	20p. H.M.S. *Leeds Castle* (patrol vessel)	1·25	1·25
863	25p. H.M.S. *Intrepid* (assault ship)	1·40	1·25
864	30p. H.M.S. *Glasgow* (destroyer)	1·50	1·50
865	40p. *St. Helena I* supplying H.M.S. *Brecon* and H.M.S. *Ledbury* (minesweepers)	2·00	2·25
866	50p. H.M.S. *Courageous* (submarine)	2·25	2·75
861/6	*Set of 6*	8·75	9·25

(Des A. Robinson. Litho Questa)

2002 (5 Aug). Queen Elizabeth the Queen Mother Commemoration. T **215** and similar vert designs. W w **14**. P 14½×14.

No.	Description	Unused	Used
867	20p. blackish brown, gold and purple	80	80
868	25p. multicoloured	90	90
869	30p. blackish brown, gold and purple	1·00	1·00
870	50p. multicoloured	1·50	2·25
867/70	*Set of 4*	3·75	4·50
MS871	145×70 mm. 35p. black and gold; £1 multicoloured. Wmk sideways	4·00	4·50

Designs:— 25p. Queen Mother at Cheltenham Races; 30p. Lady Elizabeth Bowes-Lyon, 1923; 35p. Queen Elizabeth, 1945; 50p. Queen Mother at St. Patrick's Day Parade, 1984; £1 Queen Mother at Sandown Races, 1998.

Designs in No. **MS**871 omit the "1900-2002" inscription and the coloured frame.

216 Sperm Whale Pod Underwater

217 The Princess Royal in Blues and Royals' Uniform

(Des R. Hutchins. Litho B.D.T.)

2002 (3 Oct). Endangered Species. Sperm Whale. T **216** and similar horiz designs. Multicoloured. W w **14** (sideways). P 14.

No.	Description	Unused	Used
872	10p. Type **216**	65	70
	a. Strip of 4. Nos. 872/5	3·50	4·25
873	15p. Sperm Whale on surface	80	90
874	20p. Two Sperm Whales underwater	1·00	1·25
875	30p. Tail fin of Sperm Whale	1·40	1·75
872/5	*Set of 4*	3·50	4·25

In addition to sheets of 20 for each value, Nos. 872/5 were also printed in sheets of 16 (4×4) containing the four values, *se-tenant*, both horizontally and vertically.

(Litho B.D.T.)

2002 (15 Nov). Visit of the Princess Royal to St. Helena. Sheet 62×72 mm. W w **14**. P 14.

No.	Description	Unused	Used
MS876	**217** £2 multicoloured	7·00	8·00

218 Plantation House and Arms

(Des D. Miller. Litho Cartor)

2003 (8 Apr). Tourism. T **218** and similar horiz designs. Multicoloured. W w **14**. P 13½.

No.	Description	Unused	Used
877	25p. Type **218**	1·25	1·40
	a Sheetlet. Nos. 877/88	13·50	15·00
878	25p. St. Helena II (mail ship) in Jamestown harbour	1·25	1·40
879	25p. QE2 (cruise liner) off St. Helena	1·25	1·40
880	25p. Napoleon's Tomb and Briars Pavilion	1·25	1·40
881	25p. Ebony Flower and Diana's Peak	1·25	1·40
882	25p. St. Helena Sand Plover ("Wirebird") and Napoleon's House	1·25	1·40
883	25p. Broadway House	1·25	1·40
884	25p. St. Helena Golf Course	1·25	1·40
885	25p. Yacht and dolphins	1·25	1·40
886	25p. Sport fishing	1·25	1·40
887	25p. Diving	1·25	1·40
888	25p. St. Helena Museum	1·25	1·40
877/88	*Set of 12*	13·50	15·00

Nos. 877/88 were printed together, se-tenant, in sheetlets of twelve stamps arranged around four central labels showing a map of the island. No. 879 was also produced in sheets of 20 of the one design.

219 Queen Elizabeth II in Coronation Robes (photograph by Cecil Beaton)

220 Queen Elizabeth II

(Des A. Robinson. Litho DLR)

2003 (2 June). 50th Anniv of Coronation. T **219** and similar horiz design. Multicoloured. W w **14** (sideways). P 14×14½.

No.	Description	Unused	Used
889	30p. Type **219**	1·40	1·10
890	50p. Queen and Duke of Edinburgh in Coronation Coach	2·00	2·50
MS891	95×115 mm. 30p. As Type 219; 50p. As No. 890	2·40	3·35

Nos. 889/90 have scarlet frame; stamps from **MS**891 have no frame and country name in mauve panel.

(Des CASB Studio. Litho BDT)

2003 (2 June). W w **14** . P 13½.

No.	Description	Unused	Used
892	**220** £2.50 multicoloured	5·50	6·50

221 *Leonotis nepetifolia*

222 Westland WG-13 Lynx Helicopter

(Des I. Loe. Litho Walsall)

2003 (10 June). Wild Flowers. T **221** and similar vert designs. Multicoloured. W w **14** . P 14.

No.	Description	Unused	Used
893	10p. Type **221**	1·25	1·50
894	15p. *Buddleia madagascariensis*	1·60	1·50
895	20p. *Datura suaveolens*	1·75	1·25
896	25p. *Fuchsia boliviana*	1·75	1·25
897	30p. *Commelina diffusa*	2·00	1·50
898	40p. *Solanum mauritianum*	2·50	2·25
899	50p. *Tecoma stans*	2·75	2·75
900	75p. *Kalanchoe pinnata*	4·00	4·50
901	80p. *Hedychium chrysoleucum*	4·00	4·50
902	£1 *Canna indica*	4·50	5·00
903	£2 *Alpinia nutans*	7·50	9·50
904	£5 *Lantana camara*	15·00	17·00
893/904	*Set of 12*	42·00	45·00

(Des J. Batchelor. Litho DLR)

2003 (12 Aug). Centenary of Powered Flight. T **222** and similar horiz designs. Multicoloured. W w **14** . P 14.

No.	Description	Unused	Used
905	10p. Type **222**	1·25	1·25

906 15p. Douglas C-124 Globemaster .... 1·40 1·40
907 20p. British Aerospace Nimrod AEW Mk 3 .... 1·50 1·25
908 25p. Lockheed C-130 Hercules .... 1·60 1·25
909 30p. Lockheed L-1011 TriStar .... 1·75 1·60
910 50p. Wright Flyer .... 2·50 3·25
905/10 *Set of 6* .... 9·00 9·00
MS911 115×65 mm. £1.80, Supermarine Walrus. Wmk sideways .... 8·00 9·00

223 Large Magellanic Cloud

224 Christiaan Barnard (heart transplant pioneer)

(Des R. Watton. Litho BDT)

2003 (6 Oct). Christmas. The Southern Sky. T **223** and similar horiz designs. Multicoloured. W w **14** (sideways). P 13½.

912 10p. Type **223** .... 85 1·00
913 15p. Small Magellanic cloud .... 1·00 1·25
914 20p. Omega Centauri globular cluster .... 1·25 1·25
915 25p. Eta Carinae nebula ("ETA CARRNAE") .... 1·40 1·40
916 30p. Southern Cross constellation .... 1·50 1·75
912/16 *Set of 5* .... 5·50 6·00

(Des N. Shewring. Litho BDT)

2004 (19 Mar). Medical Pioneers. T **224** and similar vert designs. Multicoloured. W w **14** (sideways). P 14.

917 10p. Type **224** .... 1·25 1·25
918 25p. Marie Curie (developer of X-radiography) .... 2·00 1·40
919 30p. Louis Pasteur (bacteriologist) .... 2·00 1·60
920 50p. Sir Alexander Fleming (discoverer of penicillin) .... 3·00 4·00
917/20 *Set of 4* .... 7·50 7·50

225 Freesia

226 St. Matthew

(Des R. Watton. Litho BDT)

2004 (25 May). Bicentenary of Royal Horticultural Society. T **225** and similar horiz designs. Multicoloured. W w **14** (sideways). P 14.

921 10p. Type **225** 40 50
922 15p. Bottle Brush 60 60
923 30p. Ebony .... 1·10 1·10
924 50p. Olive .... 1·50 2·00
921/4 *Set of 4* .... 3·25 3·75
MS925 111×111 mm. £1 Maurandya .... 2·50 3·00

(Des V. Ambrus. Litho BDT)

2004 (5 Oct). Christmas. Stained Glass Windows. T **226** and similar vert designs. Multicoloured. W w **14** (inverted). P 14.

926 10p. Type **226** 45 60
927 15p. St. John 65 65
928 20p. St. Peter 80 65
929 30p. St. James .... 1·10 1·00
930 50p. St. Paul .... 2·00 3·50
926/30 *Set of 5* .... 4·50 5·75

227 SS *Umtata*

228 The Friar

(Des A. Theobald. Litho Enschedé)

2004 (4 Nov). Merchant Ships. T **227** and similar horiz designs. Multicoloured. W w **14** (sideways). P 13×13½.

931 20p. Type **227** .... 1·75 1·25
932 30p. SS *Umzinto* .... 2·50 1·75
933 50p. SS *Umtali* .... 3·50 3·50
934 80p. SS *Umbilo* .... 5·50 6·50
931/4 *Set of 4* .... 12·00 11·50

(Des R. Richards. Litho BDT)

2005 (14 Jan). Rock Formations. T **228** and similar horiz designs. Multicoloured. W w **14** (sideways). P 14.

935 35p. Type **228** .... 2·50 3·00
a Horiz strip of 4. Nos. 935/8 .... 10·00 11·50
936 40p. Sugar Loaf .... 2·50 3·00
937 50p. The Turk's Cap .... 2·50 3·00
938 £1 Lot's Wife .... 3·50 4·00
935/8 *Set of 8* .... 10·00 11·50

Nos. 935/8 were printed together, se-tenant, in horizontal strips of 4 stamps.

229 HMS *Bellerophon*, *Aigle* and *Monarca*

(Des J. Batchelor. Litho and thermograph (30p.) Cartor)

2005 (10 May). Bicentenary of the Battle of Trafalgar (1st issue). T **229** and similar multicoloured designs. No wmk (30p.) or W w **14** (sideways on 10p., 20p. or inverted on 50p., 60p., 75p., 80p.) P 13½.

939 10p. Type **229** .... 1·00 1·00
940 20p. British 18 Pdr Naval Pattern canon .... 1·50 1·00
941 30p. HMS *Victory* .... 2·50 1·50
942 50p. First Lieutenant in the Royal Navy, 1805 (*vert*) .... 3·25 3·25
943 60p. HMS *Conqueror* (*vert*) .... 3·50 4·00
944 80p. Vice-Admiral Sir Horatio Nelson (*vert*) .... 4·75 6·00
939/44 *Set of 6* .... 15·00 15·00
MS945 120×79 mm. 75p. Admiral Cuthbert Collingwood (vert); 75p. HMS *Royal Sovereign* (*vert*) .... 8·00 8·50

See also Nos. 969/71.

Nos. 939/44 were each printed in sheets of 6 with decorative margins and the Trafalgar Festival 2005 logo at foot.

Nos. 941 contains traces of powdered wood from HMS *Victory*.

230 HMS *Milford* (sloop)

(Des R. Watton. Litho BDT)

2005 (24 June). 60th Anniv of the End of World War II. T **230** and similar horiz designs. Multicoloured. W w **14** (sideways). P 14.

946 20p. Type **230** .... 1·75 1·75
a Sheetlet. Nos. 946/55 .... 16·00 16·00
947 20p. HMS *Nelson* (battleship) .... 1·75 1·75
948 20p. RFA *Darkdale* (tanker) .... 1·75 1·75
949 20p. HMS *St Helena* (frigate) .... 1·75 1·75
950 20p. Atlantic Star medal .... 1·75 1·75
951 30p. Alan M. Turing (codebreaker) and Enigma code machine .... 1·75 1·75
952 30p. Captain Johnnie Walker and HMS *Starling* (sloop) .... 1·75 1·75
953 30p. Winston Churchill .... 1·75 1·75
954 30p. Churchill infantry tank .... 1·75 1·75
955 30p. Hawker Hurricanes .... 1·75 1·75
946/55 *Set of 10* .... 16·00 16·00

Nos. 946/55 were printed together, *se-tenant*, in sheetlets of 10 stamps.

231 Pope John Paul II

232 Sir Francis Drake

(Des A. Robinson. Litho BDT)

2005 (31 Aug). Pope John Paul II Commemoration. W w **14** (inverted). P 14.

956	**231**	50p. multicoloured	2·50	2·50

No. 956 was printed in sheetlets of eight stamps with an enlarged, illustrated right margin.

2005 (7 Sept). Famous Elizabethans. T **232** and similar vert designs. Multicoloured. W w **14**. P 14.

957	10p. Type **232**	1·00	1·00
	a. Horiz pair. Nos. 957/8	2·00	2·00
958	10p. *The Golden Hind*	1·00	1·00
959	15p. Sir Walter Raleigh	1·40	1·40
	a. Horiz pair. Nos. 959/60	2·75	2·75
960	15p. *The Ark Royal*	1·40	1·40
961	25p. Queen Elizabeth I	1·75	1·75
	a. Horiz pair. Nos. 961/2	3·50	3·50
962	25p. The Armada	1·75	1·75
963	£1 William Shakespeare	4·50	4·50
	a. Horiz pair. Nos. 963/4	9·00	9·00
964	£1 The Old Globe Theatre	4·50	4·50
957/65 *Set of 8*		15·00	15·00

Nos. 957/8, 959/60, 961/2, 963/4 were each printed together, *se-tenant*, in horizontal pairs.

2005 (4 Oct). Christmas and Birth Bicentenary of Hans Christian Andersen (writer). Vert designs as T **220** of Ascension. Multicoloured. W w **14** (inverted). P 14.

965	10p. *The Little Fir Tree*	55	65
966	25p. *The Ugly Duckling*	90	90
967	30p. *The Snow Queen*	1·00	1·25
968	£1 *The Little Mermaid*	3·25	4·75
965/8 *Set of 4*		5·25	6·75

234 HMS *Victory*

235 1961 Tristan Relief Fund Stamps and Postcard

(Des J. Batchelor (50p) or Pauline Gyles (£1.20). Litho Cartor)

2005 (18 Oct). Bicentenary of the Battle of Trafalgar (2nd issue). T **234** and similar multicoloured designs. P 13½.

969	50p. Type **234**	2·75	1·75
970	80p. Ships engaged in battle (*horiz*)	4·00	4·00
971	£1.20 Admiral Lord Nelson	6·00	7·00
969/71 *Set of 3*		11·50	11·50

(Des A. Robinson. Litho BDT)

2006 (16 Jan). 150th Anniv of the First St. Helena Postage Stamp. Treasures of the British Library. T **235** and similar horiz designs. Multicoloured. W w **14** (sideways). P 14×15.

972	10p. Type **235**	1·00	1·00
973	20p. Cape of Good Hope 1855–63 1s. deep dark green triangular	1·50	1·00
974	25p. USA (1918) 24c. inverted Curtiss JN-4 "Jenny" variety	1·60	1·10
975	30p. (1856) 6d. blue (first St. Helena stamp)	1·60	1·25
976	80p. (1840) penny black	3·75	3·75
977	£1.20 Mauritius (1847) 2d. deep blue	5·50	6·50
972/7 *Set of 6*		13·50	13·00
MS978 100×60 mm. £2 As No. 975		8·00	9·50

236 Stars holding EU Flag

(Des D. Miller. Litho BDT)

2006 (6 Feb). 50th Anniv of the First Europa Stamps. T **236** and similar horiz designs. Multicoloured. P 14.

979	10p. Type **236**	75	75
980	30p. Stars in circle and holding letter	1·00	80
981	80p. Stars and ball	2·50	2·75
982	£1.20 Stars in circle and holding stamp	3·25	4·00
979/82 *Set of 4*		6·75	7·50
MS983 122×77 mm. Nos. 979/82		6·00	6·50

237 Princess Elizabeth

(Litho BDT)

2006 (21 Apr). 80th Birthday of Queen Elizabeth II. T **237** and similar horiz designs. Multicoloured. W w **14** (sideways). P 14.

984	10p. Type **237**	1·50	1·50
985	30p. Queen Elizabeth wearing tiara, c. 1952	2·25	1·25
986	80p. Wearing tiara and fur stole	4·75	4·75
987	£1.20 In close-up	6·00	6·50
984/7 *Set of 4*		13·00	12·50
MS988 144×75 mm. £1 Wearing tiara and pearl drop earrings, c. 1952; £1 Wearing cream sweater		7·00	8·50

238 Orange flowers (Emma-Jane Yon)

239 A Partridge in a Pear Tree

(Des D. Miller. Litho BDT)

2006 (20 May). St. Helena Arts and Crafts. T **238** and similar vert designs showing artwork from exhibition at Museum of St. Helena. Multicoloured. W w **14**. P 14.

989	30p. Type **238**	1·10	1·25
	a. Sheetlet. Nos. 989/1004	15·00	17·00
990	30p. Arum lily (Emma-Jane Yon)	1·10	1·25
991	30p. Hibiscus (Christina Stroud)	1·10	1·25
992	30p. Dolphins off coast (Christina Stroud)	1·10	1·25
993	30p. Pattern of blue flowers (Muriel Gardener)	1·10	1·25
994	30p. Wood turning by Jackie Essex	1·10	1·25
995	30p. Pottery dish by Corinda Essex	1·10	1·25
996	30p. Fish (Laura Lawrence)	1·10	1·25
997	30p. Peeled orange (Emma-Jane Yon)	1·10	1·25
998	30p. Sculptures by Sandy Walters and Johnny Drummond	1·10	1·25
999	30p. Pottery bowl by Serena Thorpe	1·10	1·25
1000	30p. Shells on beach (Christina Stroud)	1·10	1·25
1001	30p. Flower arrangement (Christina Stroud)	1·10	1·25
1002	30p. Succulent (Laura Lawrence)	1·10	1·25
1003	30p. Two fish (Laura Lawrence)	1·10	1·25
1004	30p. Pink fish (Laura Lawrence)	1·10	1·25
990/1004 *Set of 15*		15·00	17·00

Nos. 989/1004 were printed together, *se-tenant*, in sheetlets of sixteen stamps.

(Des J. Vasarhelyi. Litho Cartor)

2006 (31 Aug). Christmas. "The Twelve Days of Christmas" (carol) (1st issue). T **239** and similar square designs. Multicoloured. W w **14**. P 14.

1005	10p. Type **239**	65	75
1006	15p. Two turtle doves	80	90
1007	25p. Three French hens	1·00	1·10

1008	30p. Four calling birds	1·10	1·25
1009	50p. Five gold rings	1·75	2·50
1010	£1 Six geese a-laying	3·00	4·25
1005/10	*Set of* 6	7·50	8·50

Nos. 1005/10 were each perforated in a circle contained within an outer perforated square.

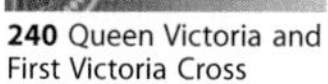

240 Queen Victoria and First Victoria Cross

241 Napoleon II (1811–32) Award Ceremony, 1857

(Des D. Miller. Litho BDT)

2006 (3 Nov). Exploration and Innovation. Anniversaries. T **240** and similar vert designs. Multicoloured. W w **14**. P 14.

1011	20p. Type **240**	2·25	2·25
	a. Horiz pair. Nos. 1011/12	4·50	4·50
1012	20p. Victoria Cross (150th anniv) and Charge of the Light Brigade	2·25	2·25
1013	25p. Charles Darwin (170th anniv of visit to St. Helena)	2·50	2·50
	a. Horiz pair. Nos. 1013/14	5·00	5·00
1014	25p. St. Helena sand plover ("Wirebird") and landscape near Sandy Bay	2·50	2·50
1015	30p. Isambard Kingdom Brunel (birth bicent) and coal railway, Cardiff Docks	2·75	2·75
	a. Horiz pair. Nos. 1015/16	5·50	5·50
1016	30p. RMS *St. Helena*, Cardiff Docks	2·75	2·75
1017	£1 Charles Dickens and Dingley Dell cricket match	5·00	5·00
	a. Horiz pair. Nos. 1017/18	10·00	10·00
1018	£1 Samuel Pickwick and cricket match (170th anniv of "The Pickwick Papers")	5·00	5·00
1011/18	*Set of* 8	22·00	22·00

Nos. 1011/12, 1013/14, 1015/16 and 1017/18 were each printed together, *se-tenant*, in horizontal pairs in sheetlets of eight stamps, each pair forming a composite background design.

(Des J. Vasarhelyi. Litho BDT)

2007 (16 Jan). The Napoleons. T **241** and similar vert designs. Multicoloured. W w **14** (inverted). P 15×14.

1019	25p. Type **241**	1·50	1·00
1020	30p. Napoleon I (1769–1821)	1·75	1·25
1021	£1 Napoleon III (1808–73)	4·00	5·00
1019/21	*Set of* 3	6·50	6·50
MS1022	156×75 mm. Nos. 1019/21	6·50	6·50

242 Princess Elizabeth and Duke of Edinburgh

243 Black Noddy

(Litho BDT)

2007 (26 Apr). Diamond Wedding of Queen Elizabeth II and Duke of Edinburgh. T **242** and similar vert designs. Multicoloured. W w **14**. P 14.

1023	25p. Type **242**	1·50	90
1024	35p. Princess Elizabeth on her wedding day	1·75	1·25
1025	40p. Wedding photograph	1·75	1·25
1026	£2 Princess Elizabeth getting out of car	8·50	10·00
1023/6	*Set of* 4	11·50	12·00
MS1027	125×85 mm. £2 Wedding photograph (42×46 *mm*). Wmk sideways	8·50	10·00

Nos. 1023/6 were each printed in sheetlets of six stamps with enlarged illustrated margins.

(Des Derek Miller. Litho Lowe-Martin, Canada)

2007 (12 June). BirdLife International (2nd series). Seabirds. T **243** and similar horiz designs. Multicoloured. W w **14** (sideways). P 12½×13.

1028	15p. Type **243**	1·25	1·00
1029	30p. Madeiran storm petrel	2·25	1·40
1030	50p. Masked booby	3·00	2·25
1031	£2 Sooty tern	8·00	10·00
1028/31	*Set of* 4	13·00	13·00

244 Scout Emblems

245 'Seven Swans a-Swimming'

(Des Andrew Robinson. Litho BDT)

2007 (9 July). Centenary of Scouting. T **244** and similar multicoloured designs. W w **14** (sideways). P 14.

1032	15p. Type **244**	90	80
1033	30p. Lord Baden-Powell inspecting scouts, May 1936	1·25	1·00
1034	50p. Lord Baden-Powell and Rev. L. C. Walcott	2·00	2·00
1035	£1 Lord Baden-Powell	3·50	5·00
1032/5	*Set of* 4	7·00	8·00
MS1036	90×65 mm. £1 Badge of 1st Jamestown Scout Group (*vert*); £1 Lord Baden-Powell (150th birth anniv) (*vert*)	6·50	8·00

(Des Julian Vasarhelyi. Litho Cartor)

2007 (3 Sept). Christmas. 'The Twelve Days of Christmas' (carol). T **245** and similar circular designs. Multicoloured. W w **14**. P 13½.

1037	10p. Type **245**	55	70
1038	15p. 'Eight Maids a-Milking'	80	1·00
1039	25p. 'Nine Ladies Dancing'	1·25	1·40
1040	30p. 'Ten Lords a-Leaping'	1·25	1·40
1041	50p. 'Eleven Pipers Piping'	1·75	2·00
1042	£1 'Twelve Drummers Drumming'	3·25	3·75
1037/42	*Set of* 6	8·00	9·25

Nos. 1037/42 were each perforated in a circle contained within an outer perforated square.

246 SS *Savannah*, (first steamship crossing), 1819

(Des Nick Shewring. Litho BDT)

2007 (6 Nov). Atlantic Firsts. T **246** and similar horiz designs. Multicoloured. W w **14** (sideways). P 14.

1043	25p. Type **246**	1·75	1·10
1044	40p. Alcock and Brown's Vickers FB-27 Vimy, 1919 (first aeroplane crossing)	2·50	2·25
1045	45p. Alain Gerbault's sloop *Firecrest*, 1923 (first east-west solo sailing)	2·50	2·25
1046	£1.20 Charles Lindbergh's *Spirit of St. Louis* (first solo flight)	6·50	7·50
1043/6	*Set of* 4	12·00	12·00

247 Airco D.H.9

(Litho BDT)

2008 (1 Apr). 90th Anniv of the Royal Air Force. T **247** and similar horiz designs. Multicoloured. W w **14** (sideways). P 14.

1047	15p. Type **247**	1·50	1·40
1048	25p. Hawker Hurricane	2·00	1·40
1049	35p. Handley Page Hastings	2·75	2·25

1050 40p. English Electric Lightning 3·00 2·50
1051 50p. Harrier GR7 3·50 4·00
1047/51 *Set of 5* 11·50 10·50
MS1052 110×70 mm. £1.50 Berlin Airlift, June 1948–September 1949 6·50 7·50

Nos. 1047/51 were each printed in sheetlets of eight stamps with a central label showing anniversary emblem and enlarged illustrated margins.

248 Longwood House, 1821

(Litho Enschedé)

2008 (7 May). 150th Anniv of the Purchase of Longwood House and Napoleon's Tomb. Sheet 165×95 mm containing T **248** and similar horiz designs. Multicoloured. W w **14** (sideways). P 13½×14.

MS1053 90p. Type **248**; £1 Napoleon's Tomb; £1.25 Longwood House, 2008 14·00 17·00

249 Brown Booby

250 Deepwater Bullseye (*Cookeolus japonicus*)

(Des Derek Miller. Litho Lowe-Martin)

2008 (17 July). Sea Birds (2nd series). T **249** and similar horiz designs. Multicoloured. W w **14** (sideways). P 12½×13.

1054 15p. Type **249** 1·25 1·00
1055 35p. Brown noddy 2·00 1·60
1056 40p. Fairy tern 2·25 1·60
1057 £1.25 Red-billed tropic bird 5·00 6·00
1054/6 *Set of 4* 9·50 9·25

(Des Derek Miller. Litho BDT)

2008 (19 Aug). Fish. T **250** and similar horiz designs. Multicoloured. W w **14** (sideways). P 14.

1058 5p. Type **250** 50 1·00
1059 10p. Five finger (*Abudefduf saxatilis*) 70 1·00
1060 15p. Deepwater greenfish (*Holanthias fronticinctus*) 1·25 1·25
1061 20p. Hardback soldier (*Holocentrus adscensionis*) 1·50 1·25
1062 25p. Deepwater gurnard (*Scorpaena mellissii*) 1·75 1·25
1063 35p. Red mullet (*Apogon axillaris*) 2·25 1·50
1064 40p. Softback soldier (*Myripristis jacobus*) 2·50 1·75
1065 50p. Rock bullseye (*Heteropriacanthus cruentatus*) 3·00 2·50
1066 80p. Gurnard (*Scorpaena plumieri*) 4·50 4·50
1067 £1 Cunningfish (*Chaetodon sanctaehelenae*) 5·00 6·00
1068 £2 Hogfish (*Acanthostracion notacanthus*) 9·00 11·00
1069 £5 Marmalade razorfish (*Xyrichtys blanchardi*) 16·00 18·00
1058/69 *Set of 12* 42·00 45·00
MS1070 171×167 Nos. 1058/69 48·00 50·00

251 St. Helena Flag

252 African Lily (*Agapanthus africanus*)

2008 (19 Aug). St. Helena Island Flag. Self-adhesive. Die-cut.

1071 **251** 35p. multicoloured 2·50 2·75
a. Booklet pane. No. 1071×12 21·00

(Litho Lowe Martin Group)

2008 (1 Sept). Flowers at Christmas. T **252** and similar vert designs. Multicoloured. P 13×12½.

1072 15p. Type **252** 1·00 80
1073 25p. Christmas cactus (*Delosperma cooperi*) 1·50 1·00
1074 35p. Honeysuckle (*Lonicera periclymenem*) 1·75 1·40
1075 40p. St. John's lily (*Lilium longiflorum*) 1·75 1·40
1076 £1 Crucifix orchid (*Epidendrum radicans*) 3·50 5·00
1072/6 *Set of 5* 8·50 8·75

253 Rupert Brooke (1914) and *The Soldier*

254 Henry VIII (as young man)

(Litho BDT)

2008 (16 Sept). 90th Anniv of the End of World War I. T **253** and similar vert designs showing war poets and extracts from their poems. Multicoloured. W w **18** (inverted). P 14.

1077 10p. Type **253** 1·00 1·25
1078 15p. Siegfried Sassoon (1919) and *Aftermath* 1·40 1·40
1079 25p. Wilfred Owen (1917) and *Anthem for Doomed Youth* 1·75 1·40
1080 35p. Laurence Binyon (1914) and *For the Fallen* 2·50 2·25
1081 40p. John McCrae (1915) and *In Flanders Fields* 2·75 2·50
1082 50p. Edward Thomas (1915) and *In Memoriam* 3·00 3·50
1077/82 *Set of 6* 11·00 11·00
MS1083 110×70 mm. £2 Cenotaph, St. Helena 8·00 9·50

Nos. 1077/82 were printed in separate sheetlets of six stamps with enlarged illustrated bottom margins.

(Litho Enschedé)

2009 (9 Jan). 500th Birth Anniv of King Henry VIII. T **254** and similar vert designs. Multicoloured. W w **14**. P 14.

1084 50p. Type **254** 2·50 2·50
a. Sheetlet. Nos. 1084/93 22·00 22·00
1085 50p. Catherine of Aragon 2·50 2·50
1086 50p. Anne Boleyn 2·50 2·50
1087 50p. Jane Seymour 2·50 2·50
1088 50p. Henry VIII (in middle age) 2·50 2·50
1089 50p. *Mary Rose* (galleon) 2·50 2·50
1090 50p. Anne of Cleves 2·50 2·50
1091 50p. Catherine Howard 2·50 2·50
1092 50p. Katherine Parr 2·50 2·50
1093 50p. Hampton Court 2·50 2·50
1085/93 *Set of 10* 22·00 22·00

Nos. 1084/93 were printed together, *se-tenant*, in sheetlets of ten stamps with enlarged illustrated.

255 Westland Sea King Helicopter

(Des Tim O'Brien. Litho BDT)

2009 (17 Apr). Centenary of Naval Aviation. T **255** and similar horiz designs. Multicoloured. P 14.

1094 15p. Type **255** 2·25 1·50
1095 35p. Fairey Swordfish 3·25 2·75
1096 40p. BAe Harrier 3·25 3·00
1097 50p. Blackburn Buccaneer 3·50 4·00
1094/7 *Set of 4* 11·00 10·00
MS1098 110×70 mm. £1.50 Pioneer naval aviator Lt. E. L. Gerrard in cockpit of aircraft, Central Flying School, 1913 9·00 9·00

Nos. 1094/7 were each printed in sheetlets of eight stamps with a central label and enlarged illustrated bottom margins.

256 The Briars Pavilion, c. 1857

257 Deep Space Tracking Station, Ascension Island

(Litho Enschedé)

2009 (26 May). 50th Anniv of Donation of the Briars Pavilion (Emperor Napoleon's home 18 October to 10 December 1815) to the French Government. Sheet 95×166 mm containing T **256** and similar horiz designs. Multicoloured. W w **14** (sideways). P 13×13½.

MS1099	90p. Type **256**; £1 Napoleon and Betsy Balcombe; £1.25 The Briars Pavilion, 2008	15·00	17·00

(Litho Lowe-Martin)

2009 (20 July). International Year of Astronomy. 40th Anniv of First Moon Landing. T **257** and similar multicoloured designs. W w **18** (sideways). P 13.

1100	15p. Type **257**	75	75
1101	35p. Early experiment by Dr. Robert Goddard	1·50	1·50
1102	40p. Apollo 11 launch, 1969	1·50	1·50
1103	90p. STS41: *Discovery* Landing, 1984	3·00	3·50
1104	£1.20 Working on International Space Station, 2001	3·75	5·00
1100/4	*Set of* 5	9·50	11·00
MS1105	100×80 mm. £1.20 *Surveyor III, I Presume* (astronauts Pete Conrad and Alan Bean approach Surveyor III) (Alan Bean) (39×59 *mm*). Wmk upright	4·25	4·75

Nos. 1100/4 were printed in separate sheetlets of six stamps with enlarged illustrated margins.

258 Father Christmas in Street Parade

259 St. Paul's Cathedral

(Ross Watton. Litho BDT)

2009 (1 Sept). Christmas. T **258** and similar horiz designs. Multicoloured. W w **18** (sideways). P 14.

1106	15p. Type **258**	75	75
1107	25p. Nativity play in church	1·00	75
1108	40p. Church lit at night	1·50	1·50
1109	£1 Street at night with Christmas tree and lights	3·25	4·50
1106/9	*Set of* 4	6·00	6·75

(Litho BDT)

2009 (30 Oct). 150th Anniv of Diocese. T **259** and similar vert designs. Multicoloured. W w **18** (inverted). P 14.

1110	15p. Type **259**	75	75
1111	35p. St. Matthew's Church	1·50	1·50
1112	40p. St. James' Church	1·50	1·50
1113	£1 Piers Calveley Claughton	3·25	4·00
1110/13	*Set of* 4	6·25	7·00

260 Charles I

261 Children in Bomb Shelter

(Litho BDT)

2010 (29 Jan). 350th Anniv of the Restoration of King Charles II. 'Revolution to Restoration'. T **260** and similar vert designs. Multicoloured. W w **18** (inverted). P 14.

1114	50p. Type **260**	2·50	2·50
	a. Sheetlet. Nos. 1114/23	22·00	22·00
1115	50p. Charles II	2·50	2·50
1116	50p. Prince Rupert	2·50	2·50
1117	50p. Oliver Cromwell	2·50	2·50
1118	50p. Richard Cromwell	2·50	2·50
1119	50p. Charles I arrests MPs	2·50	2·50
1120	50p. New Model Army	2·50	2·50
1121	50p. Execution of Charles I	2·50	2·50
1122	50p. Dissolution of Parliament	2·50	2·50
1123	50p. Coronation of Charles II	2·50	2·50
1114/23	*Set of* 10	22·00	22·00

Nos. 1114/23 were printed together, *se-tenant*, in sheetlets of ten stamps.

(Litho Lowe-Martin)

2010 (18 Mar). 70th Anniv of the Battle of Britain. The Blitz. T **261** and similar vert designs. Multicoloured. W w **18** (inverted). P 13.

1124	15p. Type **261**	1·25	1·25
1125	25p. Firemen	2·50	1·50
1126	35p. Milkman	2·50	1·75
1127	40p. Wrecked bus	3·00	2·00
1128	90p. Aircraft trails over city	4·25	4·75
1129	£1 Warden with binoculars watching for enemy aircraft	4·50	5·00
1124/9	*Set of* 6	16·00	14·50
MS1130	110×70 mm. £1.50 Sir Douglas Bader	7·50	8·50

262 Great Britain King George V 1912 1d. Stamp

263 Football Player and Globe

(Litho BDT)

2010 (8 May). Centenary of Accession of King George V. Sheet 110×70 mm. W w **18**. P 14.

MS1131	**262** multicoloured	6·50	8·00

2010 (14 May). World Cup Football Championship, South Africa. 'World of Football'. T **263** and similar vert designs. Multicoloured. Litho. W w **18**. P 14×14½.

1132	40p. Type **263**	1·50	1·60
1133	40p. Globe showing South Africa	1·50	1·60
1134	40p. Two players and globe	1·50	1·60
1132/4	*Set of* 3	4·00	4·25
MS1135	130×100 mm. Nos. 1132/4	4·00	4·50

264 Rainbows

265 Crucifix Orchid and Jacob's Ladder

(Litho BDT)

2010 (23 Aug). Centenary of Girlguiding. T **264** and similar horiz designs. Multicoloured. W w **18** (sideways). P 14.

1136	15p. Type **264**	75	75
1137	25p. Brownies	1·25	90
1138	40p. Guides	1·75	1·75
1139	90p. Lord and Lady Baden-Powell	3·25	4·00
1136/9	*Set of* 4	6·25	6·75

(Litho BDT)

2010 (25 Oct). Christmas. T **265** and similar horiz designs showing flowers and St. Helena landscapes. Multicoloured. W w **18** (sideways). P 13½.

1140	15p. Type **265**	75	75
1141	25p. St. John's lily and Diana's Peak	1·25	90

1142	40p. Agapanthus and High Knoll Fort	1·75	1·75
1143	£1 Honeysuckle and Heart Shaped Waterfall	3·25	4·00
1140/3	*Set of 4*	6·25	6·75

266 R.M.S. *St. Helena* 2010

(Litho BDT)

2010 (19 Nov). 20th Anniv of R.M.S. *St. Helena*. T **266** and simiilar horiz designs. Multicoloured. W w **18** (sideways). P 14×14½.

1144	15p. Type **266**	1·25	1·00
1145	35p. Arrival at St. Helena on her maiden voyage	1·75	1·25
1146	40p. Launch of R.M.S. *St. Helena*, 1990	2·00	1·75
1147	90p. Captain's table	4·25	4·75
1144/7	*Set of 4*	8·25	8·00

267 Queen Elizabeth II

(Litho BDT)

2011 (7 Feb). Queen Elizabeth II and Prince Philip 'A Lifetime of Service'. T **267** and similar diamond-shaped designs. Multicoloured. P 13½.

1148	15p. Type **267**	50	50
1149	25p. Queen Elizabeth II and Prince Philip (wearing tweed jacket), c. 1960	85	85
1150	35p. Queen Elizabeth II and Prince Philip, c. 1955	1·25	1·25
1151	40p. Queen Elizabeth II (wearing yellow) and Prince Philip, 1970s	1·40	1·60
1152	40p. Queen Elizabeth II (wearing turquoise-green jacket and hat) and Prince Philip, 1970s	1·40	1·60
1153	90p. Prince Philip, 1970s	3·00	3·50
1148/53	*Set of 6*	8·00	9·00
MS1154	175×164 mm. Nos. 1148/53 and three stamp-size labels	8·00	9·00
MS1155	110×70 mm. £1.50 Queen Elizabeth II and Prince Philip, c. 2010	5·00	6·00

Nos. 1148/53 were printed in separate sheetlets of eight stamps.

No. **MS**1154 forms a diamond shape but with the left, right and top corners removed.

267a Prince William and Miss Catherine Middleton

267b Miss Catherine Middleton and Maid of Honour Pippa Middleton arriving at Westminster Abbey

(Litho BDT)

2011 (29 Apr). Royal Wedding. Sheet 118×90 mm. W w **18** (sideways). P 14½×14.

MS1156	**267a** **£3** multicoloured	11·00	12·00

(Litho Enschedé)

2011 (1 Sept). Royal Wedding (2nd issue). T **267b** and similar multicoloured designs. W w **18** (sideways on horiz designs). P 14.

1157	15p. Type **267b**	75	70
1158	35p. Duke and Duchess of Cambridge waving from State Landau	1·25	1·25
1159	40p. Duke and Duchess of Cambridge at Westminster Abbey after wedding	1·40	1·40
1160	60p. Duke and Duchess of Cambridge waving from Buckingham Palace balcony (*vert*)	2·10	2·10
1161	£1 Duke and Duchess of Cambridge kissing on Buckingham Palace balcony (*vert*)	3·25	3·50
1157/61	*Set of 5*	8·00	8·00

268 Island Hogfish (male)

269 RFA *Gold Rover*

(Des Andrew Robinson. Litho BDT)

2011 (31 Oct). Endangered Species. Island Hogfish (*Bodianus insularis*). T **268** and similar horiz designs. Multicoloured. W w **18** (sideways). P 14.

1162	35p. Type **268**	1·60	1·60
	a. Strip of 5. Nos. 1162/5	8·00	8·00
1163	40p. Island hogfish (juvenile)	1·75	1·75
1164	50p. Island hogfish (immature female)	2·00	2·00
1165	£1.20 Island hogfish (male, on reef)	3·50	3·50
1162/5	*Set of 4*	8·00	8·00
MS1166	94×64 mm. £1.50 As No. 1165	5·00	5·00

Nos. 1162/5 were printed together, *se-tenant*, as horizontal and vertical strips of five in sheets of 16, and also in separate sheets of 20 (2 panes of 10).

(Des Derek Miller. Litho BDT)

2011 (14 Nov). Christmas. Royal Fleet Auxiliary Ships. T **269** and similar horiz designs. Multicoloured. W w **18** (sideways). P 13½.

1167	35p. Type **269**	1·10	1·10
1168	50p. RFA *Black Rover*	1·75	1·75
1169	60p. RFA *Lyme Bay*	2·25	2·25
1170	£1.20 RFA *Darkdale*	3·50	3·50
1167/70	*Set of 4*	7·75	7·75

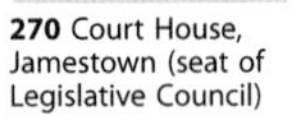

270 Court House, Jamestown (seat of Legislative Council)

271 Queen Elizabeth II

(Des Andrew Robinson. Litho Cartor)

2011 (28 Nov). Centenary of Commonwealth Parliamentary Association. T **270** and similar vert designs. Multicoloured. W w **18**. P 13½×13.

1171	50p. Type **270**	1·60	1·60
1172	50p. Royal Charter	1·60	1·60
1173	50p. CPA Headquarters, 7 Millbank, London	1·60	1·60
1171/3	*Set of 3*	4·25	4·25
MS1174	120×80 mm. Nos. 1171/3	5·00	5·00

(Litho BDT)

2012 (6 Feb). Diamond Jubilee (1st issue). T **271** and similar diamond-shaped designs. Multicoloured. P 13½.

1175	20p. Type **271**	1·40	1·40

1176	35p. Queen Elizabeth II wearing tiara and diamond earrings, c. 1955	2·00	2·00
1177	40p. Queen Elizabeth II wearing mauve hat, c. 1980	2·25	2·25
1178	50p. Queen Elizabeth II, c. 1990	2·50	2·50
1179	60p. Queen Elizabeth II, c. 1975	2·75	2·75
1180	£1 Queen Elizabeth II, c. 2005	4·00	4·00
1175/80	*Set of* 6	13·00	13·00
MS1181	174×164 mm. Nos. 1175/80 and three stamp-size labels	13·00	13·00
MS1182	110×71 mm. £1.50 Queen Elizabeth II wearing tiara, c. 1955	6·50	6·50

Nos. 1175/80 were printed in separate sheetlets of eight stamps.

No. **MS**1181 forms a diamond-shape but with the left, right and top corners removed.

272 Union Jack over Sea

(Des Andrew Robinson. Litho Enschedé)

2012 (12 June). Diamond Jubilee (2nd issue). Children's Paintings. T **272** and similar horiz designs. Multicoloured. W w **18** (sideways). P 14.

1183	20p. Type **272**	1·40	1·40
1184	35p. Outline map of St. Helena, tortoise, wirebird and crown	2·00	2·00
1185	50p. Outline map of St. Helena, Queen, ship and St. James' Church	2·50	2·50
1186	£1 Union Jack on map of St. Helena, leaves, torches, heart-shaped waterfall and ship	4·00	4·00
1183/6	*Set of* 4	9·00	9·00

273 Crew of RMS *St. Helena*, 1982

274 O Little Town of Bethlehem

(Litho BDT)

2012 (26 June). 30th Anniv of RMS *St. Helena's* Commission for the Falklands War. T **273** and similar horiz designs. Multicoloured. W w **18** (sideways). P 14.

1187	20p. Type **273**	1·50	1·50
1188	35p. RMS *St. Helena*, Grytviken, 1982 (winter)	2·25	2·25
1189	40p. RMS *St. Helena*, Ascension Island, 1982.	2·50	2·50
1190	50p. RMS *St. Helena*, Grytviken, 1982 (summer)	2·75	2·75
1191	£1 RMS *St. Helena* under escort, 1982	4·25	4·25
1187/91	*Set of* 5	12·00	12·00

(Des Andrew Robinson. Litho Cartor)

2012 (5 Nov). Christmas. Carols. T **274** and similar horiz designs. Multicoloured. W w **18** (sideways). P 13×13½.

1192	20p. Type **274**	1·10	1·10
1193	35p. While Shepherds Watched	1·75	1·75
1194	50p. Away in a Manger	2·25	2·25
1195	£1 Silent Night Holy Night	4·25	4·25
1192/5	*Set of* 4	8·50	8·50

275 Queen Victoria

276 Margaret Thatcher

(Litho BDT)

2013 (6 Feb). 60th Anniv of the Coronation. Coronation Souvenirs. T **275** and similar multicoloured designs. W w **18** (sideways on Nos. 1196/200). P 14½×14 (MS1201) or 14 (others).

1196	20p. Type **275**	75	75
1197	35p. King Edward VII and Queen Alexandra.	1·25	1·25
1198	40p. King George V	1·40	1·40
1199	50p. Coronation souvenir of King George VI and Queen Elizabeth	1·60	1·60
1200	£1 Queen Elizabeth II, c. 1952 and Buckingham Palace	3·00	3·00
1196/200	*Set of* 5	7·25	7·25
MS1201	111×70 mm. £2 Queen Elizabeth II in recent years (32×48 *mm*)	6·00	6·50

(Des Andrew Robinson. Litho BDT)

2013 (8 Aug). Margaret Thatcher (1925–2013, Prime Minister 1979–90) Commemoration. T **276** and similar horiz designs. Multicoloured. W w **18** (sideways). P 13½.

1202	40p. Type **276**	1·75	1·50
1203	50p. Margaret Thatcher	1·75	1·50
1204	60p. Margaret Thatcher (with hand on chin)	2·00	2·00
1205	£1 Margaret Thatcher at microphone speaking	3·50	4·00
1202/5	*Set of* 4	8·00	8·00
MS1206	147×82 mm. Nos. 1202/5	8·00	8·00

277 Prince William holding Prince George

(Litho Cartor)

2013 (6 Nov). Birth of Prince George of Cambridge. T **277** and similar vert designs. Multicoloured. W w **18**. P 13½×13.

1207	25p. Type **277**	75	75
1208	40p. Catherine, Duchess of Cambridge holding Prince George	1·40	1·40
1209	60p. Prince George	1·75	1·75
1210	£1 Duke and Duchess of Cambridge with Prince George	3·00	3·00
1207/10	*Set of* 4	6·25	6·25

STAMP BOOKLETS

1962 (2 Mar). Black on green cover. Stitched.

SB1 4s.6d. booklet containing 1d., 1½d., 2d., 3d. and 6d. (Nos. 176/9, 181), each in block of 4 ... 55·00

1969. Black on grey-green cover. Stapled.

SB2 5s.4d. booklet containing 1d., 2d., 3d., 4d. and 6d. (Nos. 227, 229/32), each in block of 4 ... 30·00

1971 (24 June). Black on green cover. Stapled.

SB3 44p. booklet containing ½p., 1p., 1½p., 2p., 2½p. and 3½p. (Nos. 261/6), each in block of 4 ... 16·00

1981 (June). Black printed cover showing St. Helena Arms. Stapled.

SB4 £1 booklet containing 1p., 3p., 5p., 6p. and 10p. (Nos. 319/22A, 325A), each in block of 4 ... 11·00

1984 (1 June). Black on blue cover showing St. Helena Arms. Stapled.

SB5 £1.04 booklet containing 1p., 3p., 7p. and 15p. (Nos. 425/6, 428, 430), each in block of 4 ... 6·00

1991 (17 June). 65th Birthday of Queen Elizabeth II and 70th Birthday of Prince Philip. Black on blue cover, 116×106 mm, showing St. Helena Arms. Stapled.

SB6 £1 booklet containing 25p. (Nos. 591/2) in block of 4 stamps and 2 labels ... 5·50

B **1** Flying Fish

2008 (19 Aug). St. Helena Island Flag. Multicoloured cover as Type B **1**. Self-adhesive.

SB7	£4.20 booklet containing pane of twelve 35p. stamps (No. 1071a)	21·00

POSTAGE DUE STAMPS

D **1** Outline Map of St. Helena

(Des L. Curtis. Litho Questa)

1986 (9 June). W w **16**. P 14½×14.

D1	D **1**	1p. deep brown and cinnamon	10	40
D2		2p. deep brown and bright orange	15	40
D3		5p. deep brown and orange-vermilion	20	45
D4		7p. black and bright reddish violet	20	50
D5		10p. black and violet-blue	25	50
D6		25p. black and pale emerald	65	1·25
D1/6 *Set of 6*			1·40	3·25

Tristan da Cunha

Although first settled in 1817 no surviving mail is known from Tristan da Cunha until two whaler's letters written in 1836 and 1843, these being carried home in other whaling ships. Then there is a long gap until the late 1800's when other letters are known—surprisingly only some seven in number, up to 1908 when the first of the island cachet handstamps came into use.

The collecting of postal history material from 1908 to 1952, when Tristan's first stamps were issued, revolves around the numerous cachets of origin which were struck on mail from the island during these 44 years. The handstamps producing these cachets were supplied over the years by various people particularly interested in the island and the islanders, and were mostly used by the clergymen who volunteered to go and serve as the community's ministers.

The postal cachets are illustrated below. The use of the different cachets on mail frequently overlapped, at one period in 1930 there were five different types of handstamp in use. As there was no official source for providing them they appeared on the island from various donors; then disappeared without trace once they became worn out. Only one of these early rubber handstamps has apparently survived, Cachet Va.

Covers bearing the cachets are recognised collector's items, but are difficult to value in general terms. As elsewhere the value is discounted by poor condition of the cover, and may be increased by use on a scarce date or with additional postal markings. Some cachets are known in more than one colour, but we do not list these variations.

Cachet Types V and VII on cover are the commonest, Type Va, used only for three months, and Type IVa are the scarcest, equalling the scarcest use of Type I examples. All cacheted covers, particularly if non-philatelic, are desirable forerunner items. Even a philatelic cover of Type V is, at present, worth in the region of £35.

Dates given are of the first recorded use.

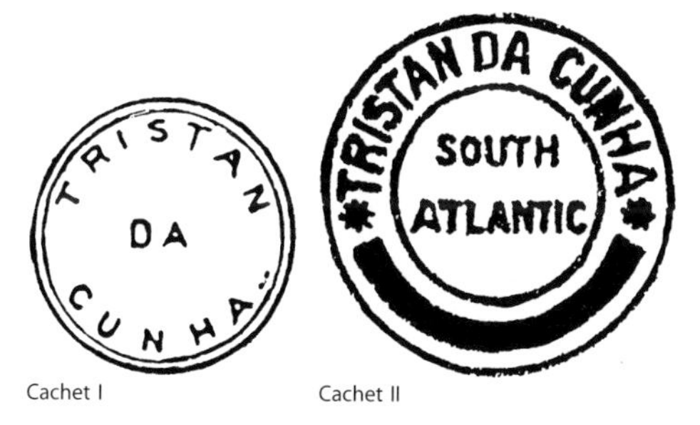

Cachet I   Cachet II

Cat. No.		*Value on cover*
C1	**1908** (May). Cachet I .... *from*	£4000
C2	**1919** (31 July). Cachet II .... *from*	£425

Cachet III

C3	**1921** (8 Feb). Cachet III .... *from*	£300

Cachet IVa

C4	**1927** (1 Oct). Cachet IV (*as* IVa, *but without centre label*) .... *from*	£850
C5	**1928** (28 Oct). Cachet IVa .... *from*	£5500

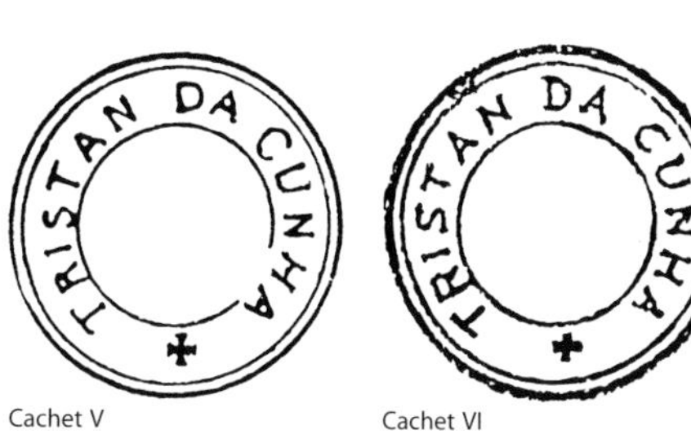

Cachet V   Cachet VI

C6	**1929** (24 Feb). Cachet V .... *from*	35·00
C7	**1929** (15 May). Cachet Va (*as* V, *but without break in inner ring. Shows* "T" "C" *and* "N" *damaged*) .... *from*	£6500
C8	**1936** (Aug). Cachet VI .... *from*	60·00

Cachet VII

C9	**1936** (1 Feb). Cachet VII .... *from*	22·00

During World War II there was little mail from the island as its function as a meteorological station was cloaked by security. Such covers as are known are generally struck with the "tombstone" naval censor mark and postmarked "maritime mail" or have South African postal markings. A few philatelic items from early in the war bearing cachets exist, but this usage was soon stopped by the military commander and the handstamps were put away until peace returned. Covers from the period would be worth from £75 to at least £350.

Cachet VIII

C10	**1946** (8 May). Cachet VIII .... *from*	90·00

Cachet IX

C11	**1948** (29 Feb). Cachet IX .... *from*	55·00

Cachet X

C12	**1948** (2 Feb). Cachet X ... *from*	45·00

This cachet with "A.B.C." below the date was in private use between 1942 and 1946.

Although an earlier example of Cachet X is now known, we have retained the traditional sequence insofar as Cachets IX and X are concerned, for the convenience of collectors.

Cachet XI

Cachet XII

RESETTLEMENT
SURVEY - 1962

Cachet XIII

Cachets XI to XIII from the 1961/63 "volcano eruption" and "return to the island" period vary in value from £30 to £120, due to philatelic usage on the one hand and scarce mailings from the small survey parties on shore during this period on the other.

TRISTAN
DA CUNHA
(1)

1952 (1 Jan). Nos. 131, 135a/40 and 149/51 of St. Helena optd with T **1**.

1	½d. violet	15	3·50
2	1d. black and green	1·00	1·50
3	1½d. black and carmine	1·00	1·50
4	2d. black and scarlet	1·00	1·50
5	3d. grey	1·00	1·50
6	4d. ultramarine	7·00	2·50
7	6d. light blue	7·00	2·50
8	8d. olive-green	7·00	8·00
9	1s. sepia	5·50	2·00
10	2s.6d. maroon	24·00	17·00
11	5s. chocolate	38·00	23·00
12	10s. purple	60·00	38·00
1/12	*Set of* 12	£140	90·00

1953 (2 June). Coronation. As No. 56 of Ascension.

13	3d. black and grey-green	1·25	2·00

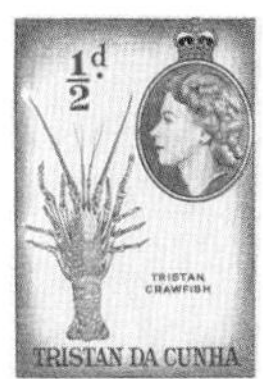

2 Tristan Crawfish

3 Carting Flax for Thatching

4 Rockhopper Penguin

5 Big Beach factory

6 Yellow-nosed Albatross

7 Island longboat

8 Tristan from the south-west

9 Girls on donkeys

10 Inaccessible Island from Tristan

11 Nightingale Island

12 St. Mary's Church

13 Southern Elephant seal at Gough Island

14 Inaccessible Island Rail

15 Island spinning wheel

(Recess D.L.R.)

1954 (2 Jan). T **2/15**. Wmk Mult Script CA. P 12½×13 (horiz) or 13×12½ (vert).

14	**2**	½d. red and deep brown	10	10
15	**3**	1d. sepia and bluish green	10	50
16	**4**	1½d. black and reddish purple	1·75	1·75
17	**5**	2d. grey-violet and brown-orange	30	20
18	**6**	2½d. black and carmine-red	1·50	60
19	**7**	3d. ultramarine and olive-green	2·25	1·75
20	**8**	4d. turquoise-blue and deep blue	60	70
21	**9**	5d. emerald and black	60	70
22	**10**	6d. deep green and violet	60	75
23	**11**	9d. reddish violet and Venetian red	60	45

24	**12**	1s. deep yellow-green and sepia	60	45
25	**13**	2s.6d. deep brown and light blue	17·00	10·00
26	**14**	5s. black and red-orange	50·00	14·00
27	**15**	10s. brown-orange and purple	24·00	14·00
14/27		*Set of* 14	90·00	40·00

16 Starfish

17 Concha Wrasse

18 Two-spined Thornfish

19 Atlantic Saury

20 Bristle Snipefish

21 Tristan Crawfish

22 False Jacopever

23 Five-fingered Morwong

24 Long-finned Scad

25 Christophersen's Medusafish

26 Blue Medusafish

27 Snoek

28 Blue Shark

29 Black Right Whale

(Des Mr. and Mrs. G. F. Harris. Recess Waterlow)

1960 (1 Feb). Marine Life. T **16/29**. W w **12**. P 13.

28	**16**	½d. black and orange	15	40
29	**17**	1d. black and bright purple	15	20
30	**18**	1½d. black and light turquoise-blue	20	70
31	**19**	2d. black and bluish green	30	1·00
32	**20**	2½d. black and sepia	55	60
33	**21**	3d. black and brown-red	1·25	2·00
34	**22**	4d. black and yellow-olive	1·25	1·25
35	**23**	5d. black and orange-yellow	1·50	1·00
36	**24**	6d. black and blue	1·75	1·00
37	**25**	9d. black and rose-carmine	1·75	1·50
38	**26**	1s. black and light brown	3·50	60
39	**27**	2s.6d. black and ultramarine	11·00	11·00
40	**28**	5s. black and light emerald	12·00	12·00
41	**29**	10s. black and violet	48·00	28·00
28/41		*Set of* 14	75·00	55·00

1961 (15 Apr). As Nos. 28/30 and 32/41 but values in South African decimal currency.

42	½c. black and orange (as ½d.)	10	1·25
43	1c. black and bright purple (as 1d.)	15	1·25
44	1½c. black and light turquoise-blue (as 1½d.)	35	1·25
45	2c. black and sepia (as 2½d.)	65	1·25
46	2½c. black and brown-red (as 3d.)	1·00	1·25
47	3c. black and yellow-olive (as 4d.)	1·00	1·25
48	4c. black and orange-yellow (as 5d.)	1·25	1·25
49	5c. black and blue (as 6d.)	1·25	1·25
50	7½c. black and rose-carmine (as 9d.)	1·25	1·25
51	10c. black and light brown (as 1s.)	2·00	1·25
52	25c. black and ultramarine (as 2s. 6d.)	8·00	7·50
53	50c. black and light emerald (as 5s.)	22·00	17·00
54	1r. black and violet (as 10s.)	50·00	32·00
42/54	*Set of* 13	80·00	60·00

Following a volcanic eruption the island was evacuated on 10 October 1961, but resettled in 1963.

TRISTAN DA CUNHA
RESETTLEMENT
1963
(**30**)

1963 (12 Apr). Tristan Resettlement. As Nos. 176/88 of St. Helena, but Wmk Mult Script CA (sideways on 1d., 2d., 7d., 10d., 2s. 6d., 10s), optd with T **30**.

55	1d. bright blue, dull violet, yellow and carmine	15	1·00
56	1½d. yellow, green, black and light drab	1·50	70
57	2d. scarlet and grey	25	1·00
58	3d. light blue, black, pink and deep blue	30	1·00
	a. Black printed double*	£300	
	w. Wmk inverted	£600	£700
59	4½d. yellow-green, green, brown and grey	50	60
60	6d. red, sepia and light yellow-olive	2·75	30
61	7d. red-brown, black and violet	50	30
62	10d. brown-purple and light blue	50	30
63	1s. greenish yellow, bluish green and brown	50	30
64	1s.6d. grey, black and slate-blue	6·00	1·00
65	2s.6d. red, pale yellow and turquoise	1·00	45
66	5s. yellow, brown and green	6·00	1·00
	w. Wmk inverted	90·00	75·00
67	10s. orange-red, black and blue	6·00	1·00
55/67	*Set of* 13	23·00	8·00

*No. 58a shows the outline round the Queen's head printed double.

1963 (2 Oct). Freedom from Hunger. As No. 84 of Ascension.

68	1s.6d. carmine	50	30

1964 (1 Feb). Red Cross Centenary. As Nos. 85/6 of Ascension.

69	3d. red and black	20	15
70	1s.6d. red and blue	30	20

31 South Atlantic Map

32 Flagship of Tristao da Cunha, 1506

33 *Heemstede* (Dutch East Indiaman), 1643

34 *Edward* (American Whaling ship), 1864

35 *Shenandoah* (Confederate warship), 1873

35a H.M.S *Challenger* (survey ship), 1873

36 H.M.S *Galatea* (screw frigate), 1867

37 H.M.S *Cilicia* (transport), 1942

38 Royal Yacht *Britannia*

39 H.M.S *Leopard* (frigate)

40 *Tjisadane* (liner)

41 *Tristania* (crayfish trawler)

42 *Boissevain* (cargo liner)

43 *Bornholm* (liner)

44 Queen Elizabeth II

44a *R.S.A.* (research vessel)

(Queen's portrait by Anthony Buckley. Des, eng and recess B.W.)

1965 (17 Feb)–**67**. Designs as T **31/44a**. W w **12** (sideways on £1). P 11½×11 (vert) or 11×11½ (horiz).

71	**31**	½d. black and ultramarine	15	30
72	**32**	1d. black and emerald-green	1·00	15
73	**33**	1½d. black and blue	1·00	15
74	**34**	2d. black and purple	1·00	15
75	**35**	3d. black and turquoise-blue	1·00	15
75*a*	**35a**	4d. black and orange (1.9.67)	4·00	4·00
76	**36**	4½d. black and brown	1·00	15
77	**37**	6d. black and green	1·25	15
78	**38**	7d. black and rose-red	2·00	30
79	**39**	10d. black and chocolate	1·25	55
80	**40**	1s. black and carmine	1·25	30
81	**41**	1s.6d. black and yellow-olive	6·50	2·50
82	**42**	2s.6d. black and orange-brown	3·50	3·75
83	**43**	5s. black and violet	9·00	3·50
84	**44**	10s. deep blue and carmine	1·75	1·25
84*a*	**44a**	10s. black and deep turquoise-blue (1.9.67)	15·00	11·00
84*b*	**44**	£1 deep blue and orange-brown (1.9.67)	13·00	11·00
71/84*b*		*Set of* 17	55·00	35·00

1965 (11 May*). I.T.U. Centenary. As Nos. 87/8 of Ascension.

85	3d. orange-red and grey	20	15
86	6d. reddish violet and yellow-orange	30	15

*This is the local date of issue; the stamps were not released in London until 17 May.

1965 (25 Oct). International Co-operation Year. As Nos. 89/90 of Ascension.

87	1d. reddish purple and turquoise-green	20	15
88	6d. deep bluish green and lavender	50	25

1966 (24 Jan). Churchill Commemoration. As Nos. 91/4 of Ascension.

89	1d. new blue	35	40
	a. Value omitted	£1300	
90	3d. deep green	1·00	50
91	6d. brown	1·25	65
92	1s.6d. bluish violet	1·40	70
89/92	*Set of* 4	3·50	2·00

No. 89a was caused by misplacement of the gold and also shows the country inscription moved to the right.

45 H.M.S. *Falmouth* (frigate) at Tristan and Soldier of 1816

(Des V. Whiteley. Litho Harrison)

1966 (15 Aug). 150th Anniv of Tristan Garrison. W w **12** (sideways*). P 14½.

93	**45**	3d. multicoloured	15	10
		w. Wmk Crown to right of CA	7·00	
94		6d. multicoloured	15	15
95		1s.6d. multicoloured	20	25
96		2s.6d. multicoloured	25	25
93/6		*Set of* 4	65	65

*The normal sideways watermark shows Crown to left of CA, *as seen from the back of the stamp.*

1966 (1 Oct*). World Cup Football Championship. As Nos. 95/6 of Ascension.

97	3d. violet, yellow-grn, lake & yellow-brown	20	10
98	2s.6d. chocolate, blue-green, lake and yellow-brown	50	20

*Released in St. Helena on 1 July in error.

1966 (1 Oct). Inauguration of W.H.O. Headquarters, Geneva. As Nos. 97/8 of Ascension.

99	6d. black, yellow-green and light blue	65	30
100	5s. black, light purple and yellow-brown	1·10	70

1966 (1 Dec). 20th Anniv of U.N.E.S.C.O. As Nos. 107/9 of Ascension.

101	10d. slate-violet, red, yellow and orange	25	15
	w. Wmk Crown to right of CA	45·00	
102	1s.6d. orange-yellow, violet and deep olive	40	20
103	2s.6d. black, bright purple and orange	45	25
101/3	*Set of* 3	1·00	55

*The normal sideways watermark shows Crown to left of CA, *as seen from the back of the stamp.*

46 Calshot Harbour

(Des V. Whiteley. Litho D.L.R.)

1967 (2 Jan). Opening of Calshot Harbour. P 14×14½.

104	**46**	6d. multicoloured	10	10
105		10d. multicoloured	10	10
106		1s.6d. multicoloured	10	15
107		2s.6d. multicoloured	15	20
104/7		*Set of* 4	30	45

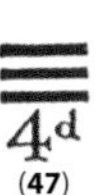

(47)

48 Prince Alfred, First Duke of Edinburgh

1967 (10 May). No. 76 surch with T **47**.

108	4d. on 4½d. black and brown	10	10

(Des M. Goaman. Litho Harrison)

1967 (10 July). Centenary of First Duke of Edinburgh's Visit to Tristan. W w **12**. P 14½.

109	**48**	3d. multicoloured	10	10
110		6d. multicoloured	10	10

111	1s.6d. multicoloured	10	10
112	2s.6d. multicoloured	15	15
109/12	*Set of 4*	30	30

49 Wandering Albatross

53 Union Jack and Dependency Flag

(Des V. Whiteley. Photo Harrison)

1968 (15 May). Birds. T **49** and similar horiz designs. Multicoloured. W w **12**. P 14×14½.

113	4d. Type **49**	30	30
114	1s. Wilkins's Finch	35	30
115	1s.6d. Tristan Thrush	40	55
116	2s.6d. Greater Shearwater	60	65
113/16	*Set of 4*	1·50	1·60

(Des Jennifer Toombs. Litho D.L.R.)

1968 (1 Nov). 30th Anniv of Tristan da Cunha as a Dependency of St. Helena. T **53** and similar horiz design. W w **12** (sideways). P 14.

117	**53**	6d. multicoloured	20	30
118	–	9d. sepia, blue and turquoise-blue	20	35
119	**53**	1s.6d. multicoloured	30	40
120	–	2s.6d. carmine, blue and turquoise-blue	40	40
117/20		*Set of 4*	1·00	1·25

Design:—9d., 2s.6d. St. Helena and Tristan on chart.

55 Frigate

59 Sailing Ship off Tristan da Cunha

(Des and recess B.W.)

1969 (1 June). Clipper Ships. T **55** and similar horiz designs. W w **12**. P 11×11½.

121	4d. new blue	60	40
122	1s. carmine (full-rigged ship)	60	45
123	1s.6d. blue-green (barque)	65	90
124	2s.6d. chocolate (full-rigged clipper)	70	95
121/4	*Set of 4*	2·25	2·40

(Des Jennifer Toombs. Litho Format)

1969 (1 Nov). United Society for the Propagation of the Gospel. T **59** and similar horiz designs. Multicoloured. W w **12** (sideways). P 14½×14.

125	4d. Type **59**	60	30
126	9d. Islanders going to first Gospel service	15	30
127	1s.6d. Landing of the first minister	15	40
128	2s.6d. Procession outside St. Mary's Church	20	40
125/8	*Set of 4*	1·00	1·25

63 Globe and Red Cross Emblem

(Des and litho B.W.)

1970 (1 June). Centenary of British Red Cross. T **63** and similar designs. W w **12** (sideways on vert designs). P 13.

129	**63**	4d. light emerald, scarlet & deep bluish green	10	25
130		9d. bistre, scarlet and deep bluish green	15	30
131	–	1s.9d. light drab, scarlet and ultramarine	25	45
132	–	2s.6d. reddish purple, scarlet and ultramarine	30	55
129/32		*Set of 4*	70	1·40

Design: *Vert*—1s.9d., 2s.6d., Union Jack and Red Cross Flag.

64 Crawfish and Longboat

(65)

(Des Harrison. Litho Enschedé)

1970 (1 Nov). Crawfish Industry. T **64** and similar horiz design. Multicoloured. W w **12**. P 12½×13.

133	4d. Type **64**	30	30
134	10d. Packing and storing Crawfish	35	35
135	1s.6d. Type **64**	45	60
136	2s.6d. As 10d.	45	70
133/6	*Set of 4*	1·40	1·75

1971 (14 Feb*). Decimal Currency. As Nos. 72/4, 75a, 77/83 and 84a surch as T **65**, by B.W. in typo. Glazed paper.

137	½p. on 1d. black and emerald-green	15	15
138	1p. on 2d. black and purple	15	15
139	1½p. on 4d. black and orange	30	15
140	2½p. on 6d. black and green	30	15
141	3p. on 7d. black and rose-red	30	15
142	4p. on 10d. black and chocolate	30	20
143	5p. on 1s. black and carmine	30	20
144	7½p. on 1s.6d. black and yellow-olive	1·25	1·75
145	12½p. on 2s.6d. black and orange-brown	1·25	2·25
146	15p. on 1½d. black and blue	1·25	2·50
147	25p. on 5s. black and violet	1·25	4·50
148	50p. on 10s. black and deep turquoise-blue	1·25	9·00
137/48	*Set of 12*	7·25	19·00

*This was the local release date, but the Crown Agents issued the stamps one day later.

66 *Quest*

(Des V. Whiteley. Litho J.W.)

1971 (1 June). 50th Anniv of Shackleton-Rowett Expedition. T **66** and similar horiz designs. W w **12** (sideways). P 13½×14.

149	1½p. multicoloured	70	30
150	4p. sepia, pale green and apple-green	70	40
151	7½p. black, bright purple and pale green	70	40
152	12½p. multicoloured	75	45
149/52	*Set of 4*	2·50	1·40

Designs:—4p. Presentation of Scout Troop flag; 7½p. Cachet on pair of 6d. G.B. stamps; 12½p. Shackleton, postmarks and longboat taking mail to the *Quest*.

67 H.M.S. *Victory* at Trafalgar and Thomas Swain catching Nelson

68 Cow Pudding

(Des R. Granger Barrett. Litho Questa)

1971 (1 Nov). Island Families. T **67** and similar horiz designs showing ships and the names of families associated with them. Multicoloured. W w **12** (sideways). P 13½.

153	1½p. Type **67**	20	40
154	2½p. *Emily of Stonington* (American schooner) (P. W. Green)	20	50
155	4p. *Italia* (barque) (Lavarello and Repetto)	25	60
156	7½p. H.M.S. *Falmouth* (frigate) (William Glass)	30	70
157	12½p. American whaling ship (Rogers and Hagan)	30	85
153/7	*Set of 5*	1·10	2·75

(Des M. and Sylvia Goaman. Recess and litho B.W. (50p., £1); Litho A. & M. (others))

1972 (29 Feb). T **68** and similar multicoloured designs showing flowering plants. W w **12** (sideways* on horiz designs). P 13.

No.	Description		
158	½p. Type **68**	20	15
	w. Wmk inverted	30	30
159	1p. Peak Berry	40	15
	w. Wmk inverted	50	40
160	1½p. Sand Flower (*horiz*)	40	20
161	2½p. N.Z. Flax (*horiz*)	40	20
	w. Wmk Crown to right of CA	1·00	1·00
162	3p. Island Tree	40	20
	w. Wmk inverted	1·10	80
163	4p. Bog Fern	40	25
	w. Wmk inverted	1·10	1·10
164	5p. Dog Catcher	3·00	30
	w. Wmk inverted	3·25	1·00
165	7½p. Celery	4·50	1·50
	w. Wmk inverted	4·75	1·50
166	12½p. Pepper Tree	1·25	60
	w. Wmk inverted	35·00	32·00
167	25p. Foul Berry (*horiz*)	1·25	1·50
	w. Wmk Crown to right of CA	3·00	3·50
168	50p. Tussock	7·00	2·50
169	£1 Tussac (*horiz*)	1·75	2·50
158/69	*Set of* 12	18·00	8·50

*The normal sideways watermark shows Crown to left of CA, *as seen from the back of the stamp.*

69 Launching

(Des R. Svensson. Litho Walsall)

1972 (1 June). Tristan Longboats. T **69** and similar multicoloured designs. W w **12** (sideways on 2½p. and 4p.). P 14.

No.	Description		
170	2½p. Type **69**	25	15
171	4p. Under oars	30	15
172	7½p. Coxswain Arthur Repetto (*vert*)	30	20
173	12½p. Under sail for Nightingale Island (*vert*)	35	25
170/3	*Set of* 4	1·10	65

70 Tristan Thrushes and Wandering Albatrosses

(Des (from photographs by D. Groves) and photo Harrison)

1972 (20 Nov). Royal Silver Wedding. Multicoloured; background colours given. W w **12**. P 14×14½.

No.	Description		
174	**70** 2½p. red-brown	25	30
	w. Wmk inverted	5·50	
175	7½p. dull ultramarine	10	30
	w. Wmk inverted	£140	

71 Church Altar

(Des J. Cooter. Litho Questa)

1973 (8 July). Golden Jubilee of St. Mary's Church. W w **12**. P 13½.

No.	Description		
176	**71** 25p. multicoloured	40	40

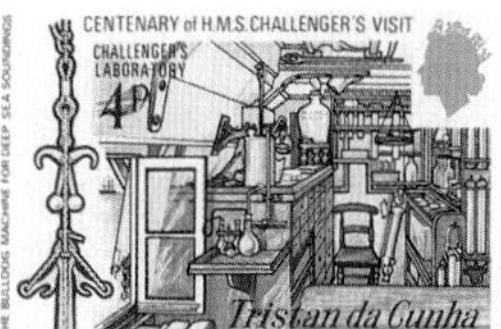

72 H.M.S. *Challenger's* Laboratory

(Des V. Whiteley Studio. Litho Questa)

1973 (15 Oct). Centenary of H.M.S. *Challenger's* Visit. T **72** and similar horiz designs. Multicoloured. W w **12**. P 13½.

No.	Description		
177	4p. Type **72**	25	25
178	5p. H.M.S. *Challenger* off Tristan	25	25
179	7½p. *Challenger's* pinnace off Nightingale Is.	25	30
180	12½p. Survey route	35	40
177/80	*Set of* 4	1·00	1·10
MS181	145×96 mm. Nos. 177/80	1·10	2·75

73 Approaching English Port

(Des Jennifer Toombs. Litho Questa)

1973 (10 Nov). Tenth Anniv of Return to Tristan da Cunha. T **73** and similar horiz designs. Multicoloured (except 4p.). W w **12**. P 14.

No.	Description		
182	4p. Type **73** (reddish brn, lemon & gold)	20	25
183	5p. Survey party	20	25
184	7½p. Embarking on *Bornholm*	20	35
	w. Wmk inverted	£300	
185	12½p. Approaching Tristan	30	45
	w. Wmk inverted	1·50	
182/5	*Set of* 4	80	1·10

1973 (14 Nov). Royal Wedding. As Nos. 178/9 of Ascension.

No.	Description		
186	7½p. bright blue	15	10
187	12½p. light turquoise-green	15	10

74 Rockhopper Penguin and Egg

(Des R. Granger Barrett. Litho Questa)

1974 (1 May). Rockhopper Penguins. T **74** and similar horiz designs. W w **12**. P 14.

No.	Description		
188	2½p. Type **74**	1·00	75
189	5p. Rockhopper Colony, Inaccessible Island	1·25	1·00
190	7½p. Penguin fishing	1·50	1·25
	w. Wmk inverted		
191	25p. Adult and fledgling	1·75	1·50
188/91	*Set of* 4	5·00	4·00

75 Map with Rockhopper Penguin and Wandering Albatross

(Des J.W. Litho Questa)

1974 (1 Oct). "The Lonely Island". Sheet 154×104 mm. W w **12** (sideways*). P 13½.

No.	Description		
MS192	**75** 35p. multicoloured	3·50	4·00
	w. Wmk Crown to right of CA	£375	

*The normal sideways watermark shows Crown to left of CA, *as seen from the back of the stamp.*

76 Blenheim Palace

(Des Sylvia Goaman. Litho Questa)

1974 (30 Nov). Birth Centenary of Sir Winston Churchill. T **76** and similar horiz design. W w **14** (sideways). P 14.

193	7½p. pale yellow and black	10	10
194	25p. black, sepia and grey	30	25
MS195	93×93 mm. Nos. 193/4. W w **12** (sideways)	55	1·60

Design:—25p. Churchill with Queen Elizabeth II.

77 *Plocamium fuscorubrum*

(Des Sylvia Goaman. Litho Harrison)

1975 (16 Apr). Sea Plants. T **77** and similar horiz designs. W w **12** (sideways*). P 13×13½.

196	4p. rose-carmine, light lilac and black	15	10
197	5p. apple-green, light violet-blue and deep bluish green	15	15
198	10p. red-orange, stone and brown-purple	20	15
	w. Wmk Crown to right of CA	£140	
199	20p. multicoloured	30	25
196/9	*Set of 4*	70	60

Designs:—5p. *Ulva lactua*; 10p. *Epymenia flabellata*; 20p. *Macrocystis pyrifera*.

*The normal sideways watermark shows Crown to left of CA, *as seen from the back of the stamp.*

78 Killer Whale

(Des G. Drummond. Litho Walsall)

1975 (1 Nov). Whales. T **78** and similar horiz designs. Multicoloured. W w **12** (sideways). P 13½.

200	2p. Type **78**	65	35
201	3p. Rough-toothed Dolphin	65	35
202	5p. Black Right Whale	75	40
203	20p. Fin Whale	1·40	85
200/3	*Set of 4*	3·00	1·75

79 ½d. Stamp of 1952

80 Island Cottage

(Des C. Abbott. Litho J.W.)

1976 (27 May*). Festival of Stamps, London. T **79** and similar designs. W w **14** (sideways on 5 and 25p). P 13½.

204	5p. black, violet and light lilac	15	15
205	9p. black, deep green and turquoise	20	15
206	25p. multicoloured	30	40
204/6	*Set of 3*	60	65

Designs: *Vert*—9p. 1953 Coronation stamp. *Horiz*—25p. Mail carrier *Tristania II*.

*This is the local date of issue. The stamps were released by the Crown Agents on 4 May.

For miniature sheet containing No. 206 see No. **MS**218 of Ascension.

(Des C. Abbott. Litho Questa)

1976 (4 Oct). Paintings by Roland Svensson (1st series). T **80** and similar multicoloured designs. W w **14** (sideways on 5p., 10p. and **MS**211). P 14.

207	3p. Type **80**	15	15
208	5p. The potato patches (*horiz*)	15	15
209	10p. Edinburgh from the sea (*horiz*)	20	20
210	20p. Huts, Nightingale Island	30	35
207/10	*Set of 4*	70	70
MS211	125×112 mm. Nos. 207/10	1·50	2·00

See also Nos. 234/8 and 272/6.

81 The Royal Standard

(Des and litho J.W.)

1977 (7 Feb). Silver Jubilee. T **81** and similar horiz designs. Multicoloured. W w **14** (sideways). P 13.

212	10p. Royal Yacht *Britannia*	15	20
213	15p. Type **81**	15	20
214	25p. Royal family	20	20
212/14	*Set of 3*	45	55

For Nos. 213/14 surcharged, see Nos. 232/3.

82 H.M.S. *Eskimo* (frigate)

(Des L. Curtis. Litho Walsall)

1977 (1 Oct). Ships' Crests. T **82** and similar horiz designs. Multicoloured. W w **14** (sideways). P 14.

215	5p. Type **82**	15	15
216	10p. H.M.S. *Naiad* (frigate)	20	15
217	15p. H.M.S. *Jaguar* (frigate)	25	25
218	20p. H.M.S. *London* (destroyer)	30	30
215/18	*Set of 4*	80	75
MS219	142×140 mm. Nos. 215/18	1·00	1·50

83 Great-winged Petrel

(Des BG Studio. Litho Walsall)

1977 (1 Dec). Multicoloured designs as T **83** showing birds. W w **14** (sideways on 1 and 2p.). P 13½.

220	1p. Type **83**	15	60
221	2p. White-faced Storm Petrel	20	90
222	3p. Hall's Giant Petrel	20	90
223	4p. Soft-plumaged Petrel	60	1·00
224	5p. Wandering Albatross	60	1·00
225	10p. Kerguelen Petrel	60	1·00
226	15p. Swallow-tailed Tern	60	1·00
227	20p. Greater Shearwater	1·00	1·00
228	25p. Broad-billed Prion	1·00	1·00
229	50p. Great Skua	1·25	1·00
230	£1 Common Diving Petrel	1·50	1·00
231	£2 Yellow-nosed Albatross	3·00	1·75
220/31	*Set of 12*	9·50	11·00

The 3p. to £2 are vertical designs.

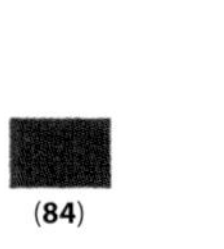

(84)	½ Normal	½ Straight top to serif in "½" (Pl 1C R. 5/1-5)

1978 (19 Jan*). Provisional definitives. Nos. 213/14 surch as T **84**.

No.	Description	Unused	Used
232	4p. on 15p. Type **81**	80	2·50
233	7½p. on 25p. Royal family	80	2·50
	a. Straight top to serif	14·00	

*This is the local date of issue. Covers dated 26 November 1977 are philatelic mail forwarded to the island for cancellation, the stamps having been released in London on 31 October 1977. Supplies for the island population did not arrive until 19 January.

(Des C. Abbott. Litho Questa)

1978 (1 Mar). Paintings by Roland Svensson (2nd series). Horiz designs as T **80**. Multicoloured. W w **14** (sideways*). P 14.

No.	Description	Unused	Used
234	5p. St. Mary's Church	15	15
235	10p. Longboats	15	15
236	15p. A Tristan home	20	25
237	20p. The harbour, 1970	20	25
	w. Wmk Crown to right of CA	£110	
234/7	*Set of 4*	65	70
MS238	115×128 mm. Nos. 234/7	1·50	2·00

*The normal sideways watermark shows Crown to left of CA, *as seen from the back of the stamp.*

85 King's Bull

86 Sodalite

(Des Jennifer Toombs. Litho Questa)

1978 (21 Apr). 25th Anniv of Coronation. T **85** and similar vert designs. W w **14**. P 15.

No.	Description	Unused	Used
239	25p. bistre, bright violet and silver	25	30
	aw. Wmk inverted	20·00	
	b. Sheetlet. Nos. 239/41×2	1·10	
	bw. Wmk inverted	£110	
240	25p. multicoloured	25	30
	aw. Wmk inverted	20·00	
241	25p. bistre, bright violet and silver	25	30
	aw. Wmk inverted	20·00	
239/41	*Set of 3*	65	80

Designs:—No. 239, Type **85**; No. 240, Queen Elizabeth II; No. 241, Tristan crawfish.

Nos. 239/41 were printed together in small sheets of 6, containing two *se-tenant* strips of 3, with horizontal gutter margin between.

(Des J.W. Litho Questa)

1978 (9 June). Local Minerals. T **86** and similar horiz designs. Multicoloured. W w **14** (sideways). P 13½.

No.	Description	Unused	Used
242	3p. Type **86**	25	25
243	5p. Aragonite	30	30
244	10p. Sulphur	45	45
245	20p. Lava containing pyroxene crystal	65	65
242/5	*Set of 4*	1·50	1·50

87 Two-spined Thornfish

88 R.F.A. *Orangeleaf* (tanker)

(Des R. Granger Barrett. Litho Harrison)

1978 (29 Sept). Fish. T **87** and similar horiz designs. W w **14** (sideways). P 14.

No.	Description	Unused	Used
246	5p. black, yellow-brown and yellow-green	10	10
247	10p. black, yellow-brown and emerald	15	15
248	15p. multicoloured	20	20
249	20p. multicoloured	30	25
246/9	*Set of 4*	65	60

Designs:—10p. Five-fingered Morwong; 15p. Concha Wrasse; 20p. Tristan Jacopever.

(Des R. Granger Barrett. Litho Cartor)

1978 (24 Nov). Royal Fleet Auxiliary Vessels. T **88** and similar horiz designs. Multicoloured. W w **14** (sideways). P 12½×12.

No.	Description	Unused	Used
250	5p. Type **88**	15	10
251	10p. R.F.A. *Tarbatness* (store carrier)	15	10
252	20p. R.F.A. *Tidereach* (tanker)	20	25
253	25p. R.F.A. *Reliant* (store carrier)	25	30
250/3	*Set of 4*	65	65
MS254	136×140 mm. Nos. 250/3 (Wmk inverted)	65	2·75

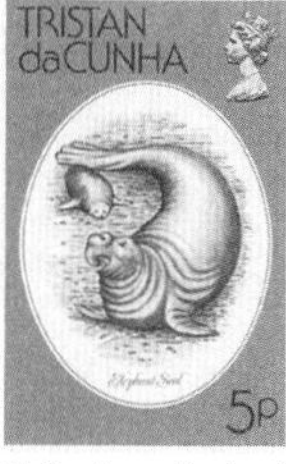

89 Southern Elephant Seal

90 Tristan Longboat

(Des J.W. Litho Questa)

1979 (3 Jan). Wildlife Conservation. T **89** and similar vert designs. Multicoloured. W w **14**. P 14.

No.	Description	Unused	Used
255	5p. Type **89**	10	10
256	10p. Afro-Australian Fur Seal	15	15
257	15p. Tristan Thrush	25	20
258	20p. Nightingale Finch	35	25
255/8	*Set of 4*	75	60

(Des R. Granger Barrett. Litho Questa)

1979 (8 Feb). Visit of *Queen Elizabeth 2*. T **90** and similar horiz designs. Multicoloured. W w **14** (sideways*). P 14½.

No.	Description	Unused	Used
259	5p. Type **90**	15	15
	w. Wmk Crown to right of CA	1·50	2·50
260	10p. *Queen Mary* (liner)	15	15
261	15p. *Queen Elizabeth* (liner)	20	25
262	20p. *Queen Elizabeth 2* (liner)	20	25
259/62	*Set of 4*	65	70
MS263	148×96 mm. 25p. *Queen Elizabeth 2* (liner) (131×27 *mm*)	75	1·50
	w. Wmk Crown to right of CA	7·00	

*The normal watermark for both stamps and minature sheet has Crown to left of CA, *as seen from the back of the stamp.*

91 1952 "TRISTAN DA CUNHA" overprinted St. Helena 10s. Definitive

(Des J.W. Litho Questa)

1979 (27 Aug). Death Centenary of Sir Rowland Hill. T **91** and similar designs showing stamps. W w **14** (sideways* on 5 and 10p.). P 14.

No.	Description	Unused	Used
264	5p. black, lilac and bistre-yellow	10	15
	w. Wmk Crown to right of CA	15·00	
265	10p. black, red and apple-green	15	20
266	25p. multicoloured	30	30
	w. Wmk inverted	4·00	
264/6	*Set of 3*	50	60
MS267	83×103 mm. 50p. black and vermilion	60	70

Designs: *Horiz*—10p. 1954 5s. definitive. *Vert*—25p. 1963 3d. Tristan da Cunha Resettlement commemorative; 50p. 1946 1d. 4 Potatoes local label.

*The normal sideways watermark shows Crown to left of CA, *as seen from the back of the stamp.*

92 "The Padre's House"

93 *Tristania II* (crayfish trawler)

(Des G. Hutchins. Litho Questa)

1979 (26 Nov). International Year of the Child. Children's Drawings. T **92** and similar horiz designs. Multicoloured. W w **14** (sideways). P 14.

268 5p. Type **92** ... 10 10
269 10p. "Houses in the Village" ... 15 15
270 15p. "St. Mary's Church" ... 15 15
271 20p. "Rockhopper Penguins" ... 20 25
268/71 *Set of* 4 ... 50 60

(Des C. Abbott. Litho Questa)

1980 (29 Feb). Paintings by Roland Svensson (3rd series). Landscapes. Multicoloured designs as T **80**. W w **14** (sideways on 5 and 10p.). P 14.

272 5p. "Stoltenhoff Island" (*horiz*) ... 10 10
273 10p. "Nightingale from the East" (*horiz*) ... 15 20
274 15p. "The Administrator's Abode" ... 15 25
275 20p. "Ridge where the Goat jump off" ... 20 30
272/5 *Set of* 4 ... 50 75
MS276 126×109 mm. Nos. 272/5 (wmk sideways) ... 70 1·25

(Des C. Abbott. Litho Walsall)

1980 (6 May). "London 1980" International Stamp Exhibition. T **93** and similar vert designs. Multicoloured. W w **14**. P 14.

277 5p. Type **93** ... 10 10
278 10p. Unloading mail at Calshot Harbour ... 15 15
279 15p. Tractor transporting mail to Post Office ... 15 20
280 20p. Ringing the "dong" to summons people to Post Office ... 20 20
281 25p. Distributing mail ... 25 25
277/81 *Set of* 5 ... 70 80

94 Queen Elizabeth the Queen Mother at Royal Opera House, 1976

95 *Golden Hind*

(Des Harrison. Litho Questa)

1980 (11 Aug*). 80th Birthday of Queen Elizabeth the Queen Mother. W w **14** (sideways). P 14.

282 **94** 14p. multicoloured ... 25 25

*This is the local date of issue. The Crown Agents released this stamp in London on 4 August.

(Des G. Vasarhelyi. Litho Walsall)

1980 (6 Sept). 400th Anniv of Sir Francis Drake's Circumnavigation of the World. T **95** and similar vert designs. Multicoloured. W w **14**. P 14½×14.

283 5p. Type **95** ... 10 10
284 10p. Drake's route ... 15 15
285 20p. Sir Francis Drake ... 20 20
286 25p. Queen Elizabeth I ... 25 25
283/6 *Set of* 4 ... 65 65

96 "Humpty Dumpty"

(Des G. Vasarhelyi. Litho J.W.)

1980 (31 Oct). Christmas. Scenes from Nursery Rhymes. T **96** and similar horiz designs. Multicoloured. W w **14** (sideways). P 13.

287 15p. Type **96** ... 15 25
a. Sheetlet. Nos. 287/95 ... 1·25 1·75
288 15p. "Mary had a little Lamb" ... 15 25
289 15p. "Little Jack Horner" ... 15 25
290 15p. "Hey Diddle Diddle" ... 15 25
291 15p. "London Bridge" ... 15 25
292 15p. "Old King Cole" ... 15 25
293 15p. "Sing a Song of Sixpence" ... 15 25
294 15p. "Tom, Tom the Piper's Son" ... 15 25
295 15p. "The Owl and the Pussy Cat" ... 15 25
287/95 *Set of* 9 ... 1·25 1·75

Nos. 287/95 were printed together, *se-tenant*, within a small sheet of 9 stamps.

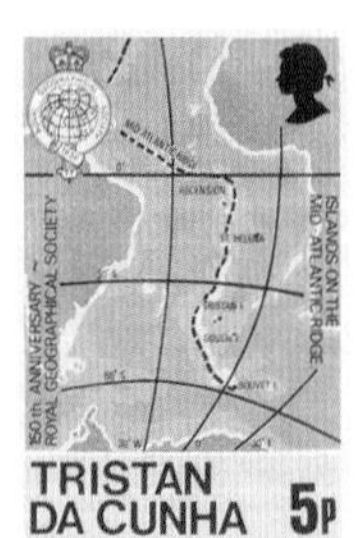

97 South Atlantic Ocean showing Islands on Mid-Atlantic Ridge

98 Revd. Edwin Dodgson as Young Man

(Des A. Crawford, adapted BG Studio. Litho Rosenbaum Bros, Vienna)

1980 (15 Dec). 150th Anniv of Royal Geographical Society. Maps. T **97** and similar vert designs. Multicoloured. W w **14**. P 13½.

296 5p. Type **97** ... 15 20
297 10p. Tristan da Cunha group (Beaufort's Survey, 1806) ... 15 25
298 15p. Tristan Island (Crawford, 1937-38) ... 20 30
299 20p. Gough Island (1955-56) ... 25 40
296/9 *Set of* 4 ... 65 1·00

(Des Jennifer Toombs. Litho Questa)

1981 (23 Mar). Centenary of Revd. Edwin Dodgson's Arrival on Tristan da Cunha. T **98** and similar multicoloured designs. W w **14** (sideways on 20p.). P 14.

300 10p. Type **98** ... 10 15
301 20p. Dodgson and view of Tristan da Cunha (*horiz*) ... 20 30
302 30p. Dodgson with people of Tristan da Cunha ... 25 45
300/2 *Set of* 3 ... 50 80
MS303 140×134 mm. Nos. 300/2. Wmk sideways* ... 75 1·40
w. Wmk Crown to right of CA ... 32·00

*The normal sideways watermark on No. **MS**303 shows Crown to left of CA, *as seen from the back of the stamp.*

99 Detail from Captain Denham's Plan, 1853

(Des L. McCombie. Litho Questa)

1981 (22 May). Early Maps. T **99** and similar horiz designs. Multicoloured. W w **14** (sideways*). P 13½×14.

304 5p. Type **99** ... 15 10
w. Wmk Crown to right of CA ... 65·00
305 14p. Detail from map by A. Dalrymple, 17 March 1781 ... 20 20
306 21p. Detail from Captain Denham's plan, 1853 (*different*) ... 25 30
304/6 *Set of* 3 ... 55 55
MS307 110×70 mm. 35p. Detail from map by J. van Keulen, *circa* 1700 ... 50 60
w. Wmk Crown to right of CA ... 95·00

*The normal sideways watermark shows Crown to left of CA, *as seen from the back of the stamp or miniature sheet.*

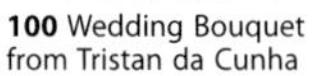

100 Wedding Bouquet from Tristan da Cunha

101 Explorer with Rucksack

(Des J.W. Litho Walsall)

1981 (22 July). Royal Wedding. T **100** and similar vert designs. Multicoloured. W w **14**. P 14.

308	5p. Type **100**	10	10
309	20p. Prince of Wales at Investiture	15	15
310	50p. Prince Charles and Lady Diana Spencer	45	45
308/10	*Set of 3*	60	60

(Des BG Studio. Litho Questa)

1981 (14 Sept). 25th Anniv of Duke of Edinburgh Award Scheme. T **101** and similar vert designs. Multicoloured. W w **14**. P 14.

311	5p. Type **101**	10	10
312	10p. Explorer at campsite	10	10
313	20p. Explorer map reading	20	20
314	25p. Duke of Edinburgh	25	25
311/14	*Set of 4*	55	55

102 Inaccessible Island Rail on Nest

(Des R. Granger Barrett. Litho Walsall)

1981 (1 Nov). Inaccessible Island Rail. T **102** and similar horiz designs. Multicoloured. W w **14** (sideways*). P 13½×14.

315	10p. Type **102**	20	30
	a. Strip of 4. Nos. 315/18	65	1·10
	aw. Wmk Crown to right of CA (strip of 4)	£190	
316	10p. Inaccessible Island Rail eggs	20	30
317	10p. Rail chicks	20	30
318	10p. Adult Rail	20	30
315/18	*Set of 4*	65	1·10

*The normal sideways watermark shows Crown to left of CA, *as seen from the back of the stamp.*

Nos. 315/18 were printed together, *se-tenant*, in horizontal and vertical strips of 4 throughout the sheet.

103 Six-gilled Shark

(Des I. Loe. Litho Enschedé)

1982 (8 Feb). Sharks. T **103** and similar horiz designs. Multicoloured. W w **14** (sideways*). P 13½.

319	5p. Type **103**	25	10
	w. Wmk Crown to right of CA	95·00	
320	14p. Porbeagle	25	20
	w. Wmk Crown to right of CA	£100	
321	21p. Blue Shark	25	35
322	35p. Golden Hammerhead	35	50
319/22	*Set of 4*	1·00	1·00

*The normal sideways watermark shows Crown to left of CA, *as seen from the back of the stamp.*

104 *Marcella* (barque)

105 Lady Diana Spencer at Windsor, July 1981

(Des J. Cooter. Litho Questa)

1982 (5 Apr). Sailing Ships (1st series). T **104** and similar horiz designs. Multicoloured. W w **14** (sideways). P 13½.

323	5p. Type **104**	20	20
324	15p. *Eliza Adams* (full-rigged ship)	20	20
325	30p. *Corinthian* (American whaling ship)	30	30
326	50p. *Samuel and Thomas* (American whaling ship)	40	40
323/6	*Set of 4*	1·00	1·00

See also Nos. 341/4.

(Des Jennifer Toombs. Litho Walsall)

1982 (1 July). 21st Birthday of Princess of Wales. T **105** and similar vert designs. Multicoloured. W w **14**. P 14½×14.

327	5p. Tristan da Cunha coat of arms	10	10
328	15p. Type **105**	25	20
329	30p. Prince and Princess of Wales in wedding portrait	30	40
330	50p. Formal portrait	60	60
327/30	*Set of 4*	1·10	1·10

106 Lord Baden-Powell

1ST PARTICIPATION
COMMONWEALTH
GAMES 1982

(**107**)

(Des C. Abbott. Litho J.W.)

1982 (20 Sept). 75th Anniv of Boy Scout Movement. T **106** and similar multicoloured designs. W w **14** (sideways on No. 333). P 13×13½ (50p.) or 13½×13 (others).

331	5p. Type **106**	15	15
332	20p. First Scout camp, Brownsea, 1907	20	35
333	50p. Local Scouts on parade (*horiz*)	45	75
331/3	*Set of 3*	70	1·10
MS334	88×104 mm. 50p. Moral of the Acorn and the Oak. P 14	75	1·40

1982 (28 Sept). Commonwealth Games, Brisbane. Nos. 224 and 228 optd with T **107**.

335	5p Wandering Albatross	15	10
336	25p. Broad-billed Prion	40	30
	w. Wmk inverted	35·00	35·00

108 Formation of Island

109 Tractor pulling Trailer

(Des J.W. Litho Questa)

1982 (1 Nov). Volcanoes. T **108** and similar horiz designs. Multicoloured. W w **14** (sideways). P 14×14½.

337	5p. Type **108**	15	15
338	15p. Plan of surface cinder cones and cross-section of volcano showing feeders	25	35
339	25p. Eruption	35	50
340	35p. 1961 Tristan eruption	40	70
337/40	*Set of 4*	1·00	1·50

(Des J. Cooter. Litho Questa)

1983 (1 Feb). Sailing Ships (2nd series). Multicoloured designs as T **104**. W w **14** (sideways on 20p., 35p.). P 13½.

No.	Description	Unused	Used
341	5p. *Islander* (barque) (*vert*)	15	15
342	20p. *Roscoe* (full-rigged ship)	25	25
343	35p. *Columbia* (whaling ship)	35	40
344	50p. *Emeline* (schooner) (*vert*)	50	60
341/4	*Set of 4*	1·10	1·25

(Des C. Abbott. Litho Format)

1983 (2 May). Land Transport. T **109** and similar horiz designs. Multicoloured. W w **14** (sideways). P 14.

No.	Description	Unused	Used
345	5p. Type **109**	10	15
346	15p. Pack donkeys	15	25
347	30p. Bullock cart	20	40
348	50p. Landrover	30	60
345/8	*Set of 4*	65	1·25

110 Early Chart of South Atlantic

111 "Christ's Charge to St. Peter" (detail) (Raphael)

(Des L. Curtis. Litho Questa)

1983 (1 Aug). Island History. T **110** and similar horiz designs. Multicoloured (except 50p. black, bright scarlet and buff). W w **14** (sideways*). P 14.

No.	Description	Unused	Used
349	1p. Type **110**	30	50
350	3p. Tristao da Cunha's caravel	40	50
351	4p. Notice left by Dutch on first landing, 1643	40	50
352	5p. 17th-century views of the island	40	50
353	10p. British army landing party, 1815	45	50
354	15p. 19th-century view of the settlement	55	70
355	18p. Governor Glass's house	55	70
356	20p. The Revd. W. F. Taylor and Peter Green.	65	75
357	25p. *John and Elizabeth* (American whaling ship)	85	75
358	50p. Letters Patent declaring Tristan da Cunha a dependency of St. Helena	1·10	1·50
359	£1 Commissioning H.M.S. *Atlantic Isle*, 1944	1·25	2·50
	w. Wmk Crown to right of CA	1·25	
360	£2 Evacuation, 1961	2·00	4·00
	w. Wmk Crown to right of CA	2·00	
349/60	*Set of 12*	8·00	12·00

*The normal sideways watermark shows Crown to left of CA, *as seen from the back of the stamp.*

(Des and litho Walsall)

1983 (27 Oct). 500th Birth Anniv of Raphael. T **111** and similar designs, showing different details of "Christ's Charge to St. Peter". W w **14**. P 14½.

No.	Description	Unused	Used
361	10p. multicoloured	15	20
362	25p. multicoloured	25	35
363	40p. multicoloured	45	60
361/3	*Set of 3*	75	1·00
MS364	115×90 mm. 50p. multicoloured (*horiz*). Wmk sideways	70	80

On No. **MS**364 the Queen's head has been replaced by the Royal Cypher.

112 1952 6d. Stamp

113 *Agrocybe praecox var. cutefracta*

(Des C. Abbott. Litho Questa)

1984 (1 Jan). 150th Anniv of St. Helena as a British Colony. T **112** and similar horiz designs showing 1952 overprints on St. Helena stamps. Multicoloured. W w **14** (sideways). P 14.

No.	Description	Unused	Used
365	10p. Type **112**	20	35
366	15p. 1952 1s. stamp	25	45
367	25p. 1952 2s. 6d. stamp	30	70
368	60p. 1952 10s. stamp	60	1·25
365/8	*Set of 4*	1·25	2·50

(Des McCombie Skinner Studio. Litho Questa)

1984 (25 Mar). Fungi. T **113** and similar multicoloured designs. W w **14** (sideways on 30p., 50p.). P 14.

No.	Description	Unused	Used
369	10p. Type **113**	30	70
370	20p. *Laccaria tetraspora*	40	90
371	30p. *Agrocybe cylindracea* (*horiz*)	45	1·00
372	50p. *Sacoscypha coccinea* (*horiz*)	55	1·25
369/72	*Set of 4*	1·50	3·50

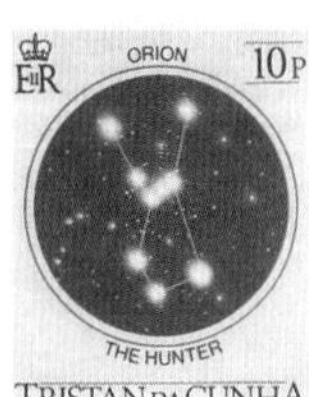

114 Constellation of "Orion"

115 Sheep-shearing

(Des Harrison. Litho Questa)

1984 (30 July). The Night Sky. T **114** and similar vert designs. Multicoloured. W w **14**. P 14½×14.

No.	Description	Unused	Used
373	10p. Type **114**	35	80
374	20p. "Scorpius"	40	90
375	25p. "Canis Major"	45	95
376	50p. "Crux"	60	1·10
373/6	*Set of 4*	1·60	3·25

(Des G. Wilby. Litho Walsall)

1984 (1 Oct). Tristan Woollens Industry. T **115** and similar vert designs. Multicoloured. W w **14**. P 14½.

No.	Description	Unused	Used
377	9p. Type **115**	15	45
378	17p. Carding wool	20	50
379	29p. Spinning	30	80
380	45p. Knitting	45	90
377/80	*Set of 4*	1·00	2·40
MS381	120×85 mm. As Nos. 377/80, but without white borders around the designs	1·00	3·00

116 "Christmas Dinner-table"

117 "H.M.S. *Julia* (sloop) Ashore, 1817" (Midshipman C. W. Browne)

(Des G. Vasarhelyi. Litho Questa)

1984 (3 Dec). Christmas. Children's Drawings. T **116** and similar horiz designs. Multicoloured. W w **14** (sideways). P 14.

No.	Description	Unused	Used
382	10p. Type **116**	20	35
383	20p. "Santa Claus in ox cart"	25	40
384	30p. "Santa Claus in longboat"	30	70
385	50p. "The Nativity"	50	80
382/5	*Set of 4*	1·10	2·00

(Des A. Crawford, adapted G. Vasarhelyi. Litho Questa)

1985 (4 Feb). Shipwrecks (1st series). T **117** and similar designs. W w **14** (sideways on 35p.). P 14×13½ (10, 25p.) or 13½×14 (35, 60p.).

No.	Description	Unused	Used
386	10p. royal blue and light grey-blue	40	80
387	25p. red-brown and emerald	50	1·40

388	35p. yellow-brown and orange-yellow	65	1·60
386/8	*Set of* 3	1·40	3·50
MS389	142×101 mm. 60p. multicoloured. Wmk sideways	75	2·25

Designs: *Vert*—25p. *Mabel Clark's* bell, St. Mary's Church. *Horiz*—5p "Barque *Glenhuntley* foundering, 1898" (John Hagan); 60p. Map of Tristan da Cunha showing sites of shipwrecks.

See also Nos. 411/14 and 426/9.

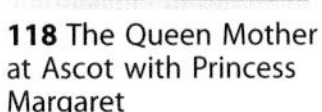

118 The Queen Mother at Ascot with Princess Margaret

119 Jonathan Lambert and "Isles of Refreshment" Flag, 1811

(Des A. Theobald (80p.), C. Abbott (others). Litho Questa)

1985 (7 June). Life and Times of Queen Elizabeth the Queen Mother. T **118** and similar vert designs. Multicoloured. W w **16**. P 14½×14.

390	10p. The Queen Mother and Prince Charles, 1954	20	30
	w. Wmk inverted	9·50	10·00
391	20p. Type **118**	30	60
	w. Wmk inverted	5·00	9·00
392	30p. Queen Elizabeth the Queen Mother	40	85
393	50p. With Prince Harry at his christening	70	1·25
390/3	*Set of* 4	1·40	2·75
MS394	91×73 mm. 80p. The Queen Mother and the young Princess Anne at Trooping the Colour. Wmk sideways	2·75	3·25

(Des D. Slater. Litho J.W.)

1985 (30 Sept). Flags. T **119** and similar multicoloured designs. W w **16** (sideways on 10p., inverted on others). P 14.

395	– 10p. Type **119**	40	90
396	– 15p. 21st Light Dragoons guidon and cannon from Fort Malcolm (1816-17) (*vert*)	50	1·00
397	– 25p. White Ensign and H.M.S. *Falmouth* (frigate) offshore, 1816 (*vert*)	60	1·40
398	– 60p. Union Jack and Tristan da Cunha (*vert*)	1·00	2·75
395/8	*Set of* 4	2·25	5·50

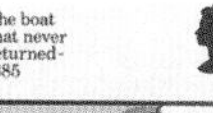

120 Lifeboat heading for Barque *West Riding*

121 Halley's Comet, 1066, from Bayeux Tapestry

(Des D. Miller. Litho Format)

1985 (28 Nov). Centenary of Loss of Island Lifeboat. T **120** and similar vert designs. Multicoloured. W w **14**. P 14×13½.

399	10p. Type **120**	25	60
	w. Wmk inverted	1·00	
400	30p. Map of Tristan da Cunha	35	1·00
	w. Wmk inverted	2·50	
401	50p. Memorial plaque to lifeboat crew	50	1·50
399/401	*Set of* 3	1·00	2·75

(Des D. Miller. Litho Walsall)

1986 (21 Apr). Appearance of Halley's Comet. T **121** and similar horiz designs. Multicoloured. W w **16** (sideways). P 14.

402	10p. Type **121**	30	75
403	20p. Path of Comet	35	1·25
404	30p. Comet over Inaccessible Island	40	1·50
405	50p. H.M.S. *Paramour* (pink) and map of South Atlantic	75	2·00
402/5	*Set of* 4	1·60	5·00

(Des A. Theobald. Litho Questa)

1986 (21 Apr). 60th Birthday of Queen Elizabeth II. Vert designs as T **110** of Ascension. Multicoloured. W w **16**. P 14½×14.

406	10p. With Prince Charles, 1950	15	35
	w. Wmk inverted	1·40	
407	15p. Queen at Trooping the Colour	20	45
408	25p. In robes of Order of the Bath, Westminster Abbey, 1972	25	70
	a. Silver (cypher and logo) omitted	£325	
409	45p. In Canada, 1977	40	1·25
	w. Wmk inverted	1·75	
410	65p. At Crown Agents Head Office, London, 1983	55	1·50
406/10	*Set of* 5	1·40	3·75

122 "*Allanshaw* wrecked on East Beach, 1893" (drawing by John Hagan)

123 Wandering Albatross

(Des A. Crawford, adapted G. Vasarhelyi. Litho J.W.)

1986 (2 June). Shipwrecks (2nd series). T **122** and similar designs. W w **16** (sideways on 9p.). P 13½×13 (9p.) or 13×13½ (others).

411	9p. dp turquoise-blue, dp grey-blue & black	65	1·00
412	20p. grey-olive, olive-yellow and black	1·00	1·50
413	40p. bright blue, bright violet and black	1·25	2·00
411/13	*Set of* 3	2·50	4·00
MS414	142×80 mm. 65p. orange-brown and black. Wmk sideways*. P 13½×13	2·25	4·00
	w. Wmk Crown to left of CA	26·00	

Designs: *Vert*—20p. Church font from wreck of *Edward Vittery*, 1881; 40p. Ship's figurehead. *Horiz*—65p. Gaetano Lavarello and Andrea Repetto, survivors from *Italia* 1892.

*The normal sideways watermark on the miniature sheet shows Crown to right of CA, *as seen from the back of the sheet.*

(Des D. Miller. Litho Questa)

1986 (23 July). Royal Wedding. Square designs as T **112** of Ascension. Multicoloured. W w **16**. P 14.

415	10p. Prince Andrew and Miss Sarah Ferguson	20	65
	w. Wmk inverted	45·00	
416	40p. Prince Andrew piloting helicopter, Digby, Canada, 1985	80	1·60
	w. Wmk inverted	50·00	

(Des A. Theobald. Litho Questa)

1986 (30 Sept). Flora and Fauna of Inaccessible Island. T **123** and similar vert designs. Multicoloured. W w **16**. P 14.

417	5p. Type **123**	30	80
418	10p. *Lagenophora nudicaulis* (daisy)	30	90
	w. Wmk inverted	60·00	27·00
419	20p. *Cynthia virginiensis* (butterfly)	50	1·40
420	25p. Wilkin's Finch	55	1·40
	w. Wmk inverted	60·00	25·00
421	50p. White-chinned Petrel	70	2·00
417/21	*Set of* 5	2·10	5·75

124 *Dimorphinoctua cunhaensis* (flightless moth) and Edinburgh

125 Castaways from *Blenden Hall* attacking Sea Elephant, 1821

(Des C. Abbott. Litho Walsall)

1987 (23 Jan). Island Flightless Insects and Birds. T **124** and similar vert designs. Multicoloured. W w **14**. P 14½.

422	10p. Type **124**	25	70
423	25p. *Tristanomyia frustilifera* (fly) and Crater Lake	35	1·40
424	35p. Inaccessible Island Rail and Inaccessible Island	65	2·25
425	50p. Gough Island Moorhen and Gough Island	80	2·50
422/5	*Set of 4*	1·75	6·25

(Des A. Crawford, adapted G. Vasarhelyi. Litho Walsall)

1987 (2 Apr*). Shipwrecks (3rd series). T **125** and similar designs. W w **16** (sideways on 17p.). P 13½×14 (17p.) or 14×13½ (others).

426	11p. black and olive-brown	65	1·25
427	17p. black and bright lilac	80	1·60
428	45p. black and deep blue-green	1·00	2·00
426/8	*Set of 3*	2·25	4·25
MS429	131×70 mm. 70p. royal blue, bright green and pale blue. Wmk sideways†. P 13½×14	3·00	3·00
	w. Wmk Crown to right of CA	55·00	

Designs: *Horiz*—17p. Barquentine *Henry A. Paull* stranded at Sandy Point, 1879; 70p. Map of Inaccessible Island showing sites of shipwrecks. *Vert*—45p. Gustav Stoltenhoff, 1871, and Stoltenhoff Island.

*This is the local date of issue. The Crown Agents placed the stamps on sale from 2 February 1987.

†The normal sideways watermark on the miniature sheet shows Crown to left of CA, *as seen from the back of the sheet.*

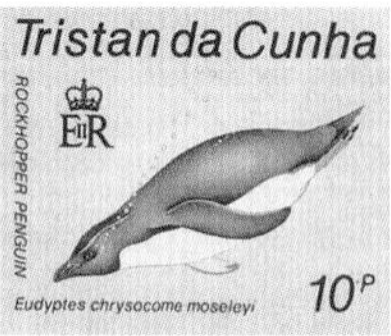

126 Rockhopper Penguin swimming

127 Microscope and Published Report

(Des I. Strange. Litho Questa)

1987 (22 June). Rockhopper Penguins. T **126** and similar horiz designs. Multicoloured. W w **16** (sideways). P 14½.

430	10p. Type **126**	1·10	1·25
431	20p. Adult with egg	1·40	1·60
432	30p. Adult with juvenile	1·90	2·25
433	50p. Head of Rockhopper Penguin	2·50	2·75
430/3	*Set of 4*	6·25	7·00

(Des N. Shewring. Litho Questa)

1987 (7 Dec). 50th Anniv of Norwegian Scientific Expedition. T **127** and similar square designs. Multicoloured. W w **16** (10p., 20p.) or w **14** (30p., 50p.) (all sideways). P 14.

434	10p. Type **127**	90	1·25
435	20p. Scientists ringing Yellow-nosed Albatross	1·90	2·25
436	30p. Expedition hut, Little Beach Point	2·25	2·75
437	50p. S.S. *Thorshammer* (whale factory ship)	3·25	3·75
434/7	*Set of 4*	7·50	9·00

1988 (9 Mar). Royal Ruby Wedding. Nos. 406/10 optd with T **119** of Ascension in silver.

438	10p. Princess Elizabeth with Prince Charles, 1950	20	25
	w. Wmk inverted		
439	15p. Queen Elizabeth II at Trooping the Colour	25	35
440	25p. In robes of Order of the Bath, Westminster Abbey, 1972	35	55
441	45p. In Canada, 1977	60	95
442	65p. At Crown Agents Head Office, London, 1983	75	1·40
438/42	*Set of 5*	1·75	3·25

128 Nightingale Finch ("Tristan Bunting")

129 Painted Penguin Eggs

(Des A. Theobald. Litho Questa)

1988 (21 Mar). Fauna of Nightingale Island. T **128** and similar vert designs. Multicoloured. W w **16**. P 14.

443	5p. Type **128**	40	65
444	10p. Tristan Thrush (immature)	55	75
445	20p. Yellow-nosed Albatross (chick)	70	1·10
446	25p. Greater Shearwater	70	1·25
447	50p. Elephant Seal	1·00	2·25
443/7	*Set of 5*	3·00	5·50

(Des O. Bell. Litho Questa)

1988 (30 May). Tristan da Cunha Handicrafts. T **129** and similar horiz designs. Multicoloured. W w **16** (sideways*). P 14×14½.

448	10p. Type **129**	25	55
	w. Wmk Crown to right of CA	50·00	
449	15p. Moccasins	35	70
	w. Wmk Crown to right of CA	35·00	
450	35p. Knitwear	75	1·40
	w. Wmk Crown to right of CA	38·00	
451	50p. Model longboat	1·10	1·75
	w. Wmk Crown to right of CA	30·00	
448/51	*Set of 4*	2·25	4·00

*The normal sideways watermark show Crown to left of CA, *as seen from the back of the stamp.*

130 Processing Blubber

131 "Government House"

(Des N. Shewring. Litho Questa)

1988 (6 Oct). 19th-century Whaling T **130** and similar horiz designs. Multicoloured. W w **16** (sideways*). P 14×14½.

452	10p. Type **130**	1·00	75
	w. Wmk Crown to right of CA	£225	
453	20p. Harpoon guns	1·25	1·00
454	30p. Scrimshaw (carved whale bone)	1·50	1·25
455	50p. Whaling ships	3·00	2·00
	w. Wmk Crown to right of CA	£100	
452/5	*Set of 4*	6·00	4·50
MS456	76×56 mm. £1 Right Whale	3·00	2·75

*The normal sideways watermark shows Crown to left of CA, *as seen from the back of the stamp.*

(Des E. Nisbet and D. Miller (25, 35p.), D. Miller (others). Litho Harrison)

1988 (7 Nov). 300th Anniv of Lloyd's of London. Designs as T **123** of Ascension. W w **16** (sideways on 25, 35p.). P 14.

457	10p. multicoloured	40	40
458	25p. multicoloured	1·50	1·10
459	35p. brownish black and emerald	2·00	1·50
460	50p. brownish black and carmine-red	2·75	1·90
457/60	*Set of 4*	6·00	4·50

Designs: *Vert*—10p. New Lloyd's Building, 1988; 50p *Kobenhavn* (cadet barque), 1928. *Horiz*—25p. *Tristania II* (crayfish trawler); 35p. *St. Helena* (mail ship).

(Des N. Harvey. Litho Walsall)

1988 (10 Dec). Augustus Earle's Paintings, 1824. T **131** and similar horiz designs. Multicoloured. W w **16** (sideways*). P 14.

461	1p. Type **131**	30	75
462	3p. "Squall off Tristan"	45	75
463	4p. "Rafting Blubber"	50	75
464	5p. "View near Little Beach"	50	75
465	10p. "Man killing Albatross"	70	75
466	15p. "View on The Summit"	90	1·25
467	20p. "Nightingale Island"	1·00	1·40
468	25p. "Earle on Tristan"	1·00	1·60
469	35p. "Solitude-Watching the Horizon"	1·00	1·75
470	50p. "Northeaster"	1·00	2·00
	w. Wmk Crown to right of CA	60·00	
471	£1 "Tristan Village"	1·25	1·75
472	£2 "Governor Glass at Dinner"	2·00	3·75
461/72	*Set of 12*	9·50	16·00

*The normal sideways watermark shows Crown to left of CA, *as seen from the back of the stamp.*

Examples of Nos. 461/72 showing Earle's dates as "1793–1835" were sold by the U.S.A. agents, and by the authorities on Ascension, in error. Supplies sent to Tristan da Cunha show the correct dates "1793–1838".

132 Hall's Giant Petrel

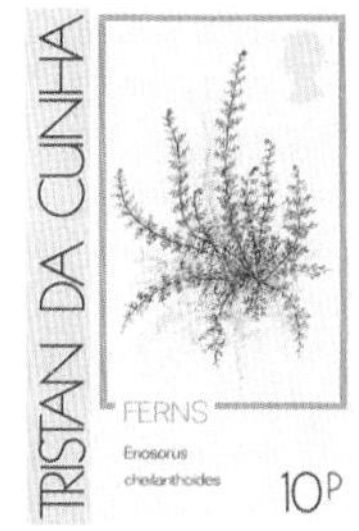

133 *Eriosorus cheilanthoides*

(Des A. Theobald. Litho Walsall)

1989 (6 Feb). Fauna of Gough Island. T **132** and similar vert designs. Multicoloured. W w **16**. P 14.

473	5p. Type **132**	1·00	1·50
474	10p. Gough Island Moorhen	1·10	1·50
475	20p. Gough Island Finch ("Gough Bunting")	1·50	1·75
476	25p. Sooty Albatross	1·60	1·75
477	50p. Amsterdam Fur Seal	2·00	3·00
473/7	*Set of 5*	6·50	8·50

(Des Jane Fern. Litho Walsall)

1989 (22 May). Ferns. T **133** and similar vert designs. Multicoloured. W w **14**. P 14×13½.

478	10p. Type **133**	65	65
479	25p. *Asplenium alvarezense*	1·10	1·10
480	35p. *Elaphoglossum hybridum*	1·40	1·40
481	50p. *Ophioglossum opacum*	1·60	1·60
478/81	*Set of 4*	4·25	4·25

134 Surgeon's Mortar

135 Cattle Egret

(Des Jennifer Toombs. Litho Questa)

1989 (25 Sept). Nautical Museum Exhibits. T **134** and similar horiz designs. Multicoloured. W w **16** (sideways). P 14.

482	10p. Type **134**	65	65
483	20p. Parts of darting-gun harpoon	1·10	1·10
484	30p. Ship's compass with binnacle-hood	1·40	1·40
485	60p. Rope-twisting device	1·75	1·75
482/5	*Set of 4*	4·50	4·50

(Des Josephine Martin and Sally Hynard. Litho Questa)

1989 (20 Nov). Vagrant Birds. T **135** and similar vert designs. Multicoloured. W w **16**. P 14.

486	10p. Type **135**	1·50	1·50
487	25p. Spotted Sandpiper	2·25	2·50
488	35p. Purple Gallinule	2·50	2·75
489	50p. Barn Swallow	2·75	3·25
486/9	*Set of 4*	8·00	9·00

136 *Peridroma saucia*

137 Sea Urchin

(Des I. Loe. Litho Questa)

1990 (1 Feb). Moths. T **136** and similar horiz designs. Multicoloured. W w **14** (sideways). P 14.

490	10p. Type **136**	90	1·00
491	15p. *Ascalapha odorata*	1·25	1·60
492	35p. *Agrius cingulata*	2·00	2·50
493	60p. *Eumorpha labruscae*	2·75	3·25
490/3	*Set of 4*	6·25	7·50

(Des Ann Hecht. Litho Questa)

1990 (12 June). Echinoderms. T **137** and similar vert designs showing starfishes. W w **14**. P 13½×14.

494	10p. multicoloured	1·00	1·00
495	20p. multicoloured	1·50	2·00
496	30p. multicoloured	1·90	2·50
497	60p. multicoloured	2·50	3·25
494/7	*Set of 4*	6·25	7·75

(Des D. Miller. Litho Questa)

1990 (4 Aug). 90th Birthday of Queen Elizabeth the Queen Mother. Vert designs as T **134** (25p.) or **135** (£1) of Ascension. W w **16**. P 14×15 (25p.) or 14½ (£1).

498	25p. multicoloured	1·00	1·25
499	£1 agate and Prussian blue	2·50	3·25

Designs:—25p. Queen Mother at the London Coliseum; £1 Queen Elizabeth broadcasting to women of the Empire, 1939.

(Des L. Curtis. Litho Walsall)

1990 (13 Sept). Maiden Voyage of *St. Helena II*. Horiz designs as T **162** of St. Helena. Multicoloured. W w **14** (sideways). P 14×14½.

500	10p. *Dunnottar Castle* (liner), 1942	1·50	1·25
501	15p. *St. Helena* (mail ship) at Tristan	2·00	1·75
502	35p. Launch of *St. Helena II* (mail ship)	2·75	3·00
503	60p. Duke of York launching *St. Helena II*	3·75	4·00
500/3	*Set of 4*	9·00	9·00
MS504	100×100 mm. £1 *St. Helena II* and outline map of Tristan da Cunha	4·25	7·00

No. **MS**504 also contains two imperforate designs of similar stamps from Ascension and St. Helena without face values.

138 H.M.S. *Pyramus* (frigate), 1829

139 *Royal Viking Sun* (cruise liner)

(Des E. Nisbet. Litho Questa)

1990 (30 Nov). Ships of the Royal Navy (1st series). T **138** and similar horiz designs. Multicoloured. W w **14** (sideways). P 14.

505	10p. Type **138**	2·50	1·50
506	25p. H.M.S. *Penguin* (sloop), 1815	3·50	2·75
507	35p. H.M.S. *Thalia* (screw corvette), 1886	3·75	3·00
508	50p. H.M.S. *Sidon* (paddle frigate), 1858	4·75	3·75
505/8	*Set of 4*	13·00	10·00

See also Nos. 509/12 and 565/8.

(Des E. Nisbet. Litho Questa)

1991 (4 Feb). Ships of the Royal Navy (2nd series). Horiz designs as T **138**. Multicoloured. W w **14** (sideways). P 14.

509	10p. H.M.S. *Milford* (sloop), 1938	2·00	1·25
510	25p. H.M.S. *Dublin* (cruiser), 1923	3·00	2·50
511	35p. H.M.S. *Yarmouth* (cruiser), 1919	3·25	2·75
512	50p. H.M.S. *Carlisle* (cruiser), 1937	3·75	3·50
509/12	*Set of 4*	11·00	9·00

No. 512 is inscribed "1938" in error.

(Des L. Curtis. Litho B.D.T.)

1991 (1 Apr). Visit of *Royal Viking Sun*. Sheet 62×47 mm. W w **16** (sideways). P 14.

MS513	**139** £1 multicoloured	6·00	8·00

140 Prince Alfred and H.M.S. *Galatea* (screw frigate), 1867

(Des D. Miller. Litho Questa)

1991 (10 June). 70th Birthday of Prince Philip, Duke of Edinburgh. T **140** and similar horiz designs. W w **16** (sideways). P 14.

514	10p. brownish black, pale blue & dp dull bl.	2·25	1·75
515	25p. brownish black, pale blue-green and myrtle-green	3·25	2·50
516	30p. black, deep brown & pale bistre-yellow	3·50	3·25
517	50p. multicoloured	4·50	3·75
514/17	*Set of 4*	12·00	10·00

Designs:—25p. Prince Philip meeting local inhabitants, 1957; 30p. Prince Philip and Royal Yacht *Britannia*, 1957; 50p. Prince Philip and Edinburgh settlement.

141 Pair of Gough Island Moorhens

142 Coats' Perch

(Des G. Vasarhelyi. Litho Questa)

1991 (10 June). Endangered Species. Birds. T **141** and similar horiz designs. Multicoloured. W w **14** (sideways). P 14.

518	8p. Type **141**	1·75	1·75
519	10p. Gough Island Finch	1·75	1·75
520	12p. Gough Island Moorhen on nest	1·90	1·90
521	15p. Gough Island Finch feeding chicks	1·90	1·90
518/21	*Set of* 4	6·50	6·50

(Des R. Watton. Litho Walsall)

1992 (23 Jan). 500th Anniv of Discovery of America by Columbus and Re-enactment Voyages. Horiz designs as T **168** of St. Helena. Multicoloured. W w **14** (sideways). P 13½×14.

522	10p. Map of re-enactment voyages and *Eye of the Wind* (cadet brig)	1·00	1·50
523	15p. Compass rose and *Soren Larsen* (cadet brigantine)	1·50	2·00
524	35p. Ships of Columbus	2·50	3·00
525	60p. Columbus and *Santa Maria*	2·75	3·25
522/5	*Set of* 4	7·00	8·75

(Des. D. Miller. Litho Questa (65p.), Walsall (others))

1992 (6 Feb). 40th Anniv of Queen Elizabeth II's Accession. Horiz designs as T **143** of Ascension. Multicoloured. W w **14** (sideways). P 14.

526	10p. Tristan from the sea	80	60
527	20p. Longboat under sail	1·25	90
528	25p. Aerial view of Edinburgh	1·25	1·00
529	35p. Three portraits of Queen Elizabeth	1·50	1·25
530	65p. Queen Elizabeth II	2·50	2·25
526/30	*Set of* 5	6·50	5·50

(Des Ann Hecht. Litho Questa)

1992 (1 June). Fish. T **142** and similar horiz designs. Multicoloured. W w **14** (sideways). P 14×13½.

531	10p. Type **142**	80	90
532	15p. Lined Trumpeter	1·25	1·40
533	35p. Karrer's Morid Cod	2·25	2·75
534	60p. Long-finned Scad	2·75	3·25
531/4	*Set of* 4	6·25	7·50

143 *Italia* leaving Greenock

144 *Stenoscelis hylastoides*

(Des E. Nisbet. Litho Questa)

1992 (16 Sept). Centenary of the Wreck of Barque *Italia*. T **143** and similar horiz designs. W w **14** (sideways). P 13½×14.

535	10p. Type **143**	1·25	1·50
536	45p. In mid-Atlantic	2·75	3·50
537	65p. Driving ashore on Stony Beach	3·25	4·00
535/7	*Set of* 3	6·50	8·00
MS538	101×75 mm. £1 *Italia* becalmed	8·50	11·00

No. **MS**538 also commemorates "Genova '92" International Thematic Stamp Exhibition.

(Des G. Marx. Litho Questa)

1993 (2 Feb). Insects. T **144** and similar vert designs. Multicoloured. W w **16**. P 14×13½.

539	15p. Type **144**	1·50	1·50
540	45p. *Trogloscaptomyza brevilamellata*	2·75	3·00
541	60p. *Senilites tristanicola*	3·25	3·75
539/41	*Set of* 3	6·75	7·50

145 Ampulla and Anointing Spoon

146 *Tristania* and *Frances Repetto* (crayfish trawlers)

(Des D. Miller. Litho Walsall)

1993 (14 June). 40th Anniv of Coronation. T **145** and similar vert designs. W w **16**. P 14½×14.

542	10p. emerald and black	90	1·00
543	15p. magenta and black	1·40	1·60
544	35p. violet and black	1·90	2·50
545	60p. new blue and black	2·50	3·25
542/5	*Set of* 4	6·00	7·50

Designs:—15p. Orb; 35p. Imperial State Crown; 60p. St. Edward's Crown.

(Des E. Nisbet. Litho Questa)

1993 (10 Nov). 30th Anniv of Resettlement of Tristan. T **146** and similar horiz designs. Multicoloured. W w **16** (sideways). P 13½×14.

546	35p. Type **146**	2·50	3·00
	a. Horiz pair. Nos. 546/7	5·00	6·00
547	35p. *Boissevain* (cargo liner)	2·50	3·00
548	50p. *Bornholm* (liner) and longboat	3·25	3·75
546/8	*Set of* 3	7·50	8·75

Nos. 546/7 were printed together, *se-tenant*, in horizontal pairs throughout the sheet.

147 "Madonna with Child" (School of Botticelli)

148 *Duchess of Atholl* (liner)

(Des D. Miller. Litho Cartor)

1993 (30 Nov). Christmas. Religious Paintings. T **147** and similar vert designs. Multicoloured. W w **14**. P 13.

549	5p. Type **147**	90	1·00
550	15p. "The Holy Family" (Daniel Gran)	2·00	2·00
551	35p. "The Holy Virgin and Child" (Rubens)	3·00	3·25
552	65p. "The Mystical Marriage of St. Catherine with the Holy Child" (Jan van Balen)	4·00	5·00
549/52	*Set of* 4	9·00	10·00

(Des R. Watton. Litho Questa)

1994 (3 Feb). Ships. T **148** and similar horiz designs. Multicoloured. W w **16** (sideways). P 14.

553	1p. Type **148**	75	1·25
554	3p. *Empress of Australia* (liner)	1·00	1·25
555	5p. *Anatolia* (freighter)	1·00	1·25
556	8p. *Viceroy of India* (liner)	1·10	1·50
557	10p. *Rangitata* (transport)	1·10	1·50
558	15p. *Caronia* (liner)	1·40	1·50
559	20p. *Rotterdam* (liner)	1·50	1·50
560	25p. *Leonardo da Vinci* (liner)	1·50	1·50
561	35p. *Vistafjord* (liner)	1·75	1·75
562	£1 *World Discoverer* (liner)	4·00	4·50
563	£2 *Astor* (liner)	7·00	8·00
564	£5 *St. Helena II* (mail ship)	12·00	14·00
553/64	*Set of* 12	30·00	35·00

(Des E. Nisbet. Litho Questa)

1994 (2 May). Ships of the Royal Navy (3rd series). Horiz designs as T **138**. Multicoloured. W w **14** (sideways). P 14×14½.

565	10p. H.M.S. *Nigeria* (cruiser), 1948	1·25	1·50
566	25p. H.M.S. *Phoebe* (cruiser), 1949	2·25	2·50
567	35p. H.M.S. *Liverpool* (cruiser), 1949	2·25	2·50
568	50p. H.M.S. *Magpie* (frigate), 1955	3·00	3·25
565/8	*Set of* 4	8·00	8·75

149 Blue Shark

(Des Ann Hecht. Litho Questa)

1994 (8 Aug). Sharks. T **149** and similar horiz designs. Multicoloured. W w **16** (sideways). P 14½.

569	10p. Type **149**	90	1·25
570	45p. Seven-gilled Shark	2·50	3·25
571	65p. Short-finned Mako	3·25	4·00
569/71	*Set of* 3	6·00	7·75

150 Pair of Donkeys

(Des Josephine Martin. Litho Questa)

1994 (21 Nov). Island Livestock (1st series). T **150** and similar horiz designs. Multicoloured. W w **14** (sideways). P 13½×14.

572	10p. Type **150**	1·10	1·25
573	20p. Cattle	1·40	1·50
574	35p. Ducks and geese	2·50	3·00
575	60p. Girl bottle-feeding lamb	3·25	4·00
572/5	*Set of* 4	7·50	8·75

See also Nos. 620/3.

151 Pick-up Truck

152 Queen Elizabeth the Queen Mother

(Des A. Theobald. Litho Walsall)

1995 (27 Feb). Local Transport. T **151** and similar horiz designs. Multicoloured. W w **16** (sideways). P 14.

576	15p. Type **151**	1·10	1·25
577	20p. Sherpa van	1·50	1·50
578	45p. Scooter and Yamaha motorcycle	2·50	3·00
579	60p. Administrator's Landrover	3·00	3·75
576/9	*Set of* 4	7·25	8·50

(Des R. Watton. Litho Cartor (Nos. 580/3) or Questa (No. **MS**584))

1995 (10 July). 50th Anniv of End of Second World War. Multicoloured designs as T **161** of Ascension. W w **14** (sideways). P 13½.

580	15p. Sailors training on Lewis guns	1·75	1·50
581	20p. Tristan Defence Volunteers	1·75	1·60
582	45p. Wireless and meteorological station	2·75	2·75
583	60p. H.M.S. *Birmingham* (cruiser)	4·50	4·50
580/3	*Set of* 4	9·75	9·25
MS584	75×85 mm. £1 Reverse of 1939-45 War Medal (*vert*). Wmk upright. P 14	2·00	2·75

(Des Jennifer Toombs. Litho Questa)

1995 (4 Aug). 95th Birthday of Queen Elizabeth the Queen Mother. Sheet 75×103 mm. W w **14** (sideways). P 14½×14.

MS585	**152** £1.50 multicoloured	7·00	7·50

153 Sub-Antarctic Fur Seal on Rock

153a Bedford 4-ton Lorry

(Des R. Watton. Litho Cartor)

1995 (3 Nov). Seals. T **153** and similar horiz designs. Multicoloured. W w **14** (sideways). P 14×13½.

586	10p. Type **153**	90	1·25
587	35p. Sub-Antarctic Fur Seals with pups	2·00	2·50
588	45p. Southern Elephant Seal asleep with pups	2·50	3·00
589	50p. Southern Elephant Seals in water	2·50	3·00
586/9	*Set of* 4	7·00	8·75

(Des A. Theobald. Litho Cartor)

1996 (23 Jan). 50th Anniv of United Nations. T **153a** and similar horiz designs. Multicoloured. W w **14** (sideways). P 13½×13.

590	20p. Type **153a**	1·75	1·75
591	30p. Saxon armoured personnel carrier	2·00	2·00
592	45p. Mi26 heavy lift helicopter	3·50	3·50
593	50p. R.F.A. *Sir Tristram* (landing ship)	3·50	3·50
590/3	*Set of* 4	9·75	9·75

(Des D. Miller. Litho Cartor)

1996 (22 Apr). 70th Birthday of Queen Elizabeth II. Vert designs as T **165** of Ascension, each incorporating a different photograph of the Queen. W w **14**. P 13½×14.

594	15p. Tristan from the sea	70	1·10
595	20p. Traditional cottage	80	1·40
596	45p. The Residency	1·75	2·75
597	60p. The Queen and Prince Philip	2·25	3·25
594/7	*Set of* 4	5·00	7·75

154 Old Harbour and *St. Helena I* (mail ship)

155 Gough Island Moorhen

(Des C. Abbott. Litho Cartor)

1996 (5 July). Construction of New Harbour. T **154** and similar horiz designs. Multicoloured. W w **14** (sideways). P 13 (15, 60p.) or 14×13½ (20, 45p.).

598	15p. Type **154**	2·00	2·00
599	20p. Excavator and dump truck (44×27 *mm*)	2·00	2·00
600	45p. Construction of new mole (44×27 *mm*)	3·00	3·00
601	60p. New harbour and *St. Helena II* (mail ship)	4·00	4·50
598/601	*Set of* 4	10·00	10·50

(Des I. Loe. Litho Walsall)

1996 (1 Oct). Declaration of Gough Island as World Heritage Site. Birds. T **155** and similar vert designs. Multicoloured. W w **14**. P 14.

602	15p. Type **155**	1·25	1·40
603	20p. Wandering Albatross	1·40	1·50
604	45p. Sooty Albatross	2·50	2·75
605	60p. Gough Island Finch ("Gough Bunting")	3·35	3·50
602/5	*Set of* 4	7·50	8·25

For 60p. design in miniature sheet see No. **MS**619.

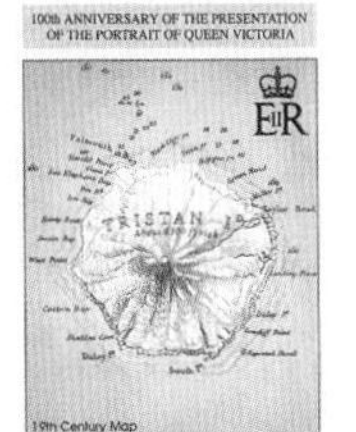

156 19th-century Map

157 Archelon (turtle)

(Des G. Vasarhelyi. Litho Cartor)

1996 (18 Dec). Centenary of the Presentation of the Queen Victoria Portrait to Tristan. T **156** and similar vert designs. Multicoloured. W w **14**. P 13½.

606	20p. Type **156**	1·25	1·25
607	30p. H.M.S. *Magpie* (gunboat)	1·75	2·00
608	45p. Governor Peter Green	1·90	2·25

609 50p. "Queen Victoria" (H. von Angeli) (detail) 2·00 2·50
606/9 *Set of 4* 6·25 7·25

(Des N. Shewring. Litho B.D.T.)

1997 (10 Feb). Atlantic Marine Fauna (1st series). Cretaceous Period. Sheet 92×100 mm containing T **157** and similar horiz designs. Multicoloured. W w **16** (sideways). P 14.

MS610 35p. Type **157**; 35p. Trinacromerum; 35p. Platecarpus; 35p. Clidastes 5·00 5·50

See also No. **MS**638.

158 Smoke Signals

159 *Hilary* and *Melodie*

(Des D. Miller. Litho Walsall)

1997 (1 May). Visual Communications. T **158** and similar horiz designs. Multicoloured. W w **16** (sideways). P 14×14½.

611	10p. Type **158**	40	75
	a. Horiz pair. Nos. 611/12	80	1·50
612	10p. H.M.S. *Eurydice* (frigate)	40	75
613	15p. H.M.S. *Challenger* (survey ship)	60	1·00
	a. Horiz pair. Nos. 613/14	1·20	2·00
614	15p. Flag hoists	60	1·00
615	20p. Semaphore	70	1·00
	a. Horiz pair. Nos. 615/16	1·40	2·00
616	20p. H.M.S. *Carlisle* (cruiser)	70	1·00
617	35p. Aldis lamp	80	1·10
	a. Horiz pair. Nos. 617/18	1·60	2·20
618	35p. H.M.S. *Cilicia* (transport)	80	1·10
611/18	*Set of 8*	4·50	7·00

Nos. 611/12, 613/14, 615/16 and 617/18 were each printed together, *se-tenant*, in horizontal pairs forming composite designs.

(Litho Walsall)

1997 (20 June). Return of Hong Kong to China. Sheet, 130×90 mm, containing design as No. 605, but with "1997" imprint date. W w **14**. P 14.

MS619 60p. Gough Island Finch ("Gough Bunting") 1·75 3·00

(Des Josephine Martin. Litho Walsall)

1997 (26 Aug). Island Livestock (2nd series). Horiz designs as T **150**. Multicoloured. W w **16** (sideways). P 13½×14.

620	20p. Chickens	1·00	1·10
621	30p. Bull	1·40	1·60
622	45p. Sheep	1·90	2·50
623	50p. Collie dogs	3·75	3·75
620/3	*Set of 4*	7·25	8·00

(Des N. Shewring (No. **MS**630), D. Miller (others). Litho Questa (No. **MS**630), B.D.T. (others))

1997 (20 Nov). Golden Wedding of Queen Elizabeth and Prince Philip. Multicoloured designs as T **173** of Ascension. W w **14**. P 13½.

624	15p. Queen Elizabeth	1·25	1·25
	a. Horiz pair. Nos. 624/5	2·50	2·50
625	15p. Prince Philip playing polo	1·25	1·25
626	20p. Queen Elizabeth with horse	1·25	1·25
	a. Horiz pair. Nos. 626/7	2·50	2·50
627	20p. Prince Philip	1·25	1·25
628	45p. Queen Elizabeth with Prince Philip in R.A.F. uniform	1·90	2·00
	a. Horiz pair. Nos. 628/9	3·75	4·00
629	45p. Princess Anne on horseback	1·90	2·00
624/9	*Set of 6*	8·00	8·00

MS630 110×70 mm. £1.50 Queen Elizabeth and Prince Philip in landau (*horiz*). Wmk sideways. P 14×14½ 10·00 11·00

Nos. 624/5, 626/7 and 628/9 were each printed together, *se-tenant*, in horizontal pairs throughout the sheetlets with the backgrounds forming composite designs.

(Des N. Shewring. Litho Questa)

1998 (6 Feb). 50th Anniv of First Lobster Survey. Lobster Trawlers. T **159** and similar vert designs. Multicoloured. W w **14**. P 14½×14.

631	15p. Type **159**	60	80
632	20p. *Tristania II* and *Hekla*	70	90
633	30p. *Pequena* and *Frances Repetto*	90	1·25
634	45p. *Tristania* and *Gillian Gaggins*	1·50	1·75
635	50p. *Kelso* and *Edinburgh*	1·50	2·00
631/5	*Set of 5*	4·75	6·00

MS636 100×80 mm. £1.20 Revd. C. P. Lawrence and lobster 4·75 7·00

(Des D. Miller. Litho Questa)

1998 (15 May). Diana, Princess of Wales Commemoration. Sheet, 145×70 mm, containing vert designs as T **177** of Ascension. Multicoloured. W w **14** (sideways). P 14½×14.

MS637 35p. Wearing pink jacket, 1993; 35p. Wearing white jacket, 1990; 35p Laughing, in striped dress, 1991; 35p. Wearing blue and white dress, 1989 (*sold at* £1.40 + 20p. *charity premium*) 2·00 3·25

(Des N. Shewring. Litho B.D.T.)

1998 (8 July). Atlantic Marine Fauna (2nd series). Miocene Epoch. Sheet, 92×100 mm, containing horiz designs as T **157**. Multicoloured. W w **16** (sideways). P 14.

MS638 45p. Carcharodon (shark); 45p Orycterocetus (sperm whale); 45p Eurhinodelphis (dolphin); 45p. Hexanchus (shark) and Myliobatis (ray) 14·00 15·00

160 *Livonia*

(Des J. Batchelor. Litho B.D.T.)

1998 (15 Sept). Cruise Ships. T **160** and similar horiz designs. Multicoloured. W w **14** (sideways). P 14.

639	15p. Type **160**	2·00	2·25
640	20p. *Professor Molchanov*	2·25	2·50
641	45p. *Explorer*	2·75	3·25
642	60p. *Hanseatic*	3·00	3·50
639/42	*Set of 4*	9·00	11·00

161 *H. G. Johnson* (barque)

(Des J. Batchelor. Litho Questa)

1998 (23 Nov). Maritime Heritage (1st series). T **161** and similar horiz designs. Multicoloured. W w **16** (sideways). P 14½.

643	15p. Type **161**	2·00	2·25
644	35p. *Theodore* (full-rigged ship)	2·75	3·00
645	45p. *Hesperides* (full-rigged ship)	3·25	3·50
646	50p. *Bessfield* (barque)	3·25	3·50
643/6	*Set of 4*	10·00	11·00

(Des J. Batchelor. Litho Questa)

1999 (19 Mar). Maritime Heritage (2nd series). Horiz designs as T **161**. Multicoloured. W w **16** (sideways). P 14½.

647	20p. *Derwent* (full-rigged ship)	2·00	2·25
648	30p. *Strathgryfe* (full-rigged ship)	2·75	3·00
649	50p. *Celestial Empire* (full-rigged ship)	3·25	3·50
650	60p. *Lamorna* (full-rigged ship)	3·25	3·50
647/50	*Set of 4*	10·00	11·00

162 Wandering Albatross Courtship Dance

(Des Josephine Martin. Litho Walsall)

1999 (27 Apr). Endangered Species. Wandering Albatross. T **162** and similar horiz designs. Multicoloured. W w **14** (sideways*). P 14.

651	5p. Type **162**	75	1·00
	a. Strip of 4. Nos. 651/4	2·75	3·50
	b. Panda emblem printed twice	24·00	
	w. Wmk Crown to left of CA	1·25	1·50
	wa. Strip of 4. Nos. 651w/4w	4·50	5·50
652	8p. Adult and chick	75	1·00
	w. Wmk Crown to left of CA	1·25	1·50
653	12p. Adult with spread wings	75	1·00
	w. Wmk Crown to left of CA	1·25	1·50
654	15p. Two adults in flight	75	1·00
	w. Wmk Crown to left of CA	1·25	1·50
651/4	*Set of 4*	2·75	3·50

*The normal sideways watermark shows Crown to right of CA, *as seen from the back of the stamp*.

Nos. 651/4 were printed in sheets of individual values, or in sheets of 16 containing the four stamps *se-tenant*, both horizontally and vertically.

No. 651b occurs on R. 2/4 of those *se-tenant* sheets with the watermark sideways Crown to right. There is a second image of the W.W.F. Panda emblem shown over the left-hand bird in addition to the normal position at bottom right.

(Des D. Miller. Litho Walsall)

1999 (18 June). Royal Wedding. Vert designs as T **185** of Ascension. Multicoloured. W w **16**. P 14.

655	45p. Photographs of Prince Edward and Miss Sophie Rhys-Jones	1·75	1·25
656	£1.20 Engagement photograph	3·75	4·50

(Des D. Miller. Litho Cartor)

1999 (18 Aug). "Queen Elizabeth the Queen Mother's Century". Horiz designs as T **187** of Ascension. Multicoloured (except £1.50). W w **16** (sideways). P 13½.

657	20p. With King George VI and Princess Elizabeth, 1944	80	1·00
658	30p. King George and Queen Elizabeth at Balmoral, 1951	1·00	1·25
659	50p. Family group outside Clarence House, 1994	1·50	2·00
660	60p. Inspecting The Black Watch	2·00	2·25
657/60	*Set of 4*	4·75	6·00
MS661	145×70 mm. £1.50 Lady Elizabeth Bowes-Lyon, 1905, and Hurricane squadron, Battle of Britain, 1940 (black)	4·50	6·50

163 Winter Sunrise

164 King Manuel I of Portugal

(Des D. Miller. Litho Questa)

2000 (1 Jan). New Millennium. T **163** and similar horiz designs. Multicoloured. W w **14** (sideways). P 14.

662	20p. Type **163**	2·75	2·00
663	30p. Spring sunrise	3·25	2·50
664	50p. Summer sunrise	4·00	3·50
665	60p. Autumn sunrise	4·50	4·00
662/5	*Set of 4*	13·00	11·00

(Litho Questa)

2000 (1 Feb). Monarchs connected with Tristan da Cunha. T **164** and similar vert designs. Multicoloured (except 1p. and 5p.). W w **16**. P 14.

666	1p. Type **164** (black, stone and olive-brown)	60	1·25
667	3p. Frederick Henry, Prince of Orange	80	1·25
668	5p. Empress Maria Theresa of Austria (blackish olive, stone and black)	1·00	1·25
669	8p. King George III	1·50	1·50
670	10p. King George IV	1·50	1·50
671	15p. King William IV	1·75	1·75
672	20p. Queen Victoria	1·75	1·75
673	25p. King Edward VII	1·75	1·75
674	35p. King George V	2·50	2·50
675	£1 King Edward VIII	5·50	6·00
676	£2 King George VI	9·00	9·50
677	£5 Queen Elizabeth II	15·00	17·00
666/77	*Set of 12*	38·00	42·00

165 Longboat under Oars

(Des J. Batchelor. Litho Questa)

2000 (22 May). "The Stamp Show 2000" International Stamp Exhibition. Visit of *Cutty Sark* (clipper), 1876. T **165** and similar horiz designs. Multicoloured. W w **14** (sideways). P 14.

678	15p. Type **165**	1·50	1·50
679	45p. Longboat under sail	2·50	3·75
680	50p. *Cutty Sark* at sea	5·50	5·50
681	60p. *Cutty Sark* on display at Greenwich	6·00	6·00
678/81	*Set of 4*	11·00	12·00
MS682	102×65 mm. £1.50 *Cutty Sark* off Tristan da Cunha	14·00	14·00

(Des A. Robinson. Litho Questa)

2000 (21 June). 18th Birthday of Prince William. Multicoloured designs as T **191** of Ascension. W w **14** (sideways on Nos. 683/4). P 14×14½ (vert) or 14½×14 (horiz).

683	45p. Prince Charles with sons, 1985	2·00	2·25
684	45p. Prince William in 1995	2·00	2·25
685	45p. Prince William in 1999 (*horiz*)	2·00	2·25
686	45p. Prince William in overcoat and scarf (*horiz*)	2·00	2·25
683/6	*Set of 4*	7·25	8·00
MS687	175×95 mm. 45p. With Shetland Pony, 1995 (*horiz*) and Nos. 683/6. Wmk sideways. P 14½	12·00	11·00

166 *Agulhas* (South African Antarctic research ship)

(Des A. Theobald. Litho Questa)

2000 (4 Sept). Helicopters and Ships. T **166** and similar horiz designs. Multicoloured. W w **14** (sideways). P 14.

688	10p. Type **166**	1·40	1·75
	a. Horiz pair. Nos. 688/9	2·75	3·50
689	10p. S.A. 330J Puma helicopter, 1999	1·40	1·75
690	15p. H.M.S. *London* (destroyer)	1·50	1·75
	a. Horiz pair. Nos. 690/1	3·00	3·50
691	15p. Westland Wessex HAS1 helicopter, 1964	1·50	1·75
692	20p. H.M.S. *Endurance II* (ice patrol ship)	1·50	1·75
	a. Horiz pair. Nos. 692/3	3·00	3·50
693	20p. Westland Lynx HAS3 helicopter, 1996	1·50	1·75
694	50p. U.S.S. *Spiegel Grove* (landing ship)	1·75	2·00
	a. Horiz pair. Nos. 694/5	3·50	4·00
695	50p. Sikorsky UH-19F helicopter, 1963	1·75	2·00
688/95	*Set of 8*	11·00	13·00

Nos. 688/9, 690/1, 692/3 and 694/5 were each printed together, *se-tenant*, as horizontal pairs in sheets of 10, with the backgrounds forming composite designs.

167 Winston Churchill as Home Secretary and Siege of Sidney Street, 1911

(Des D. Miller. Litho Questa)

2000 (2 Oct). Centenary of Sir Winston Churchill's Election to Parliament. T **167** and similar horiz designs. Multicoloured. W w **14** (sideways). P 13½×14.

696	20p. Type **167**	2·50	1·75
697	30p. As Chancellor of the Exchequer, 1925, and with Pres. Roosevelt at signing of Atlantic Treaty, 1941	2·75	2·50
698	50p. Giving Victory sign and making V.E. Day broadcast, 1945	3·50	3·25
699	60p. In retirement and greeting Queen Elizabeth II at 10 Downing Street, 1955	3·50	3·50
696/9	*Set of 4*	11·00	10·00

168 Inaccessible Island Rail

(Des T. Thackeray. Litho Questa)

2001 (1 Feb). "HONG KONG 2001" Stamp Exhibition. Sheet, 150×90 mm, containing T **168** and similar horiz design showing island bird. Multicoloured. W w **14** (sideways). P 14.

MS700	30p. Type **168**; 45p. Black-faced Spoonbill	7·50	8·50

169 Letter from Tristan da Cunha, 1846

(Des N. Shewring. Litho Questa)

2001 (24 May). Death Centenary of Queen Victoria. T **169** and similar multicoloured designs. W w **14** (sideways on horiz designs). P 14.

701	15p. Type **169**	95	95
702	20p. Prince Alfred, Duke of Edinburgh (*vert*)	1·10	1·10
703	30p. H.M.S. *Galatea* (screw frigate)	1·60	1·75
704	35p. Queen Victoria (*vert*)	1·60	1·75
705	50p. Charles Dickens (*vert*)	2·00	2·25
706	60p. Longboats resupplying warship	2·00	2·25
701/6	*Set of* 6	8·25	9·00
MS707	104×80 mm. £1.50, Queen Victoria outside St. Paul's during Diamond Jubilee celebrations	4·50	6·50

170 Longboat under Sail

HURRICANE RELIEF 2001
(**171**)

(Litho Questa)

2001 (12 July). Tristan Longboats. T **170** and similar horiz designs. Multicoloured. W w **14** (sideways). P 14.

708	30p. Type **170**	1·75	1·75
	a. Sheetlet. Nos. 708/15	12·50	12·50
709	30p. Two longboats at sea (face value at bottom right)	1·75	1·75
710	30p. Two longboats at sea (face value at bottom left)	1·75	1·75
711	30p. Longboat with multicoloured mainsail near island	1·75	1·75
712	30p. Longboat with blue and white striped sail near island	1·75	1·75
713	30p. Longboat with white mainsail near island	1·75	1·75
714	30p. Longboat with violet blue mainsail near island	1·75	1·75
715	30p. Longboat in harbour	1·75	1·75
708/15	*Set of* 8	12·50	12·50

Nos. 708/15 were printed together, *se-tenant*, in sheetlets of 8 with enlarged illustrated and inscribed margins.

2001 (17 Sept). Hurricane Relief. Nos. 688/95 optd with T **171** in blue.

716	10p. Type **166**	2·00	2·25
	a. Horiz pair. Nos. 716/17	4·00	4·50
717	10p. S.A. 330J Puma Helicopter, 1999	2·00	2·25
718	15p. H.M.S. *London* (destroyer)	2·50	2·75
	a. Horiz pair. Nos. 718/19	5·00	5·50
719	15p. Westland Wessex HAS1 helicopter, 1964	2·50	2·75
720	20p. H.M.S. *Endurance II* (ice patrol ship)	2·50	2·75
	a. Horiz pair. Nos. 720/1	5·00	5·50
721	20p. Westland Lynx HAS3 helicopter, 1996	2·50	2·75
722	50p. U.S.S. *Spiegel Grove* (landing ship)	3·25	3·50
	a. Horiz pair. Nos. 722/3	6·50	7·00
723	50p. Sikorsky UH-19F helicopter, 1963	3·25	3·50
716/23	*Set of* 8	18·00	20·00

172 Head of White-chinned Petrel ("Spectacled Petrel")

173 H.M.S. *Julia* (sloop), 1817

(Des A. Robinson. Litho Questa)

2001 (1 Oct). BirdLife International (1st Series). World Bird Festival. Spectacled Petrel. Sheet, 175×80 mm, containing T **172** and similar multicoloured designs. W w **14** (sideways). P 14½.

MS724	35p. Type **172**; 35p. Petrel in front of cliffs (*vert*); 35p. Petrel descending to sea (*vert*); 35p. Petrel flying; 35p. Petrel chick	15·00	16·00

See also Nos. 770/4.

(Des J. Batchelor. Litho Enschedé)

2001 (31 Oct). Royal Navy Connections with Tristan da Cunha. T **173** and similar horiz designs. Multicoloured. W w **14** (sideways). P 14.

725	20p. Type **173**	2·25	2·50
726	20p. H.M.S. *Penguin* (sloop), 1815	2·25	2·50
727	35p. H.M.S. *Beagle* (screw sloop), 1901	3·00	3·25
728	35p. H.M.S. *Puma* (frigate), 1962	3·00	3·25
729	60p. H.M.S. *Monmouth* (frigate), 1997	4·50	5·00
730	60p. H.M.S. *Somerset* (frigate), 1999	4·50	5·00
725/30	*Set of* 6	18·00	19·00

174 Procession at St. Mary's Anglican Church

175 1952 Overprints on St. Helena 3d., 4d., 1s. and 2s.6d.

(Litho Cartor)

2001 (27 Nov). 150th Anniv of Arrival of First U.S.P.G. Missionary on Tristan da Cunha. T **174** and similar designs. Multicoloured (except No. 731). W w **14** (sideways on horiz designs). P 13½.

731	35p. Type **174** (olive-brown, black and yellow)	2·75	3·00
732	35p. St. Joseph's Catholic Church	2·75	3·00
733	60p. Altar, St. Mary's Church (*vert*)	5·00	5·50
734	60p. Stained glass, St. Joseph's Church (*vert*)	5·00	5·50
731/4	*Set of* 4	14·00	15·00

(Litho B.D.T.)

2002 (1 Jan). 50th Anniv of First Stamp Issue. T **175** and similar horiz designs. Multicoloured (except 60p.). W w **14** (sideways). P 13½.

735	15p. Type **175**	2·50	1·75
736	20p. 1952 6d., 8d., 5s. and 10s. overprinted stamps	2·50	1·75
737	50p. 1952 ½d., 1d., 1½d. and 2d. overprinted stamps	5·50	6·00
738	60p. Buying stamps, 1952 (black, olive-sepia and olive-bistre)	6·00	6·50
735/8	*Set of* 4	15·00	14·50
MS739	146×90 mm. 45p.×4 As Nos. 735/8, but each inscr "Tristan da Cunha" in mock manuscript	9·50	11·00

(Des A. Robinson. Litho Questa)

2002 (6 Feb). Golden Jubilee. Designs as T **211** of St. Helena. W w **14** (sideways). P 14½.

740	15p. grey-black, Indian red and gold	1·25	1·00
741	30p. multicoloured	1·90	1·75
742	45p. multicoloured	2·50	2·75
743	50p. multicoloured	2·50	2·75
740/3	*Set of* 4	7·25	7·25
MS744	162×95 mm. Nos. 740/3 and 60p. multicoloured. P 13½ (60p.) or 14½ (others)	8·50	9·00

Designs: *Horiz* (*as Type* **211** *of St. Helena*)— 15p. Princess Elizabeth, 1947; 30p. Queen Elizabeth in evening dress, Buckingham Palace, 1991; 45p. Queen Elizabeth in multicoloured turban; 50p. Queen Elizabeth at Newmarket, 1997. *Vert* (38×51 *mm*)—60p. Queen Elizabeth after Annigoni.

Designs as Nos. 740/3 in No. **MS**744 omit the gold frame around each stamp and the "Golden Jubilee 1952-2002" inscription.

176 Pelagic Armourhead (fish)

177 Gray's Beaked Whale

(Des N. Shewring. Litho B.D.T.)

2002 (8 May). Extension of Fishing Industry to New Species. T **176** and similar horiz designs. Multicoloured. W w **14** (sideways). P 14.

745	20p. Type **176**	1·50	1·25

746	35p. Yellowtail	2·25	2·25
747	50p. Splendid Alfonsino	3·00	3·25
745/7 *Set of 3*		6·00	6·00
MS748 140×75 mm. 60p. *San Liberatore* (stern trawler) and Nos. 745/7		5·00	6·00

(Des A. Robinson. Litho Questa)

2002 (5 Aug). Queen Elizabeth the Queen Mother Commemoration. Vert designs as T **215** of St. Helena. W w **14**. P 14½×14.

749	20p. brownish black, gold and purple	1·50	70
750	£1.50 multicoloured	5·50	6·50
MS751 145×70 mm. 75p. black and gold; 75p. multicoloured. Wmk sideways		7·50	8·50

Designs:— 20p. Queen Elizabeth visiting shipyard, 1942; 75p. black and gold (No. **MS**751) Duchess of York with Princess Margaret, 1930; 75p. multicoloured (No. **MS**751) Queen Mother at Cheltenham Races; £1.50 Queen Mother on her birthday, 1995.

Designs in No. **MS**751 omit the "1900-2002" inscription and the coloured frame.

(Des. R. Watton. Litho B.D.T.)

2002 (24 Sept). Marine Mammals. T **177** and similar square designs. Multicoloured. W w **14** (inverted). P 13½.

752	30p. Type **177**	3·50	3·50
	a. Sheetlet. Nos. 752/7	19·00	19·00
753	30p. Dusky Dolphin	3·50	3·50
754	30p. False Killer Whale	3·50	3·50
755	30p. Long-finned Pilot Whale	3·50	3·50
756	30p. Sperm Whale	3·50	3·50
757	30p. Shepherd's Beaked Whale	3·50	3·50
752/7 *Set of 6*		19·00	19·00
MS758 81×92 mm. £2 Humpback Whale. Wmk upright		16·00	17·00

Nos. 752/7 were printed together, *se-tenant*, in sheetlets of 6 forming a composite design.

178 Captain Denham and Officers of H.M.S. *Herald* (survey ship)

(Litho B.D.T.)

2002 (11 Nov). 150th Anniv of Survey by H.M.S. *Herald*. T **178** and similar horiz designs. Multicoloured (except 20p.). W w **14** (sideways). P 14×15.

759	20p. Type **178** (ochre and agate)	1·50	1·10
760	35p. H.M.S. *Herald* in Bay of Biscay	2·00	2·00
761	50p. H.M.S. *Herald* off Tristan da Cunha, 1852	2·50	2·50
762	60p. H.M.S. *Herald* and H.M.S. *Torch* (paddle steamer) at sunset	2·75	3·25
759/62 *Set of 4*		8·00	8·00

179 Great Barrier Reef, Australia (longest reef)

180 Atlantic Yellow-nosed Albatross (pair)

(Litho B.D.T.)

2003 (10 Jan). World Geographical Records. T **179** and similar horiz designs. Multicoloured. W w **14**(sideways). P 14.

763	30p. Type **179**	1·40	1·75
764	30p. Greenland (biggest island)	1·40	1·75
765	30p. Sahara (biggest desert)	1·40	1·75
766	30p. River Amazon (longest river)	1·40	1·75
767	30p. Mt Everest (highest mountain)	1·40	1·75
768	30p. Edinburgh, Tristan da Cunha (most remote inhabited island)	1·40	1·75
763/8 *Set of 6*		7·50	9·50
MS769 90×68 mm. £2 Closer view of Edinburgh		8·50	10·00

Nos. 763/8 were printed together, *se-tenant*, in sheetlets of 6 with enlarged inscribed margins.

(Des A. Harris. Litho DLR)

2003 (7 May). BirdLife International (2nd series). Atlantic Yellow-nosed Albatross. T **180** and similar multicoloured designs. W w **14** (sideways on 30p, 45p). P 14½×14 (horiz) or 14×14½ (vert).

770	15p. Type **180**	1·40	1·25
771	30p. Albatross on nest (*vert*)	2·25	2·25
772	45p. Albatross in flight (*vert*)	2·75	2·75
773	50p. Two albatrosses in flight	2·75	3·00
770/3 *Set of 4*		8·25	8·25
MS774 175×80 mm. Nos. 770/3 and £1 Pair in flight. Wmk sideways. P 14½		8·50	9·50

(Des A. Robinson. Litho DLR)

2003 (2 June). 50th Anniv of Coronation. Horiz designs as T **219** of St. Helena. Multicoloured. W w **14** (sideways). P 14×14½.

775	30p. Queen Elizabeth II with Royal family	70	70
776	£1.50 Archbishop and bishops paying homage to Queen	4·25	4·50
MS777 95×115 mm. 75p. As 20p.; 75p. As £1.50		4·25	5·00

Nos. 775/6 have scarlet frame; stamps from **MS**777 have no frame and country name in mauve panel.

(Des CASB Studio. Litho BDT)

2003 (2 June). As T **220** of St. Helena. W w **14**. P 13½.

778	£2.80 black, dull mauve and cream	6·00	6·50

(Des A. Robinson. Litho DLR)

2003 (23 June). 21st Birthday of Prince William of Wales. Square designs as T **208** of Ascension. Multicoloured. P 14½.

779	50p. Prince William at Sighthill Community Education Centre, 2001 and playing polo, 2002	2·00	2·00
	a. Horiz pair. Nos. 779/80	4·00	4·00
780	50p. In Scotland, 2001 and on Raleigh International Expedition, 2000	2·00	2·00

Nos. 779/80 were printed together, *se-tenant*, as horizontal pairs in sheets of ten (2×5) with enlarged illustrated left-hand margins.

181 Corporal William Glass arriving on HMS Falmouth (1816)

182 RFA *Tideflow*

(Des R. Watton. Litho DLR)

2003 (24 Nov). 150th Death Anniv of William Glass (founding settler of Tristan). T **181** and similar horiz designs. Multicoloured. W w **14** (sideways). P 14×14½.

781	30p. Type **181**	1·75	1·75
	a. Sheetlet. Nos. 781/6	9·50	9·50
	ab. Imperf		
782	30p. Corporal Glass with other Royal Artillerymen	1·75	1·75
783	30p. William Glass and family remaining on Tristan (1817)	1·75	1·75
784	30p. William Glass and family	1·75	1·75
785	30p. Governor William Glass conducting marriage of eldest daughter Mary (1833)	1·75	1·75
786	30p. Governor William Glass as old man (1853)	1·75	1·75
781/6 *Set of 6*		9·50	9·50

Nos. 781/6 were printed together, *se-tenant*, in sheetlets of six, with a small *se-tenant* label describing the stamp design at the foot of each stamp.

(Des A. Theobald. Litho DLR)

2003 (8 Dec). Royal Navy Connections with Tristan da Cunha (2nd series). T **182** and similar horiz designs. Multicoloured. W w **14**. P 14.

787	20p. Type **182**	1·75	2·00
	a. Horiz pair. Nos. 787/8	3·50	4·00
788	20p. RFA *Tidespring* (tanker)	1·75	2·00
789	35p. RFA *Gold Rover* (tanker)	2·50	2·75
	a. Horiz pair. Nos. 789/90	5·00	5·50
790	35p. RFA *Diligence* (repair ship)	2·50	2·75
791	60p. RFA *Wave Chief*	4·00	4·50
	a. Horiz pair. Nos. 791/2	8·00	9·00
792	60p. Royal Yacht *Britannia*	4·00	4·50
787/92 *Set of 6*		15·00	17·00

Nos. 787/8, 789/90 and 791/2 were each printed together, *se-tenant*, in horizontal pairs in sheets of 10.

Nos. 791/2 have no white margins and form a composite background design.

183 Pigment Blocks and Cave Painting

(Des A. Robinson. Litho DLR)

2004 (8 Jan). History of Writing. T **183** and similar horiz designs. Multicoloured. W w **14** (sideways). P 13½×14.

793	15p. Type **183**	95	95
794	20p. Clay tablet	1·10	1·10
795	35p. Egyptian writing palette	1·90	2·00
796	45p. Goose quill pen	2·00	2·25
797	50p. Fountain pen	2·00	2·25
798	60p. Ballpoint pen	2·50	2·75
793/8	*Set of* 6	9·50	10·50
MS799	60p. 100×90 mm. £1.50 Word processing	6·50	7·50

184 Subantarctic Fur Seal

185 Flag

(Des J. Pointer. Litho BDT)

2004 (12 July). Endangered Species. Subantarctic Fur Seal. T **184** and similar horiz designs. Multicoloured. W w **14** (sideways). P 14.

800	35p. Type **184**	1·40	1·60
	a. Horiz strip of 4. Nos. 800/3	5·00	5·75
801	35p. Seal swimming	1·40	1·60
802	35p. Two seals	1·40	1·60
803	35p. Seal on rocks	1·40	1·60
800/3	*Set of* 4	5·00	5·75

Nos. 800/3, were printed together, *se-tenant*, in horizontal strips of four as well as in separate sheets.

(Litho Walsall)

2004 (27 July). New Island Flag. Self-adhesive. Die-cut imperf.

804	**185**	30p. multicoloured	1·00	1·00
		a. Booklet pane. No. 804×12	10·00	10·00

No. 804 is die-cut with horizontal wavy lines to simulate the movement of a flag, and was only printed in £3.60 self-adhesive stamp booklets.

(Des A. Theobald. Litho Enschedé)

2004 (9 Nov). Merchant Ships. Horiz designs as T **227** of St. Helena. Multicoloured. W w 14 (sideways). P 13×13½.

805	20p. RMS *Dunnottar Castle*	1·75	1·90
806	20p. RMS *Caronia*	1·75	1·90
807	35p. MV *Edinburgh*	2·50	2·75
808	35p. SA *Agulhas*	2·50	2·75
809	60p. MV *Hanseatic*	4·00	4·50
810	60p. MV *Explorer*	4·00	4·50
805/10	*Set of* 6	15·00	16·00

186 Nelson's Quadrant

187 Rockhopper Penguins

(Des J. Batchelor. Litho and thermograph (60p.) Cartor)

2005 (20 Jan). Bicentenary of the Battle of Trafalgar (1st issue). T **186** and similar multicoloured designs. P 13½.

811	15p. Type **186**	1·60	1·75
812	20p. HMS Royal *Sovereign* breaks the line (*horiz*)	2·25	2·50
813	25p. Thomas Swain helping wounded Lord Nelson (*horiz*)	2·25	2·50
814	35p. HMS *Victory* breaks the line (*horiz*)	3·25	3·50
815	50p. Lord Nelson	3·50	3·75
816	60p. HMS *Victory*	4·25	4·50
811/16	*Set of* 6	15·00	17·00
MS817	120×79 mm. 75p. Captain Sir Thomas Hardy; 75p. HMS *Victory* firing signal Shot	11·00	12·00

See also Nos. 846/8.

Nos. 811/16 were each printed in sheets of 6 with decorative margins and with the Trafalgar Festival 2005 logo at foot.

(Des D. Miller. Litho BDT)

2005 (21 Feb). Islands (1st issue). Tristan da Cunha. T **187** and similar horiz designs. Multicoloured. W w **14** (sideways). P 14.

818	50p. Type **187**	2·00	2·25
	a. Horiz strip of 5. Nos. 818/22	9·00	10·00
819	50p. Southern Elephant Seals	2·00	2·25
820	50p. Tristan Rock Lobster	2·00	2·25
821	50p. Crowberry	2·00	2·25
822	50p. Island settlement and volcano	2·00	2·25
818/22	*Set of* 5	9·00	10·00

Nos. 818/22 were printed together, *se-tenant*, in horizontal strips of five stamps within sheets of 25.

See also Nos, 823/7, 828/32, 850/4, 855/9, 866/70 and **MS**871.

(Des D. Miller. Litho BDT)

2005 (28 Mar). Islands (2nd issue). Gough Island. Horiz designs as T **187**. Multicoloured. W w **14** (sideways). P 14.

823	50p. Gough Moorhen	2·00	2·25
	a. Horiz strip of 5. Nos. 823/7	9·00	10·00
824	50p. Subantarctic Fur Seal	2·00	2·25
825	50p. Bluefish	2·00	2·25
826	50p. Gough Tree Fern	2·00	2·25
827	50p. South African Weather Station	2·00	2·25
823/7	*Set of* 5	9·00	10·00

Nos. 823/7 were printed together, *se-tenant*, in horizontal strips of five stamps within sheets of 25.

(Des D. Miller. Litho BDT)

2005 (18 Apr). Islands (3rd issue). Inaccessible Island. Horiz designs as T **187**. Multicoloured. W w **14** (sideways). P 14.

828	50p. Inaccessible Island Rail	2·00	2·25
	a. Horiz strip of 5. Nos. 828/32	9·00	10·00
829	50p. Dusky Dolphin	2·00	2·25
830	50p. Soldierfish	2·00	2·25
831	50p. Pepper Tree	2·00	2·25
832	50p. Waterfall	2·00	2·25
828/32	*Set of* 5	9·00	10·00

Nos. 828/32 were printed together, *se-tenant*, in horizontal strips of five stamps within sheets of 25.

188 Kerguelen Petrel

189 HMS *Victory*

(Des R. Gorringe. Litho BDT)

2005 (1 June). Birds. T **188** and similar horiz designs. Multicoloured. W w **14** (sideways*). P 14×15.

833	1p. Type **188**	45	60
834	3p. Sooty Albatross	60	70
835	5p. Antarctic Tern	75	80
836	8p. Nightingale Finch ("Tristan Bunting")	1·00	1·25
837	10p. Pintado ("Cape") Petrel	1·00	1·25
838	15p. Gough Island Coot ("Tristan Moorhen")	1·50	1·25
839	20p. Giant Petrel ("Fulmar")	1·75	1·25
	w. Wmk Crown to right of CA	£250	
840	25p. Brown Skua	1·75	1·40
841	35p. Great-winged Petrel	2·00	1·50
842	£1 Broad-billed Prion	4·75	5·00
843	£2 Soft-plumaged Petrel	8·50	9·50
844	£5 Rockhopper Penguin	14·00	17·00
833/44	*Set of* 12	35·00	38·00

*The normal sideways watermark shows Crown to left of CA, *as seen from the back of the stamp.*

(Des A. Robinson. Litho BDT)

2005 (18 Aug). Pope John Paul II Commemoration. Vert design as T **231** of St. Helena. W w **14** (inverted). P 14.

845	50p. multicoloured	2·75	3·00

No. 845 was printed in sheetlets of eight stamps with an enlarged, illustrated right margin.

(Des J. Batchelor (20p) or Pauline Gyles (£1). Litho Cartor)

2005 (18 Oct). Bicentenary of the Battle of Trafalgar (2nd issue). T **189** and similar multicoloured designs. P 13½.

846	20p. Type **189**	3·25	2·00
847	70p. Ships engaged in battle (*horiz*)	5·50	6·00
848	£1 Admiral Lord Nelson	7·00	7·50
846/8	*Set of* 3	14·00	14·00

190 Portuguese Admiral Tristao d'Acunha and First Sighting of Tristan da Cunha

(Des R. Watton. Litho BDT)

2006 (2 Feb). 500th Anniv of Discovery of Tristan da Cunha (1st issue). T **190** and similar horiz designs. Multicoloured. W w **14** (sideways). P 14×15.

MS849 Two sheets, each 160×100 mm. (a) 30p. Type **190**; 30p. French frigate *L'heure du Berger* (first survey), 1767; 30p. Jonathan Lambert and establishment of trading station, 1810; 50p. William Glass and elephant seal, 1816; 50p. Crew rowing away from wreck of *Emily*, 1836; 80p. *Duke of Gloucester*, 1824. (b) 30p. Thomas Swain as old man and with wounded Nelson at Battle of Trafalgar; 30p. HMS *Challenger*, 1873; 30p. Arrival of Reverend Dodgson, 1881; 50p. Crew of wrecked *Italia* coming ashore, 1892; 50p. HMS *Milford*, 1938; 80p. Outline map (Norwegian expedition, 1937/8) ... 20·00 22·00

See also No. **MS**865.

(Des D. Miller. Litho BDT)

2006 (7 Feb). Islands (4th issue). Nightingale Island. Horiz designs as T **187**. Multicoloured. W w **14** (sideways). P 14.

850	50p. Tristan thrush	2·00	2·25
	a. Horiz strip of 5. Nos 850/4	9·00	10·00
851	50p. Southern right whales	2·00	2·25
852	50p. Fivefinger fish	2·00	2·25
853	50p. Tussock grass	2·00	2·25
854	50p. Nightingale Island	2·00	2·25
850/4	*Set of* 5	9·00	10·00

Nos. 850/4 were printed together, *se-tenant*, in horizontal strips of five stamps within sheets of 25.

(Des D. Miller. Litho BDT)

2006 (30 Mar). Islands (5th issue). Middle Island. Horiz designs as T **187**. Multicoloured. W w **14** (sideways). P 14.

855	50p. Broad-billed prion	2·00	2·25
	a. Horiz strip of 5. Nos. 855/9	9·00	10·00
856	50p. False killer whale	2·00	2·25
857	50p. Wreckfish	2·00	2·25
858	50p. *Blechnum tabulare* (fern)	2·00	2·25
859	50p. Middle Island	2·00	2·25
855/9	*Set of* 5	9·00	10·00

Nos. 855/9 were printed together, *se-tenant*, in horizontal strips of 5 stamps in sheets of 50 (2 panes of 25).

(Litho BDT)

2006 (21 Apr). 80th Birthday of Queen Elizabeth II. Horiz designs as T **237** of St. Helena. Multicoloured. W w **14** (sideways). P 14.

860	60p. Princess Elizabeth as young girl	3·00	3·25
861	60p. Queen Elizabeth II wearing black hat, c. 1955	3·00	3·25
862	60p. Wearing red hat	3·00	3·25
863	60p. Recent photograph of Queen Elizabeth II	3·00	3·25
860/3	*Set of* 4	11·00	11·50
MS864	144×75 mm. 50p. As No. 861; 50p. As No. 862	5·50	6·00

Stamps from No. **MS**864 do not have white borders.

(Des R. Watton. Litho BDT)

2006 (1 June). 500th Anniv of Discovery of Tristan da Cunha (2nd issue). Horiz designs as T **191**. Multicoloured. W w **14** (sideways). P 14×15.

MS865 Two sheets, each 160×100 mm. (a) 30p. Tristan Defence Volunteers in training, World War II; 30p. HMS *Atlantic Isle* (radio and weather station), 1944; 30p. 1946 1d. "Potato Stamp"; 50p. First Tristan da Cunha stamp, 1952 (overprinted 3d. St. Helena stamp); 50p. Volcano eruption and evacuation, 1961; 80p. Gough Island Scientific Expedition, 1955. (b) 30p. Royal Society Expedition, 1962; 30p. Resettlement, 1963; 30p. Denstone Expedition to Inaccessible Island, 1982; 50p. RMS *St. Helena*, 1992; 50p. New Coat of Arms, 2002; 80p. Hurricane disaster, 2001 ... 25·00 27·00

(Des D. Miller. Litho BDT)

2006 (27 Sept). Islands (6th issue). Stoltenhoff Island. Horiz designs as T **187**. Multicoloured. W w **14** (sideways). P 14.

866	50p. Brown skua	2·00	2·50
	a. Horiz strip of 5. Nos. 866/70	9·00	11·00
867	50p. Shepherd's beaked whales	2·00	2·50
868	50p. Snoek (fish)	2·00	2·50
869	50p. Sea bind weed	2·00	2·50
870	50p. Stoltenhoff Island	2·00	2·50
866/70	*Set of* 5	9·00	11·00

Nos. 866/70 were printed together, *se-tenant*, as horizontal strips of five stamps in sheets of 25.

(Des D. Miller. Litho BDT)

2007 (22 Jan). Islands (7th series). Sheet 160×75 mm containing horiz designs as T **187**. Multicoloured. W w **14** (sideways). P 14.

MS871 50p.×6 Map and flag of Tristan da Cunha; Wandering albatross and Inaccessible Island; Tail of humpback whale and Nightingale Island; Traditional longboats and Middle Island; Mackerel and Stoltenhoff Island; Sub-Antarctic fur seal and Gough Island ... 19·00 21·00

The stamps within **MS**871 all show an outline map of the island depicted.

191 *Wave Dancer* (fisheries patrol boat)

192 Great Shearwater

(Des Andrew Robinson. Litho Lowe-Martin, Canada)

2007 (17 Apr). Local Vehicles. T **191** and similar horiz designs. Multicoloured. P 12½×13.

872	15p. Type **191**	1·00	1·00
873	20p. Ambulance	1·75	1·25
874	30p. Inshore rescue craft	2·00	1·50
875	45p. Police Land Rover	3·50	3·25
876	50p. Fire engine	3·50	3·25
877	85p. Administrator's Land Rover	4·50	5·00
872/7	*Set of* 6	14·50	13·50

(Litho BDT)

2007 (26 Apr). Diamond Wedding of Queen Elizabeth II and Duke of Edinburgh. Vert designs as T **242** of St. Helena. Multicoloured. W w **14**. P 14.

878	50p. Princess Elizabeth and Duke of Edinburgh, c. 1947	2·25	2·50
879	50p. Princess Elizabeth looking out of carriage window on wedding day	2·25	2·50
880	50p. Princess Elizabeth on wedding day, waving from balcony	2·25	2·50
881	50p. Young Queen Elizabeth and Duke of Edinburgh in evening dress	2·25	2·50
878/81	*Set of* 4	8·00	9·00
MS882	125×85 mm. £2 Wedding photograph of Princess Elizabeth (42×56 *mm*). Wmk sideways	8·00	8·50

Nos. 878/81 were each printed in sheetlets of six stamps with enlarged illustrated margins.

(Des Richard Allen. Litho BDT)

2007 (1 July). Great Shearwater (*Puffinus gravis*). Sheet 170×85 mm containing T **192** and similar horiz designs. Multicoloured. Litho. P 14.

MS883 50p.×6 Type **192**; In flight, seen from above; On nest, head turned to left; In flight, wings raised; In close-up on nest, facing left; Chick ... 17·00 18·00

The stamps within **MS**883 form a composite design showing seabirds and headland.

(Des Andrew Robinson. Litho BDT)

2007 (9 July). Centenary of Scouting. Multicoloured designs as T **244** of St. Helena. W w **14** (sideways). P 14.

884	15p. Scout James Marr and his log of 1921–2 Antarctic expedition *Into the Frozen South*	1·50	1·00
885	20p. *Quest* frozen into Antarctic ice	1·75	1·25
886	£1.25 Scout Marr presenting Tristan Da Cunha Troop flag to Patrol Leader Donald Glass, May 1922	5·00	5·50
887	£1.40 Children of Tristan da Cunha outside schoolhouse, May 1922	5·00	5·50
884/7	*Set of* 4	12·00	12·00
MS888	90×65 mm. £1.50 Scout Marr and ship's cat "Questie" (*vert*); £1.50 Lord Baden-Powell (150th birth anniv) (*vert*). Wmk upright	12·00	13·00

193 Diana, Princess of Wales

194 Tristan Rock Lobster (*Jasus tristanii*)

(Litho Lowe-Martin, Canada)

2007 (30 Nov). Tenth Death Anniv of Diana, Princess of Wales. T **193** and similar vert designs. Multicoloured.

889	50p. Type **193**	1·90	1·90
890	50p. Wearing red dress (dark blue background)	1·90	1·90
891	50p. Wearing diamond and pearl earrings	1·90	1·90
892	50p. Wearing black	1·60	1·60
893	50p. Wearing dress with narrow straps and diamond necklace	1·90	1·90
894	50p. Wearing white dress, looking over shoulder	1·90	1·90
889/94	*Set of 6*	10·00	10·00

Nos. 889/94 were each printed in sheetlets of six stamps with enlarged illustrated margins.

(Des Derek Miller. Litho Lowe-Martin Group)

2008 (28 Jan). Marine Invertebrates. T **194** and similar square designs. Multicoloured. P 13½.

895	15p. Type **194**	80	80
896	20p. Trumpet anemone (*Parazoanthus hertwigi*)	90	90
897	35p. Starfish (*Henricia simplex*)	1·60	1·60
898	60p. Tristan urchin (*Arbacia crassispina*)	2·25	2·75
899	60p. Sponge	2·25	2·75
900	85p. Strawberry anemone (*Corynactis annulata*)	3·00	3·50
895/900	*Set of 6*	9·00	10·50

195 21st Light Dragoon Officer

196 Fishing Boats in Calshot Harbour

(Des Ross Watton. Litho BDT)

2008 (3 Mar). Military Uniforms. T **195** and similar vert designs. Multicoloured. P 14.

901	15p. Type **195**	2·00	2·00
902	15p. Corporal, Royal Artillery	2·00	2·00
903	20p. Privates, Royal Artillery	2·00	2·00
904	20p. Lieutenant, Royal Artillery	2·00	2·00
905	£1 Cape Regiment	6·50	7·00
906	£1 South Africa Army Engineering Corps	6·50	7·00
901/6	*Set of 6*	19·00	20·00

Nos. 901/6 were each printed in sheetlets of six stamps with enlarged illustrated margins.

(Litho BDT)

2008 (1 Apr). 90th Anniv of the Royal Air Force. Horiz designs as T **247** of St. Helena. Multicoloured (except **MS**912). P 14.

907	30p. Hawker Hart	2·25	2·25
908	30p. Hawker Typhoon	2·25	2·25
909	30p. Royal Aircraft Factory S.E.5a	2·25	2·25
910	30p. Avro Vulcan	2·25	2·25
911	30p. SEPECAT Jaguar	2·25	2·25
907/11	*Set of 5*	10·00	10·00
MS912	110×70 mm. £1.50 Sir Hugh Trenchard ('father of the RAF') (brownish black and brownish grey) (*vert*). Wmk inverted	7·50	8·00

Nos. 907/11 were each printed in sheetlets of eight stamps with a central label showing anniversary emblem and enlarged illustrated margins.

(Des Ross Watton. Litho Lowe-Martin Group)

2008 (1 July). 60th Anniv of Tristan Fisheries. T **196** and similar horiz designs. Multicoloured. P 13½×13.

913	15p. Type **196**	1·25	1·25
914	20p. Fishing boats	1·40	1·40
915	30p. Offloading and loading fish	2·00	2·00
916	70p. Sorting crawfish tails	3·50	3·75
917	80p. Rock lobster tails wrapped and packed	3·50	3·75
918	£1.25 Shipping for export	6·00	6·50
913/18	*Set of 6*	16·00	17·00

197 Allan B. Crawford

198 *A Battery Shelled* (Percy Wyndham Lewis) (1919)

(Des Andrew Robinson. Litho Lowe-Martin Group)

2008 (1 Aug). Allan B. Crawford (founder of Tristan da Cunha Association and author) Commemoration. T **197** and similar multicoloured designs. P 13×13½.

919	15p. Type **197**	80	80
920	20p. 1d. 'Potato stamp', 1946–7	1·00	1·00
921	50p. First map of Tristan da Cunha drawn by Allan Crawford, 1937–8	2·50	2·50
922	60p. Allan Crawford with Norwegian Scientific Expedition, 1937–8 and cover of *I Went to Tristan*, 1941 (*horiz*)	2·75	2·75
923	85p. Establishment of Meteorological Office at Marion Island, 1948 and cover of *Tristan da Cunha and the Roaring Forties*, 1982 (*horiz*)	3·25	3·50
924	£1.20 Allan Crawford on Royal Society Expedition, 1962 and cover of *Penguins, Potatoes and Postage Stamps*, 1999 (*horiz*)	4·75	5·50
919/24	*Set of 6*	13·50	14·50

(Litho BDT)

2008 (16 Sept). 90th Anniv of the End of World War I. T **198** and similar multicoloured designs showing paintings. W w **18** (inverted on vert designs, sideways on horiz). P 14.

925	50p. Type **198**	2·50	2·50
926	50p. *The Angels of Mons* (R. Crowhurst) (1914) (*vert*)	2·50	2·50
927	50p. *Oppy Wood* (John Nash) (1917)	2·50	2·50
928	50p. *Lion leads in Jutland* (W. L. Wyllie) (1916)	2·50	2·50
929	50p. *End of Richthofen* (Charles H. Hubbell) (1918)	2·50	2·50
930	50p. *Somme Tank* (Louis Dauphin) (1916)	2·50	2·50
925/30	*Set of 6*	13·50	13·50
MS931	110×70 mm. £1 The UK Overseas Territories Wreath of Remembrance (*vert*). Wmk inverted	4·00	4·50

Nos. 925/30 were printed in separate sheetlets of six stamps with enlarged illustrated bottom margins.

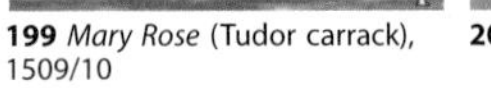

199 *Mary Rose* (Tudor carrack), 1509/10

200 Preparing Seed Potatoes

(Litho BDT)

2009 (9 Mar). Seafaring and Exploration. T **199** and similar multicoloured designs. W w **18** (sideways). P 14.

932	50p. Type **199**	2·75	2·75
933	50p. *Cutty Sark* (clipper), 1869	2·75	2·75
934	50p. *Suomen Joutsen* (full-rigged ship), 1902	2·75	2·75
935	50p. *Endurance* (barquentine), 1912 (Shackleton)	2·75	2·75
936	50p. MS *Explorer*, 1969	2·75	2·75
937	50p. RFA *Lyme Bay* (Bay Class landing ship dock), 2005	2·75	2·75
932/7	*Set of 6*	15·00	15·00

MS938 110×70 mm. £1 Tristão da Cunha (discovered Tristan da Cunha, 1506) (*vert*). Wmk inverted .... 4·75 5·50

Nos. 932/7 were each printed together, *se-tenant*, in sheetlets of six stamps with enlarged illustrated margins.

(Des Tim O'Brien. Litho BDT)

2009 (17 Apr). Centenary of Naval Aviation. Horiz designs as T **255** of St. Helena. Multicoloured. Litho. P 14.

939 25p. Felixstowe F.2A flying boat .... 2·00 2·00
940 35p. Short S.27 .... 3·00 3·00
941 50p. Sikorsky Hoverfly helicopter .... 4·00 4·00
942 50p. Blackburn Dart .... 4·00 4·00
939/42 *Set of 4* .... 11·50 11·50
MS943 110×70 mm. £1.50 Lt. Cdr. C. R. Samson in Short S.27 taking off from HMS *Hibernia*, 1912 .... 8·00 9·00

Nos. 939/42 were each printed in sheetlets of eight stamps and a central label with enlarged illustrated bottom margins.

(Litho Lowe-Martin)

2009 (20 July). International Year of Astronomy. 40th Anniv of First Moon Landing. Multicoloured designs as T **257** of St. Helena. W w **18** (sideways). P 13.

944 25p. Goddard Rocket, 1936 .... 1·40 1·40
945 35p. X-24B Spaceplane, 1972 .... 1·90 1·90
946 60p. Apollo launch, 1969 .... 3·25 3·25
947 90p. *Discovery* ferried by 747, 2005 .... 4·50 5·00
948 £1 X-43C, experimental hypersonic aircraft 4·50 5·00
944/8 *Set of 6* .... 14·00 15·00
MS949 100×80 mm. £1.50 *The Fabulous Photo We Never Took* (astronauts Alan Bean and Pete Conrad in front of Surveyor III) (Alan Bean) (39×59 *mm*). Wmk upright .... 6·00 7·00

Nos. 944/8 were printed in separate sheetlets of six stamps with enlarged illustrated margins.

(Des Andrew Robinson. Litho Lowe-Martin)

2009 (3 Aug). Potato Production. T **200** and similar horiz designs. Multicoloured. P 13.

950 25p. Type **200** .... 1·50 1·75
a. Horiz pair. Nos. 950/1 .... 3·00 3·50
951 25p. Women planting potatoes .... 1·50 1·75
952 35p. Digging out potatoes .... 2·00 2·25
a. Horiz pair. Nos. 952/3 .... 4·00 4·50
953 35p. Tractor with trailer of harvested potatoes .... 2·00 2·25
954 £1.10 Potato flowers .... 4·00 4·50
a. Horiz pair. Nos. 954/5 .... 8·00 9·00
955 £1.10 Potato patches .... 4·00 4·50
950/5 *Set of 6* .... 13·50 15·00

Nos. 950/1, 952/3 and 954/5 were printed together, *se-tenant*, in horizontal pairs throughout the sheets.

201 Sheep shearing

(Des Andrew Robinson. Litho Lowe-Martin Group)

2009 (28 Sept). Tristan da Cunha Traditions (1st series). T **201** and similar horiz designs. Multicoloured. P 13.

956 25p. Type **201** .... 1·50 1·50
957 35p. Ratting Day .... 1·75 1·75
958 70p. Longboats to Nightingale Island .... 3·00 3·50
959 £1.60 Old Year's Night Okalolies (masked men) .... 5·50 6·50
956/9 *Set of 4* .... 10·50 12·00

See also Nos. 1005/8.

202 Mail Bags arriving on Ship's Deck

(Des Andrew Robinson. Litho Lowe-Martin Group)

2009 (23 Nov). Mail to Tristan da Cunha. T **202** and similar horiz designs. Multicoloured. P 13.

960 25p. Type **202** .... 2·25 1·75
961 35p. Loading mail bags onto trailer at Calshot Harbour for transport to Post Office .... 3·00 2·25
962 £1 Hitting the gong to announce that post is ready for collection .... 7·00 7·50
963 £1.60 Giving out the mail, Prince Philip Hall .. 9·00 10·00
960/3 *Set of 4* .... 19·00 19·00

203 Battle of Hastings, 1066

204 Golden Eagle and Scotland Flag (Glass)

(Litho Lowe-Martin Group)

2010 (15 Jan). History of the British Isles (1st series). T **203** and similar square designs. Multicoloured. W w **18**. P 13½.

964 35p. Type **203** .... 1·50 1·50
965 35p. Peasants' Revolt, 1381 .... 1·50 1·50
966 35p. King Henry VIII and Hampton Court Palace .... 1·50 1·50
967 35p. Thomas Cranmer ('English Reformation') .... 1·50 1·50
968 35p. Queen Elizabeth I and Columbus' ships ('Elizabethan Era') .... 1·50 1·50
969 35p. Oliver Cromwell and King Charles I ('English Civil War') .... 1·50 1·50
970 35p. Sir Isaac Newton ('Scientific Innovation') .... 1·50 1·50
971 35p. Bonnie Prince Charlie .... 1·50 1·50
964/71 *Set of 8* .... 11·00 11·00

(Litho Lowe-Martin Group)

2010 (18 Mar). 70th Anniv of the Battle of Britain. Battle of Britain Pilots. Horiz designs as T **261** of St. Helena. Multicoloured. W w **18** (inverted). P 13.

972 25p. Pilots standing in front of plane .... 2·00 2·00
973 25p. Pilots running towards planes .... 2·00 2·00
974 50p. Group of pilots reading chart .... 3·50 3·50
975 50p. Pilots sat on grass in front of plane .... 3·50 3·50
976 70p. Pilots running to planes .... 4·50 4·50
977 70p. Group of pilots .... 4·50 4·50
972/7 *Set of 6* .... 18·00 18·00

No. **MS**978 is left for miniature sheet not yet received.

(Litho BDT)

2010 (8 May). Centenary of Accession of King George V. Sheet 110×70 mm containing vert design as T **262** of St. Helena. Multicoloured. W w **18**. P 14.

MS979 Great Britain King George V 1912 ½d. green stamp .... 5·50 6·00

(Litho Lowe-Martin Group)

2010 (16 July). History of the British Isles (2nd series). Square designs as T **203**. Multicoloured. W w **18**. P 13½.

980 35p. Murder of Archbishop Thomas Becket by four knights in Canterbury Cathedral, 1170 .... 1·90 1·90
981 35p. Bowmen and mounted knight (Battle of Agincourt, 1415) .... 1·90 1·90
982 35p. Vice Admiral Nelson and HMS *Victory* (Battle of Trafalgar, 1805) .... 1·90 1·90
983 35p. Isambard Kingdom Brunel and suspension bridge (Engineering & Transportation) .... 1·90 1·90
984 35p. Guglielmo Marconi and early wireless, 1901 (Wireless Age) .... 1·90 1·90
985 35p. Suffragettes (Votes for Women) .... 1·90 1·90
986 35p. Unemployed men (The Great Depression, 1930s) .... 1·90 1·90
987 35p. Joseph Stalin, Franklin D. Roosevelt, Winston Churchill and fighter planes (Second World War) .... 1·90 1·90
980/7 *Set of 8* .... 13·50 13·50

(Des Nick Shewring. Litho Lowe-Martin Group)

2010 (6 Sept). Island Families Surnames. T **204** and similar vert designs showing national flags and native birds of the original settlers home nations. Multicoloured. P 12½×13.

988 50p. Type **204** .... 3·50 3·50
989 50p. American bald eagle and US flag (Hagan and Rogers) .... 3·50 3·50
990 50p. Oystercatcher and Dutch flag (Green) ... 3·50 3·50
991 50p. Hoopoe and Italian flag (Repetto and Lavarello) .... 3·50 3·50

992	50p. Avocet and England flag (Swain)	3·50	3·50
988/92	*Set of* 5	16·00	16·00

205 New Conservation RIB

(Litho Lowe-Martin Group)

2010 (1 Nov). Conservation. T **205** and similar horiz designs. Multicoloured. P 13.

993	1p. Type **205**	10	10
994	3p. Eradication of New Zealand flax on Nightingale Island	20	20
995	5p. Ringing Tristan albatross	35	35
996	8p. Hag's tooth (rock formation) on Gough Island (World Heritage site)	40	40
997	10p. Inaccessible rail	60	60
998	15p. Inaccessible Island (World Heritage site)	80	80
999	25p. Counting sub-Antarctic fur seals	1·00	1·00
1000	35p. Eradication of sagina plant on Gough Island	1·25	1·25
1001	70p. Eradication of loganberry plants at Sandy Point	2·40	2·40
1002	£1 Ringing Atlantic yellow-nosed albatross	5·50	5·50
1003	£2 Gough bunting	7·50	7·50
1004	£5 Counting northern rockhopper penguins	18·00	18·00
993/1004	*Set of* 12	35·00	35·00

(Des Andrew Robinson. Litho Lowe-Martin Group)

2010 (24 Nov). Tristan Traditions (2nd series). Horiz designs as T **201**. Multicoloured. P 13.

1005	25p. Thatching	1·50	1·50
1006	35p. Bullock cart	2·25	2·25
1007	70p. Music (fiddle and accordion players)	3·25	3·50
1008	£1.60 Pillow dance	6·50	7·00
1005/8	*Set of* 4	12·00	13·00

206 Queen Elizabeth II, c. 1952

(Litho BDT)

2011 (14 Mar). Queen Elizabeth II and Prince Philip. 'A Lifetime of Service'. T **206** and similar diamond-shaped designs. Multicoloured. P 13½.

1009	25p. Type **206**	1·10	1·10
1010	35p. Princess Elizabeth and Lieut. Philip Mountbatten laughing, Clydebank, 1947	1·50	1·50
1011	50p. Queen Eliizabeth II and Prince Philip, c. 2007	2·25	2·25
1012	50p. Queen Elizabeth II (wearing red coat and hat) and Prince Philip, 1990s	2·25	2·25
1013	70p. Queen Elizabeth II and Prince Philip, c. 1972	3·50	3·50
1014	70p. Lieut. Philip Mountbatten, c. 1947	3·50	3·50
1009/14	*Set of* 6	12·50	12·50
MS1015	174×163 mm. Nos. 1009/14 and three stamp-size labels	12·00	13·00
MS1016	110×70 mm. £1.50 Queen Elizabeth II (wearing green checked dress) and Prince Philip, c. 2007	6·00	7·00

Nos. 1009/14 were printed in separate sheetlets of eight stamps.

No. **MS**1015 forms a diamond shape but with the left, right and top corners removed.

207 MV *Professor Multanocskiy*

208 Duke and Duchess of Cambridge at Westminster Abbey after Wedding Ceremony

(Litho BDT)

2011 (12 Apr). Atlantic Odyssey (voyages to Antarctica). T **207** and similar horiz designs showing cruise ships. Multicoloured. P 14×15.

1017	25p. Type **207**	1·25	1·25
1018	35p. MV *Aleksey Maryshev*	1·75	1·75
1019	70p. MV *Professor Molchanov*	3·25	3·25
1020	£1.10 MV *Plancius*	4·50	4·50
1017/20	*Set of* 4	9·75	9·75
MS1021	100×80 mm. £1.50 As No. 1020	7·00	7·50

(Litho BDT)

2011 (29 Apr). Royal Wedding. Sheet 118×90 mm containing vert design as T **267a** of St. Helena. Multicoloured. W w **18** (sideways). P 14½×14.

MS1022	£3 Prince William and Miss Catherine Middleton	11·00	12·00

(Litho Lowe-Martin)

2011 (24 May). History of the British Isles (3rd series). Square designs as T **203**. Multicoloured. W w **18**. P 13½.

1023	35p. King John signing Magna Carta, 1215	1·40	1·40
1024	35p. Mounted knights carrying standards of Houses of Lancaster and York (Wars of the Roses, 1455–85)	1·40	1·40
1025	35p. Guy Fawkes (Gunpowder Plot), 1605	1·40	1·40
1026	35p. Samuel Pepys writing in diary and London ablaze (Great Fire of London, 1666)	1·40	1·40
1027	35p. Duke of Wellington (Battle of Waterloo, 1815)	1·40	1·40
1028	35p. Factory and smoking chimneys (Industry & Commerce)	1·40	1·40
1029	35p. Queen Victoria, lion statue and Union Jack (Age of Empire)	1·40	1·40
1030	35p. Lord Kitchener and soldiers (First World War)	1·40	1·40
1023/30	*Set of* 8	10·00	10·00

(Litho Lowe-Martin)

2011 (1 Sept). Royal Wedding (2nd issue). T **208** and similar multicoloured designs. P 12½.

1031	70p. Type **208**	2·50	2·50
1032	70p. Duke and Duchess of Cambridge waving from State Landau (*horiz*)	2·50	2·50
1033	70p. Duke and Duchess of Cambridge kissing on Buckingham Palace balcony	2·50	2·50
1034	70p. Leaving Buckingham Palace in car with 'JU5T WED' numberplate (*horiz*)	2·50	2·50
1031/4	*Set of* 4	9·25	9·25

209 Tholoid (mass of lava rising above surface)

(Des Andrew Robinson. Litho BDT)

2011 (10 Oct). Volcano (1st series). 50th Anniv of the Eruption and Evacuation of Tristan da Cunha. T **209** and similar horiz designs. Multicoloured. P 14.

1035	25p. Type **209**	1·25	1·25
1036	35p. Volcanic eruption, October 1961	1·50	1·50
1037	95p. Islanders boarding *Tjisadane*, 1961	3·25	3·25
1038	£1.10 Arrival of Islanders at Cape Town	3·75	3·75
1035/8	*Set of* 4	8·75	8·75
MS1039	94×64 mm. £2 MV *Tjisadane*	8·00	8·00

(Des Andrew Robinson. Litho BDT)

2012 (30 Jan). Volcano (2nd series). 50th Anniv of the Royal Society Expedition. Horiz designs as T **209** . Multicoloured. P 14.

1040	25p. Rowing out to HMS *Protector* ('Returning with the Report')	1·25	1·25
1041	35p. Resettlement survey team	1·50	1·50
1042	95p. Whirlwind helicopter from HMS *Protector*	3·25	3·25
1043	£1.10 Royal Society members	3·75	3·75
1040/3	*Set of 4*	8·75	8·75
MS1044	94×64 mm. £2 Landing party	8·00	8·00

210 Queen Elizabeth II

(Litho BDT)

2012 (6 Feb). Diamond Jubilee. T **210** and similar diamond-shaped designs. Multicoloured. P 13½.

1045	25p. Type **210**	1·25	1·25
1046	35p. Queen Elizabeth II wearing yellow, 1970s	1·75	1·75
1047	50p. Queen Elizabeth II, c. 1952	2·00	2·00
1048	50p. Queen Elizabeth II wearing blue, c. 2005	2·00	2·00
1049	70p. Queen Elizabeth II wearing tiara and drop earrings, c. 1955	2·75	2·75
1050	70p. Queen Elizabeth II wearing tiara and drop earrings, c. 2005	2·75	2·75
1045/50	*Set of 6*	11·00	11·00
MS1051	174×164 mm. Nos. 1045/50 and three stamp-size labels	12·00	12·00
MS1052	110×70 mm. £1.50 Coronation photograph, 1953	5·00	5·00

Nos. 1045/50 were printed in separate sheetlets of eight stamps.

No. **MS**1051 forms a diamond-shape but with the left, right and top corners removed.

211 Harland and Wolff Shipyard

(Litho Cartor)

2012 (27 Feb). Centenary of the Sinking of the *Titanic*. Sheet 180×250 mm containing T **211** and similar horiz designs. Multicoloured. P 13½.

MS1053	50p.×10 Type **211**; First class dining room; *Titanic's* propellors; Sinking of the ship; Captain E. J. Smith and crew; Survivors in lifeboat; Setting sail; Newspaper reports; Passengers strolling on board; Discovery of the wreck	17·00	17·00

212 S.A. *Agulhas II*

(Litho Enschedé)

2012 (17 Sept). Maiden Voyage of S.A. *Agulhas II*. T **212** and similar horiz designs. Multicoloured. P 14.

1054	35p. Type **212**	1·75	1·75
1055	35p. S.A. *Agulhas I*	1·75	1·75
1056	70p. S.A. *Agulhas I* off Tristan da Cunha	3·00	3·00
1057	£1.10 S.A. *Agulhas II* off Tristan da Cunha	4·25	4·25
1054/7	*Set of 4*	9·75	9·75

213 HMS *Portland*, 2005

(Des Andrew Robinson. Litho Cartor)

2012 (15 Oct). Ships' Crests (2nd series). Sheet 150×150 mm containing T **213** and similar horiz designs. Multicoloured. P 13½.

MS1058	35p. Type **213**; 35p. HMS *Edinburgh*, 2006; 70p. HMS *Clyde*, 2011; 70p. HMS *Montrose*, 2012	9·00	9·00

214 James Marr and Tristan da Cunha

(Des Andrew Robinson. Litho BDT)

2012 (28 Nov). Shackleton–Rowett Expedition, 1921–2 T **214** and similar horiz designs. Multicoloured. P 14.

1059	70p. Type **214**	3·50	3·50
1060	70p. Frank Wild and Inaccessible Island	3·50	3·50
1061	70p. Frank Worsley and Nightingale Island	3·50	3·50
1062	70p. Hubert Wilkins and Gough Island	3·50	3·50
1059/62	*Set of 4*	12·50	12·50

215 Tristan Albatross Chick

(Des Andrew Robinson. Litho Cartor)

2013 (28 Jan). Endangered Species. Tristan Albatross (*Diomedea dabbenena*). T **215** and similar horiz designs. Multicoloured. P 13 (**MS**1067) or 13×13½ (others).

1063	35p. Type **215**	1·75	1·75
	a. Without white border	1·75	1·75
	ab. Strip of 4. Nos. 1063a/6a	9·50	9·50
1064	45p. Adult and chick	2·00	2·00
	a. Without white border	2·00	2·00
1065	70p. Pair	2·75	2·75
	a. Without white border	2·75	2·75
1066	£1.10 Adult in flight	4·00	4·00
	a. Without white border	4·00	4·00
1063/6	*Set of 4*	9·50	9·50
MS1067	94×64 mm. £3 Adult displaying	12·00	12·00

Nos. 1063a/6a (the stamps without white borders) were printed together, *se-tenant*, as horizontal and vertical strips of four in sheetlets of 16.

Nos. 1063/6 have white borders around the design and were printed in separate sheets of ten (2×5).

216 Recorders and 'When Fish Get the Flu'

(Des Andrew Robinson. Litho Cartor)

2013 (14 Feb). Tristan Song Project. T **216** and similar horiz designs, each showing musical instrument and words from song. Multicoloured. P 13½.

1068	35p. Type **216**	1·25	1·25
1069	45p. Violin and 'Rockhopper Penguins'	1·50	1·50
1070	70p. Guitar and 'Volcano's Black'	2·50	2·50
1071	£1.10 Accordion and 'The Molly' (albatross)	3·75	3·75
1068/71	*Set of 4*	8·00	8·00

217 Queen Victoria

(Litho BDT)

2013 (15 Apr). 60th Anniv of Coronation of Queen Elizabeth II. 'A Celebration of Coronation Commemoratives'. T **217** and similar multicoloured designs. P 14 (1072/6) or 15×14 (**MS**1077).

No.	Description	Unused	Used
1072	35p. Type **217**	1·25	1·25
1073	45p. King Edward VII and Queen Alexandra and grandstand at Charing Cross Station for Coronation procession	1·50	1·50
1074	70p. King George V and Queen Mary	2·50	2·50
1075	£1.10 King George VI and Queen Elizabeth, crowned 12 May 1937	3·75	3·75
1076	£1.50 Queen Elizabeth II and Duke of Edinburgh	4·50	4·50
1072/6	*Set of 5*	12·00	12·00
MS1077	110×70 mm. £2 Recent photograph of Queen Elizabeth II (32×48 *mm*)	7·50	7·50

(Des Andrew Robinson. Litho BDT)

2013 (11 Nov). Volcano (3rd series). 50th Anniv of the Resettlement. Horiz designs as T **209**. Multicoloured. P 14.

No.	Description	Unused	Used
1078	25p. Returned Islanders amongst their possessions	1·25	1·25
1079	35p. Islanders looking for their possessions amongst the unloaded stores	1·50	1·50
1080	95p. Islanders on shore, MV *Boissevain* and MV *Frances Repetto* offshore	3·25	3·25
1081	£1.10 Returning islanders transported by tractor and trailer	3·75	3·75
1078/81	*Set of 4*	8·75	8·75
MS1082	94×64 mm. £2 Islanders hauling longboat up beach, MV *Boissevain* and MV *Tristania* offshore.	8·00	8·00

218 St. Mary's Anglican Church, Tristan da Cunha

(Des Bee Design. Litho Cartor)

2013 (18 Nov). Christmas. Churches. T **218** and similar horiz designs. Multicoloured. P 13½.

No.	Description	Unused	Used
1083	35p. Type **218**	1·25	1·25
	a. Horiz pair with central label. Nos. 1083 and 1085	4·25	4·25
1084	35p. St. Joseph's Catholic Church, Tristan da Cunha	1·25	1·25
	a. Horiz pair with central label. Nos. 1084 and 1086	4·25	4·25
1085	£1.10 Canterbury Cathedral, England	3·00	3·00
1086	£1.10 St. Peter's Basilica, Vatican City	3·00	3·00
1083/6	*Set of 4*	8·50	8·50

Nos. 1083 and 1085, and 1084 and 1086, were each printed together, *se-tenant*, as horizontal pairs with a central label in sheetlets of ten stamps and five half stamp-size labels depicting Archbishop of Canterbury Justin Welby (1083a) or Pope Francis I (1084a).

(Des Andrew Robinson. Litho BDT)

2013 (9 Dec). Volcano (4th series). Ships of Volcano Period (1961–3). Horiz designs as T **209**. Multicoloured. P 14.

No.	Description	Unused	Used
1087	25p. HMS *Puma*	1·25	1·25
1088	35p. HMS *Jaguar*	1·50	1·50
1089	95p. MV *Tristania*	3·25	3·25
1090	£1.10 HMMV *Stirling Castle*	3·75	3·75
1087/90	*Set of 4*	8·75	8·75
MS1091	94×64 mm. £2 MV *Bornholm*	8·00	8·00

STAMP BOOKLETS

1957 (30 May)–**58**. Black on blue cover. Postmarked "MY 30 57" on back cover. Stapled.

No.	Description	Price
SB1	3s.6d. booklet containing eight ½d. and four 1d., 1½d., 3d. and 4d. (Nos. 14/16, 19/20) in blocks of 4	£350
	a. Postmarked "JA 24 58" on back cover (24.1.58)	£300
	b. Without postmark	£300

1958 (Jan). Black on red cover. Without postmark. Stapled.

No.	Description	Price
SB2	3s.6d. Contents as No. SB1	55·00

1960 (Feb). Black on green cover. Stitched.

No.	Description	Price
SB3	3s.6d. booklet containing eight ½d. and four 1d., 1½d., 3d. and 4d. (Nos. 28/30, 33/4) in blocks of 4	30·00

1965 (17 Feb). Black on green cover. Stapled.

No.	Description	Price
SB4	4s.2d. booklet containing eight ½d. and four 1d., 1½d., 3d. and 6d. (Nos. 71/3, 75, 77) in blocks of 4	6·00

The booklet covers were reprinted with amended postage rates and released by the Crown Agents on 21 September 1970.

B **1**

2004 (27 July). New Island Flag. Multicoloured cover as Type B **1**. Self-adhesive.

No.	Description	Price
SB5	£3.60 booklet containing pane of twelve 30p. stamps (No. 804a)	10·00

POSTAGE DUE STAMPS

D **1**

2d Normal

Large "d" (R. 9/6, 10/6)

Normal

3d Lower serif at left of "3" missing (R. 9/1)

d **4d.** Ball of "d" broken and serif at top damaged (R. 9/5). Other stamps in the fifth vertical row show slight breaks to the ball of the "d".

(Typo D.L.R.)

1957 (1 Feb). Chalk-surfaced paper. Wmk Mult Script CA. P 14.

No.	Type	Description	Unused	Used
D1	D **1**	1d. scarlet	1·75	15·00
D2		2d. orange-yellow	2·50	4·75
		a. Large "d"	30·00	
D3		3d. green	2·50	5·50
		a. Missing serif	50·00	
D4		4d. ultramarine	4·50	7·00
		a. Broken "d"	60·00	
D5		5d. lake	2·50	25·00
D1/5		*Set of 5*	12·00	50·00

D **2**

D **3** Outline Map of Tristan da Cunha

(Des J.W. Litho Questa)

1976 (27 May*). W w **12** (sideways). P 13½×14.

No.	Type	Description	Unused	Used
D6	D **2**	1p. magenta	10	30

D7		2p. dull emerald	15	40
D8		4p. bluish violet	20	40
D9		5p. new blue	20	40
D10		10p. chestnut	20	50
D6/10 *Set of 5*			75	1·75

*This is the local date of issue; the Crown Agents released the stamps four days later.

1976 (3 Sept). W w **14** (sideways*). P 13½×14.

D11	D **2**	1p. magenta	10	30
D12		2p. dull emerald	10	30
D13		4p. bluish violet	15	35
D14		5p. new blue	15	40
D15		10p. chestnut	15	45
		w. Wmk Crown to right of CA	£120	
D11/15 *Set of 5*			60	1·60

*The normal sideways watermark shows Crown to left of CA, *as seen from the back of the stamp.*

(Des L. Curtis. Litho Questa)

1986 (20 Nov). W w **16**. P 14½×14.

D16	D **3**	1p. deep brown and cinnamon	10	80
D17		2p. deep brown and bright orange	15	80
D18		5p. deep brown and orange-vermilion	20	80
D19		7p. black and bright reddish violet	20	80
D20		10p. black and violet-blue	25	80
D21		25p. black and pale emerald	65	1·40
D16/21 *Set of 6*			1·40	3·75

POSTAL FISCAL STAMPS

(F **1**)

(F **2**)

1970 (15 May). No. 77 optd with Type F **1** in red.

F1	6d. black and green	20	30

No. F1 was originally intended as a National Savings Stamp, but also retained postal validity.

(Handstamped locally by rubber handstamp)

1971 (14 Feb). Decimal currency. No. F1 handstamped with Type F **2**, in violet.

F2	2½p. on 6d. black and green	3·00	4·50
	a. Pair, one without handstamp	£600	£600

Beware of forgeries of this handstamp.

Dear Catalogue User,

As a collector and Stanley Gibbons catalogue user for many years myself, I am only too aware of the need to provide you with the information you seek in an accurate, timely and easily accessible manner. Naturally, I have my own views on where changes could be made, but one thing I learned long ago is that we all have different opinions and requirements.

I would therefore be most grateful if you would complete the form overleaf and return it to me. Please contact Lorraine Holcombe (lholcombe@stanleygibbons.co.uk) if you would like to be emailed the questionnaire.

Very many thanks for your help.

Yours sincerely,

Hugh Jefferies,
Editor.

Questionnaire

2014 St. Helena, Ascension & Tristan da Cunha

1. Level of detail
   Do you feel that the level of detail in this catalogue is:
   a. too specialised O
   b. about right O
   c. inadequate O

2. Frequency of issue
   How often would you purchase a new edition of this catalogue?
   a. Annually O
   b. Every two years O
   c. Every three to five years O
   d. Less frequently O

3. Design and Quality
   How would you describe the layout and appearance of this catalogue?
   a. Excellent O
   b. Good O
   c. Adequate O
   d. Poor O

4. How important to you are the prices given in the catalogue:
   a. Important O
   b. Quite important O
   c. Of little interest O
   d. Of no interest O

5. Would you be interested in an online version of this catalogue?
   a. Yes O
   b. No O

6. What changes would you suggest to improve the catalogue? E.g. Which other features would you like to see included?
   ....
   ....
   ....
   ....
   ....

7. Would you like us to let you know when the next edition of this catalogue is due to be published?
   a. Yes O
   b. No O

   If so please give your contact details below.
   Name: ....
   Address: ....
   ....
   ....
   ....
   Email: ....
   Telephone: ....

8. Which other Stanley Gibbons Catalogues are you interested in?
   a. ....
   b. ....
   c. ....
   d. ....

Many thanks for your comments.

Please complete and return it to:
Hugh Jefferies (Catalogue Editor)
Stanley Gibbons Limited, 7 Parkside, Ringwood,
Hampshire BH24 3SH, United Kingdom

or email: lholcombe@stanleygibbons.co.uk to request a soft copy

St. Helena, Ascension & Tristan da Cunha

Order Form

YOUR ORDER

Stanley Gibbons account number

Condition (mint/UM/ used)	Country	SG No.	Description	Price	Office use only
			POSTAGE & PACK-ING	£3.60	
			TOTAL		

The lowest price charged for individual stamps or sets purchased from Stanley Gibbons Ltd, is £1.

Payment & address details

Name

Address (We cannot deliver to PO Boxes)

Postcode

Tel No.

Email

PLEASE NOTE Overseas customers MUST quote a telephone number or the order cannot be dispatched. Please complete ALL sections of this form to allow us to process the order.

☐ Cheque (made payable to Stanley Gibbons)

☐ I authorise you to charge my

☐ Mastercard ☐ Visa ☐ Diners ☐ Amex ☐ Maestro

Card No. (Maestro only)

Valid from Expiry date Issue No. (Maestro only) CVC No. (4 if Amex)

CVC No. is the last three digits on the back of your card (4 if Amex)

Signature Date

4 EASY WAYS TO ORDER

Post to
Lesley Mourne, Stamp Mail Order Department, Stanley Gibbons Ltd, 399 Strand, London, WC2R 0LX, England

Call
020 7836 8444
+44 (0)20 7836 8444

Fax
020 7557 4499
+44 (0)20 7557 4499

Click
lmourne@stanleygibbons.com/co.uk?